GATHER

GATHER

GIA PUBLICATIONS, INC.
CHICAGO

NORTH AMERICAN LITURGY RESOURCES
PHOENIX

Distributed exclusively by GIA Publications, Inc.

Design based upon *Worship — Third Edition* by
Michael Tapia. Cover design by John Buscemi.
Engraved and typeset by the Hornseth Company,
Beltsville, Maryland.

Published with ecclesiastical approval, Archdiocese
of Chicago.

ISBN 0-941050-11-4

1 2 3 4 5 6 7 8 9 10 11 12 13 14 15 16 17 18 19 20

PREFACE

There is more printed music available to worshipping communities today than ever before in the history of the Church. There are more diverse styles of music now being commonly used in worship than ever before, and musical eclecticism is the call of the day.

A contemporary reality is that worshipping communities commonly use more than one worship aid. Often, one publication contains classical hymnody for the most part and the other, folk style hymns and songs. A substantial hymn book, using standard hymnal format, is not new to the Church. There have been at least a dozen published since Vatican II, all with classical hymnody as their primary contents. Music in the folk idiom, on the other hand, has been found primarily in paperback songbooks and supplements, and even hardcover editions have up to now failed to organize the contents according to any logical plan. Folk music hymnals and collections have also been characterized by containing the music of only one or two publishers.

The publication of *Gather* introduces a number of long overdue firsts. It is the first collection of contemporary folk style hymns, songs and psalms that is truly comprehensive. This hymnal "gathers" from all publishers and sources that which its editors deemed the best available in this musical idiom, and in fact, we combed every known publication and hundreds of manuscripts in choosing the contents of *Gather.* In attempting to secure the rights for the music which was selected, happily, only one publisher was un-cooperative.

When compiling *Gather,* the editors kept a constant focus on the Lectionary, so that the hymnal would not only represent a fine collection of congregational music, but music that accompanies the assembly throughout its celebration of the church year. This is the first folk hymnal which, like its classical counterpart *Worship,* is organized according to the way we celebrate.

The publication of *Gather* completes GIA's long range plan to make available in two attractive and practical volumes, the most extensive and comprehensive music repertoire ever. Although each stands alone, the *ultimate* parish resource, we believe, is the combination of *Gather* and the already critically acclaimed *Worship — Third Edition.* Together, these books contain a repertoire of more than 1,000 music selections, chosen to provide assemblies with high quality music and texts, and extensive enough so as to offer genuine choice and allow assemblies room to grow and mature in their worshiplife. In addition, the careful design, and quality of paper, printing and binding, are more consistent with the nature of this human experience we know as divine worship than are throwaway materials.

The "guitar mass" of the 60's has come a long way. Singing led by several strumming guitars has evolved into singing led by an ensemble composed of guitar, bass, piano and/or synthesizer, usually several orchestral instruments (e.g., flute, oboe, trumpet, cello, etc.), and multiple voices, often SATB. Similarly, the repertoire has evolved from simple songs printed with melody line, text and chord symbols, into a score for almost any combination of the above. And the quality of composition has certainly kept pace with the complexity of the score.

Here, then, is a collection of sophisticated music for worship in a style that is more popular than classical — although the distinction is not always clear. All selections include keyboard accompaniments, generally written for piano rather than organ, and a majority of the selections include vocal harmonies. It is a hymnal that can serve as a partner to almost any other worship aid in use today, and is experienced to the fullest when used in tandem with the hymnal it was created to compliment, *Worship — Third Edition.*

Special tribute is paid to Edward J. Harris of GIA Publications, Inc., and Raymond P. Bruno of North American Liturgy Resources, for negotiating the co-publishing agreement which made this hymnal possible. Acknowledgement is given to Neil Borgstrom, Kelly Dobbs and Michael A. Silhavy of the GIA editorial staff, for their work on this project, especially the careful attention to the many details, and to Robert H. Oldershaw for once again doing a masterful job of preparing the indexes.

That God may be glorified.

Robert J. Batastini
General Editor
Michael A. Cymbala
David Haas
Marty Haugen
Michael Joncas
Editors

Contents

Daily Prayer

1 Morning Praise
9 Evensong
18 Psalter

Mass

64 The Order of Mass - Mass of Creation
85 Setting One - Mass of Light
96 Setting Two - Mass of Remembrance
108 Setting Three - The Psallite Mass
114 Service Music

Hymns and Songs

136 Advent
144 Christmas
153 Holy Family
154 Epiphany
158 Lent & Holy Week
175 Easter
187 Ascension
189 Pentecost
194 Trinity
196 Creation
202 Providence
205 Light
210 Word
213 Praise

237 Thanksgiving
239 Petition
249 Faith
254 Trust
267 Love
274 Comfort
280 Kingdom
282 Church
283 Christian Life
289 Mission/Ministry
295 Discipleship
300 Social Concern
303 Peace
308 Unity
311 Gathering
316 Morning
318 Evening
321 Second Coming
326 Mary
328 Saints
329 Christian Initiation
335 Eucharist
349 Funeral
351 Marriage
353 Pastoral Care of the Sick
355 Penance

Indexes

358 Acknowledgements
359 Scripture Passages Related to Hymns
360 Liturgical Index
361 Topical Index
362 Index of Composers, Authors and Sources
363 Metrical Index
364 Tune Index
365 Index of First Lines and Common Titles

Morning Praise

The church's sense for how to pray in the morning comes from our Jewish heritage. Whatever the day, whatever the difficulties, the tradition has been to begin the day with praise for the creator. The sign of the cross, first traced on the Christian at baptism, is again made to begin the new day and its prayer. In the hymn and the psalms, in the scripture and intercessions, each one who prays and the community together finds what it is to stand at the beginning of a new day as a Christian. The morning's prayer gives the day its meaning when, through the years, these prayers become one's own.

OPENING DIALOG 1

Stand

J. Tasch Jordan, adapt.
David Haas, 1986
Presider:
Ho - ly God! Fill us this day with new breath!
Assembly:
And we shall be liv - ing words of praise!

2 MORNING HYMN

SUMMIT HILL, 8 8 9 9 8
David Haas, 1987

DH

1. Sing your joy, pro - claim God's glo - ry! Rise and sing, the
2. All the earth is filled with re-joic - ing, Light and life the
3. May we learn to be - come your King-dom. May we be your
4. Light our way, O God of the liv - ing, May we learn to

morn-ing has come! Bless our God and praise all cre - a - tion;
won-der of God! Christ has tri-umphed! Ris - en for ev - er!
kind-ness and truth! Love is our call - ing, gift of your pres-ence;
see with new eyes! Je - sus the Lord, our pow - er and prom-ise;

Song of the earth, and light from heav - en: God is a - live!
Joy of our hearts, and hope of our dream-ing: God is a - live!
Chil-dren of God, and spir - it of Je - sus: God is a - live!
Light for the blind, and food for the hun - gry: God is a - live!

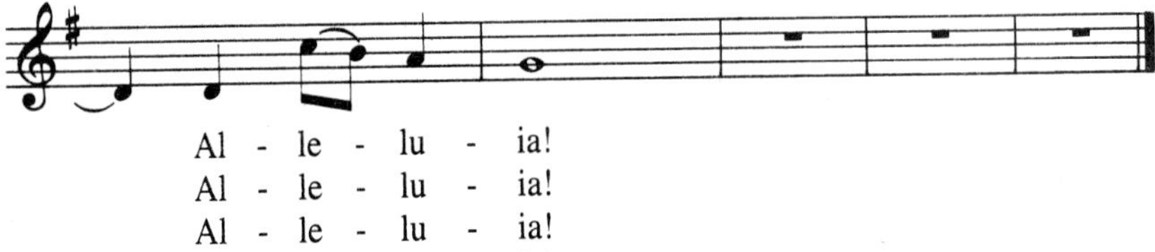
Al - le - lu - ia!
Al - le - lu - ia!
Al - le - lu - ia!
Al - le - lu - ia!

PSALMODY

The singing of one or more psalms is a central part of Morning Praise. Psalm 63, given below, is one of the premier morning psalms. Psalm 51 (# 31)–usually substituted for Psalm 63 on Wednesday and Friday, as well as during Lent – Psalm 118 (#52), and the metrical paraphrase of Psalm 19 (#18) were written by David Haas as part of this complete setting. Other appropriate psalms for morning are Psalms 33 (#25), 42/43 (#28), 47 (#29), 66 (#36), 72 (#37), 80 (#38), 85 (#41), 95 (#44), 98 (#45), 100 (#46) and 150 (#64).

PSALM 63

3

Sit

Psalm 63:2-9, adapt.
DH

David Haas, 1986

Refrain:

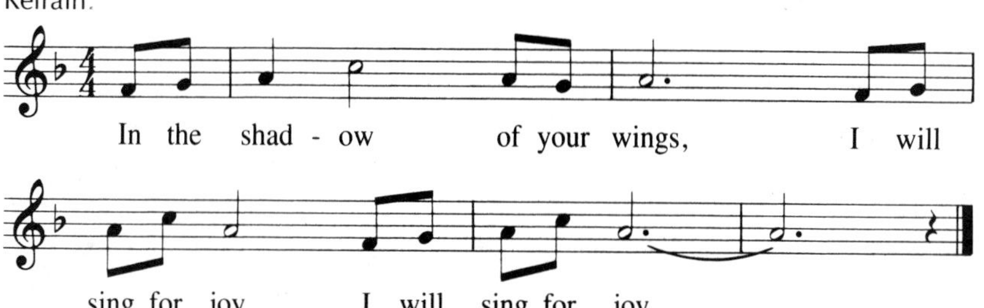
In the shad - ow of your wings, I will
sing for joy, I will sing for joy.

Verses

1. O God, you are my God,
   for you I long, I desire you.
   Like a dry and waterless land,
   my soul is thirsting for you.

2. Let me see you in your holy place,
   let me see your glory.
   Your love is better than life,
   and so I will praise you.

3. I will give you thanks, while I live,
   I will lift my hands in prayer to you.
   My soul will feast and be filled.
   I will sing glad songs of praise to you.

4. As I lie in bed I remember you,
   I think of you at night, my help.
   In the shadow of your wings I sing for joy,
   I cling to you, and your right hand keeps me safe.

5. Glory to the Father, and to the Son,
   and to the Holy Spirit;
   as it was in the beginning, is now,
   and will be for ever. Amen.

PSALM PRAYER

Stand

All respond: Amen

4 WORD OF GOD

Sit

Reader concludes: This is the word of the Lord.

Assembly: Thanks be to God.

5 GOSPEL CANTICLE

Stand. All make the sign of the cross as the canticle begins.

Luke 1:67-69
Metrical paraphrase by
James Quinn, SJ, 1969

HURON, CMD
David Haas, 1986

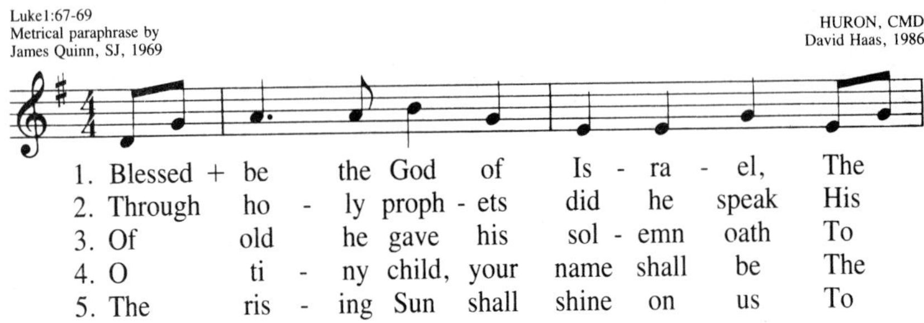
1. Blessed + be the God of Is - ra - el, The
2. Through ho - ly proph - ets did he speak His
3. Of old he gave his sol - emn oath To
4. O ti - ny child, your name shall be The
5. The ris - ing Sun shall shine on us To

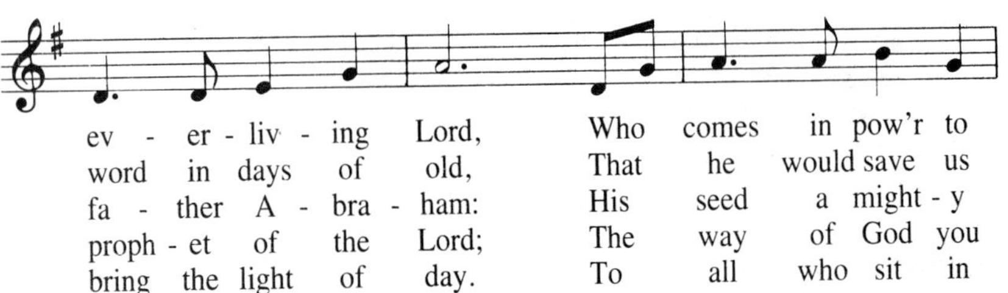
ev - er - liv - ing Lord, Who comes in pow'r to
word in days of old, That he would save us
fa - ther A - bra - ham: His seed a might - y
proph - et of the Lord; The way of God you
bring the light of day. To all who sit in

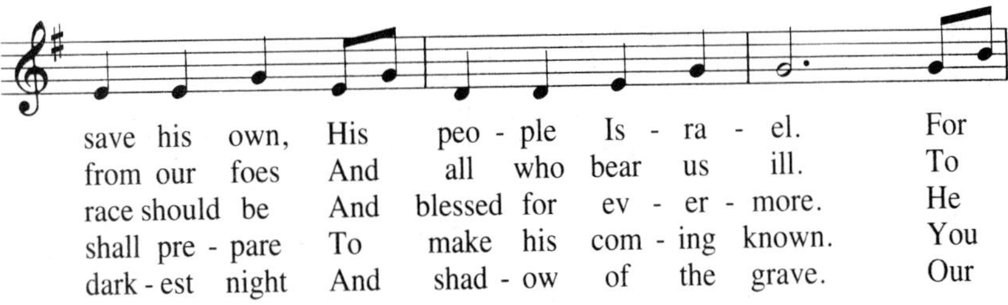
save his own, His peo - ple Is - ra - el. For
from our foes And all who bear us ill. To
race should be And blessed for ev - er - more. He
shall pre - pare To make his com - ing known. You
dark - est night And shad - ow of the grave. Our

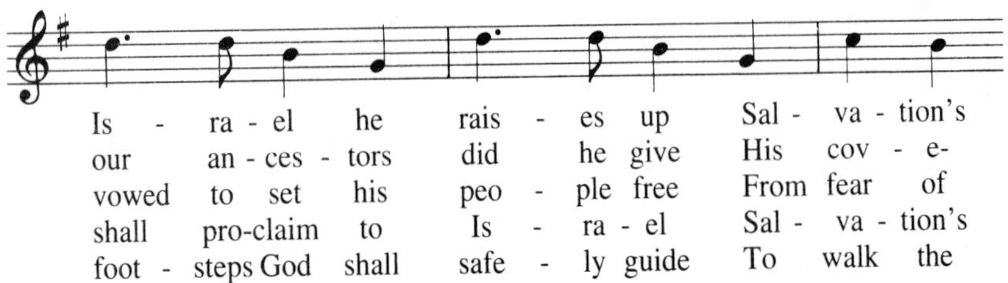
Is - ra - el he rais - es up Sal - va - tion's
our an - ces - tors did he give His cov - e-
vowed to set his peo - ple free From fear of
shall pro-claim to Is - ra - el Sal - va - tion's
foot - steps God shall safe - ly guide To walk the

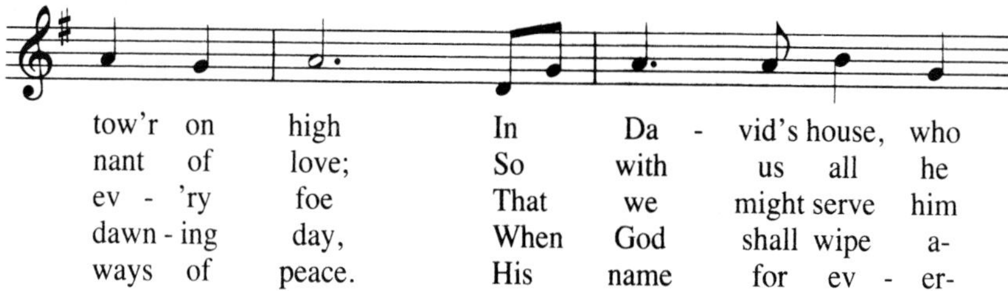
tow'r on high In Da - vid's house, who
nant of love; So with us all he
ev - 'ry foe That we might serve him
dawn - ing day, When God shall wipe a-
ways of peace. His name for ev - er-

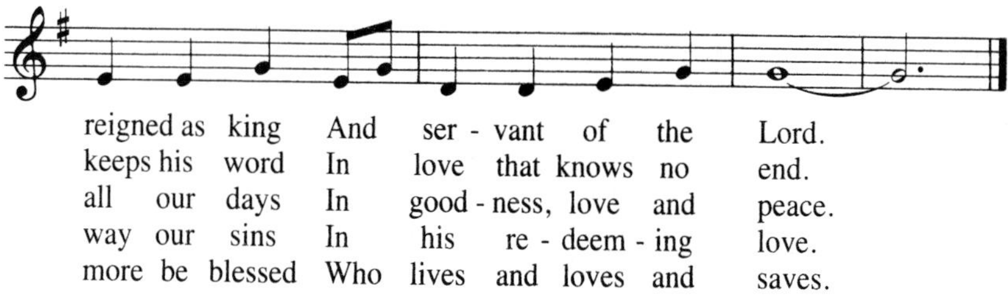
reigned as king And ser - vant of the Lord.
keeps his word In love that knows no end.
all our days In good - ness, love and peace.
way our sins In his re - deem - ing love.
more be blessed Who lives and loves and saves.

Text © 1969, James Quinn, SJ, by permission of Geoffrey Chapman, a division of Cassell Ltd.

MORNING PRAYERS 6

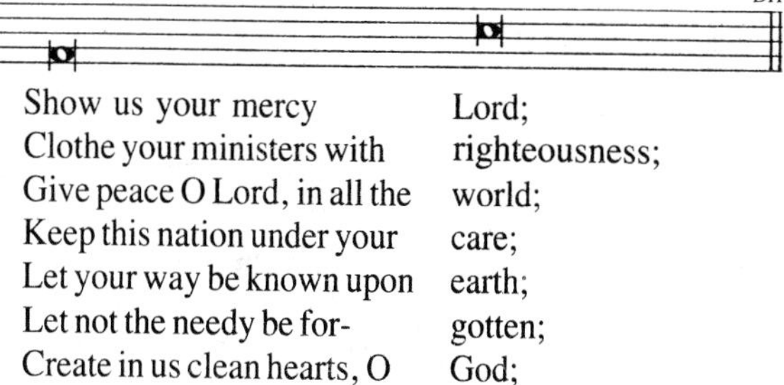
Cantor:
DH
Show us your mercy Lord;
Clothe your ministers with righteousness;
Give peace O Lord, in all the world;
Keep this nation under your care;
Let your way be known upon earth;
Let not the needy be for- gotten;
Create in us clean hearts, O God;

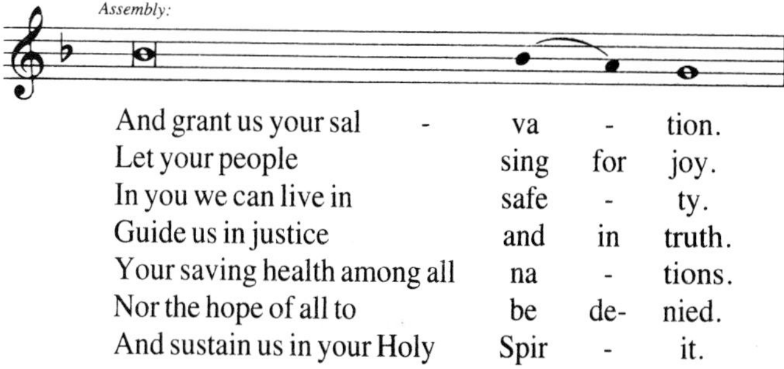
Assembly:
And grant us your sal - va - tion.
Let your people sing for joy.
In you we can live in safe - ty.
Guide us in justice and in truth.
Your saving health among all na - tions.
Nor the hope of all to be de- nied.
And sustain us in your Holy Spir - it.

CONCLUDING PRAYER

All respond: Amen

7 LORD'S PRAYER

David Haas, 1986
Our Fa - ther in heav - en, hal-low - ed be your
name, your king-dom come, your will be done, on
earth as in heav - en. Give us to - day our
dai - ly bread. For - give us our sins as we for - give
those who sin a - gainst us.
Save us from the time of trial and de - liv - er us from
e - vil, for the king-dom, the pow'r and the glo - ry are yours,
now and for ev - er.
8 FINAL BLESSING
DH
Presider:
Let us bless the Lord.
Assembly:
And give him thanks.
Presider:
May the Lord almighty bless our days and our deeds with his peace.
All:
A - men.

Evensong

The church gathers in the evening to give thanks for the day that is ending. In the earliest tradition, this began with the lighting of the lamps as darkness fell and the hymn of praise of Christ who is "radiant Light...of God the Father's deathless face." The evening psalms and the Magnificat bring the day just past to focus for the Christian: "God has cast down the mighty from their thrones, and has lifted up the lowly"; "God has remembered the promise of mercy, the promise made to our ancestors." Prayers of intercession are almost always part of the church's liturgy, but those which conclude evening prayer are especially important. As day ends, the church again and again lifts up to God the needs and sorrows and failures of all the world. Such intercession is the daily task and joy of the baptized.

LIGHT PROCLAMATION 9

Stand

Assistant or Presider:
Michael Joncas, 1979
Light and peace in Je - sus Christ our Lord.
Assembly:
Thanks be to God.

10 EVENING HYMN

Phos Hilaron
Tr. William G. Storey

Michael Joncas, 1979

1. O ra - diant Light, O
Sun di - vine, Of God the Fa - ther's
death - less face, O Im - age of the
Light sub - lime That fills the heav'n - ly
dwell - ing place,

2. O Son of God, the
Source of life, Praise is your due by
night and day. Our hap - py lips must
raise the strain Of your es - teemed and
splen - did name.

3. Lord Je - sus Christ, as
day - light fades, As shine the lights of
ev - en - tide, We praise the Fa - ther
with the Son, The Spir - it blest, and
with them one.

11 EVENING THANKSGIVING

MJ

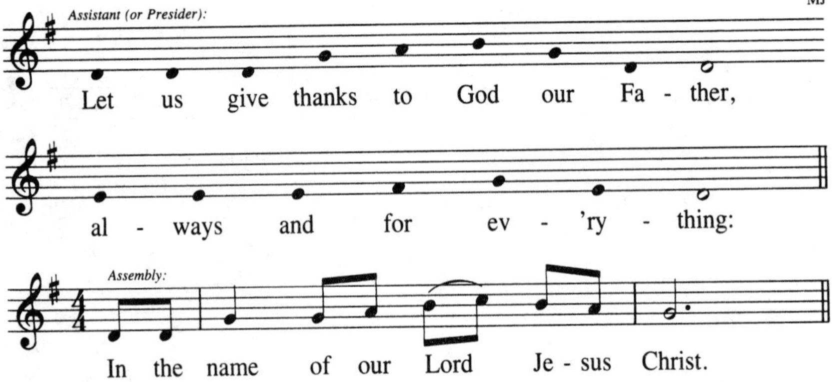
Assistant (or Presider):
Let us give thanks to God our Fa - ther,
al - ways and for ev - 'ry - thing:
Assembly:
In the name of our Lord Je - sus Christ.

The assistant sings the Thanksgiving to which all respond:

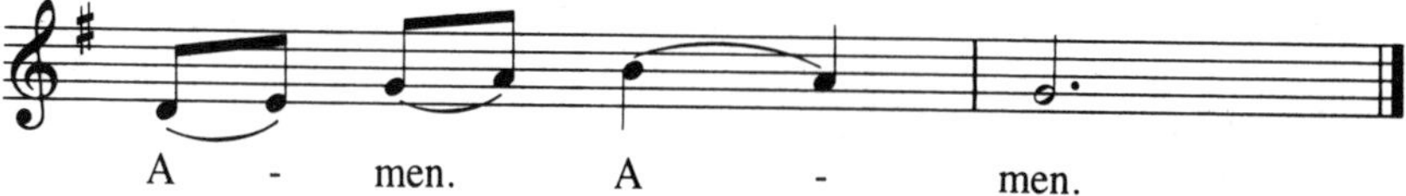

PSALMODY

The singing of one or more psalms is a central part of Evensong. Psalm 141, given below, is one of the premier evening psalms. It is customary to use incense as it is sung. Psalms 121 (#53) and 117 (#50) were written by Michael Joncas as part of this complete setting. Other appropriate psalms for evening are Psalms 19 (#18), 23 (#20), 27 (#23), 84 (#39 & 40), 91 (#43), 104 (#48), 118 (#51 & 52), 122 (#54), 130(#57 & 58), 136 (#59) and 145 (#60).

PSALM 141 / INCENSE PSALM 12

The Grail, alt.

Michael Joncas, 1987

Refrain

Like burn - ing in - cense, O Lord; let my
prayer rise up to you.

Verses

1. I have called you, Lord; hasten to help me!
   Hear my voice when I cry to you.
   Let my prayer arise before you like incense,
   the raising of my hands like an evening oblation.

2. Set, O Lord, a guard over my mouth;
   keep watch, O Lord, at the door of my lips!
   Do not turn my heart to things that are wrong,
   to evil deeds with those who are sinners.

3. Never allow me to share in their feasting.
   If the upright strike or reprove me it is kindness;
   but let the oil of the wicked not anoint my head.
   Let my prayer be ever against their malice.

4. To you, Lord God, my eyes are turned:
   in you I take refuge, spare my soul!

From the trap they have laid for me keep me safe:
keep me from the snares of those who do evil.

5. Glory to the Father, and to the Son,
and to the Holy Spirit:
as it was in the beginning, is now,
and will be for ever. Amen.

PSALM PRAYER

All respond: Amen

13 WORD OF GOD

Sit

Reader concludes: This is the Word of the Lord.
Assembly: Thanks be to God.

14 GOSPEL CANTICLE

Stand. All make the sign of the cross as the canticle begins.

Luke 1:46-55
J.T. Mueller, 1940, alt.
MAGNIFICAT LMD
Michael Joncas, 1979
1. My soul+ gives glo - ry to the Lord, In God my Sav - ior I re - joice. My low - li - ness he
2. His mer - cy goes to all who fear, From age to age and to all parts. His arm of strength to
3. He raised his ser - vant Is - ra - el, Re - mem - b'ring his e - ter - nal grace, As from of old He

did re - gard, Ex - alt - ing
all is near; He scat - ters
did fore - tell To A - bra-
me by his own choice.
those who have proud hearts.
ham and all his race.
From this day all shall
He casts the might - y
O Fa - ther, Son and
call me blest, For he has
from their throne And rais - es
Spir - it blest, In three - fold
done great things for me,
those of low de - gree;
Name are you a - dored,
Of all great names his
He feeds the hun - gry
To you be ev - 'ry
is the best, For it is
as his own, The rich de-
prayer ad - drest, From age to
ho - ly; strong is he.
part in po - ver - ty.
age the on - ly Lord.

15 PETITIONS

Invitation
Assistant:
Michael Joncas, 1987
Let us com-plete our eve-ning prayer to the Lord.
Refrain
Assembly:
Lord have mer - cy. Lord have mer - cy.
Intercessions
Assistant:
(Intention) let us pray to the Lord
(to refrain)

CONCLUDING PRAYER

All respond: Amen.

16 LORD'S PRAYER

Michael Joncas, 1987

Our Fa-ther, in heav-en, hal-lowed be your
name. Your king - dom come, your will be done on
earth as in heav-en. Give us to - day our dai - ly
bread; give us to - day our dai - ly bread.
For - give us our sins as we for-give those who sin a-
gainst us. Save us from the time of trial,
and de - liv - er us from e - vil. For the king-dom, the

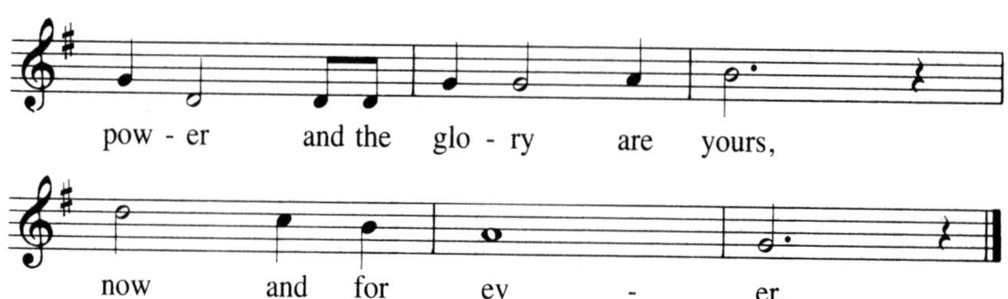
pow - er and the glo - ry are yours,
now and for ev - er.

FINAL BLESSING 17

Presider:
All:
A - men. A - men.
MJ

18 Psalm 19 Lord, You Have the Words

Refrain

Lord, you have the words of ev - er - last - ing life.

Verses

1. The law of the Lord is perfect, refreshing the soul;
   the Lord's rule is to be trusted, the simple find wisdom.

2. The fear of the Lord is holy, abiding for ever;
   the decrees of the Lord are true, all of them just.

3. The precepts of the Lord are right, they gladden the heart,
   the command of the Lord is clear, giving light to the eye.

4. They are worth more than gold, than the finest gold,
   sweeter than honey, than honey from the comb.

Text: *Psalm 19:8, 9, 10, 11;* Adapt. by David Haas, b.1957, © 1983, GIA Publications, Inc.; Refrain trans. © 1969, ICEL
Tune: David Haas, b.1957, © 1983, GIA Publications, Inc.

19 Psalm 22 My God, My God

Refrain

My God, my God, O, why have you a - ban-doned me?

Verses

1. All who see me laugh at me, they mock me and they shake their heads:
   "He relied on the Lord, let the Lord be his refuge."

2. As dogs around me, they circle me about.
   Wounded me and pierced me, I can number all my bones.

3. My clothing they divided, for my garments casting lots,
   O Lord, do not desert me, but hasten to my aid.

4. I will praise you to my people, and proclaim you in their midst.
O fear the Lord and praise him, give glory to his name.

Text: *Psalm 22:8-9, 17-18, 19-20, 23-24;* Adapt. by Marty Haugen, b. 1950, © 1983, GIA Publications, Inc.; Refrain trans. © 1969, ICEL
Tune: Marty Haugen, b. 1950, ©1983, GIA Publications, Inc.

Psalm 23 Shepherd Me, O God 20

Refrain

Shep-herd me, O God, be - yond my wants, be-
yond my fears, from death in - to life.

Verses

1. God is my shepherd, so nothing shall I want,
I rest in the meadows of faithfulness and love,
I walk by the quiet waters of peace.

2. Gently you raise me and heal my weary soul,
you lead me by pathways of righteousness and truth,
my spirit shall sing the music of your name.

3. Though I should wander the valley of death,
I fear no evil, for you are at my side,
your rod and your staff, my comfort and my hope.

4. You have set me a banquet of love in the face of hatred,
crowning me with love beyond my power to hold.

5. Surely your kindness and mercy follow me
all the days of my life;
I will dwell in the house of my God for evermore.

Text: *Psalm 23;* Para. by Marty Haugen, b. 1950
Tune: Marty Haugen, b. 1950

21 Psalm 25 To You, O Lord

Refrain

To you, O Lord, I lift my soul, to you, I lift my soul.

Verses

1. Lord, make me know your ways,
   teach me your paths
   and keep me in the way of your truth,
   for you are God, my Savior.

2. For the Lord is good and righteous,
   revealing his way to those who seek him,
   gently leading the poor and the humble.

3. To the ones who seek the Lord,
   who look to his word, who live his love,
   he will always be near,
   he will show them his mercy.

Text: *Psalm 25:4-5, 8-9, 12-14;* Para. by Marty Haugen, b.1950, © 1982, GIA Publications, Inc.; Refrain trans. © 1969, ICEL
Tune: Marty Haugen, b.1950, © 1982, GIA Publications, Inc.

22 Psalm 25 To You, O Lord

Refrain

To you, O Lord, to you, O Lord, I lift up, I lift up my soul.

Verses

1. Your ways, O Lord, make known to me;
   teach me your paths.
   Guide me in your truth and teach me
   for you are God my Savior.

2. Good and upright is the Lord;
   thus he shows sinners the way.
   The humble he guides to justice;
   he teaches the humble his way.

3. Kindness and constancy the paths of the Lord
   for those who keep cov'nant with him.
   The friendship of the Lord with those who revere him,
   his covenant for their instruction.

Text: *Psalm 25:4-5, 8-9, 10, 14;* Adapt. by Michael Joncas, b.1951, © 1985, North American Liturgy Resources; Refrain trans. © 1974, ICEL
Tune: Michael Joncas, b.1951, © 1985, North American Liturgy Resources

Psalm 27 The Lord Is My Light 23

Refrain

The Lord is my light and my sal - va - tion, of
whom should I be a - fraid, of whom should I be a - fraid?

Verses

1. The Lord is my light and my help; whom should I fear?
   The Lord is the stronghold of my life; before whom should I shrink?

2. There is one thing I ask of the Lord; for this I long;
   to live in the house of the Lord all the days of my life.

3. I believe I shall see the goodness of the Lord in the land of the living;
   hope in him, and take heart. Hope in the Lord!

Text: *Psalm 27:1-2, 4, 13-14;* Adapt. by David Haas, b.1957
Tune: David Haas, b.1957

24 Psalm 30 I Will Praise You, Lord

Refrain

I will praise you, Lord, you have res-cued me, I will
praise you, Lord, for your mer - cy. I will praise you, Lord,
you have res-cued me: I will praise you, Lord.

Verses

1. I will praise you, Lord, you have rescued me
   and have not let my enemies rejoice over me.
   O Lord, you have raised my soul from the dead,
   restored me to life from those who sink into the grave.

2. Sing psalms to the Lord, you who love him,
   give thanks to his holy name.
   His anger lasts a moment; his favor all through life.
   At night there are tears, but joy comes with dawn.

3. The Lord listened and had pity.
   The Lord came to my help.
   For me you have changed my mourning into dancing,
   O Lord my God, I will thank you for ever.

Psalm 33 Let Your Mercy Be on Us 25
The Earth is Full of the Goodness

Refrain

Let your mer - cy be on us, O God,
as we place our trust in you.
Alternate refrain
The earth is full of the good - ness of
God, the good - ness of our God.

Verses

1. Your words, O God, are truth indeed,
   and all your works are ever faithful;
   you love justice and right,
   your compassion fills all creation.

2. See how the eye of God is watching,
   ever guarding all who wait in hope,
   to deliver them from death
   and sustain them in time of famine.

3. Exult you just in the Lord,
   for praise is the song of the righteous!
   How happy the people of God,
   the ones whom God has chosen!

4. Our soul is waiting for God,
   for God is our help and our shield.
   May your kindness and love be on us
   who place our hope in you.

26 Psalm 34 The Cry of the Poor

Refrain

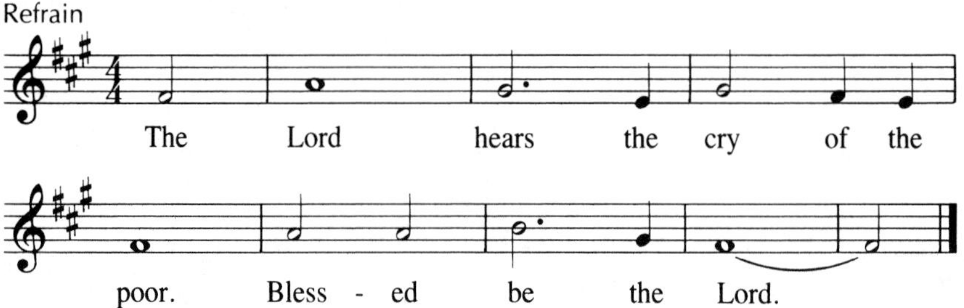
The Lord hears the cry of the
poor. Bless - ed be the Lord.

Verses

1. I will bless the Lord at all times,
his praise ever in my mouth.
Let my soul glory in the Lord,
for he hears the cry of the poor.

2. Let the lowly hear and be glad:
the Lord listens to their pleas,
and to hearts broken he is near,
for he hears the cry of the poor.

3. Ev'ry spirit crushed he will save;
will be ransom for their lives;
will be safe shelter for their fears,
for he hears the cry of the poor.

4. We proclaim the greatness of God,
his praise ever in our mouth;
ev'ry face brightened in his light,
for he hears the cry of the poor.

Text: *Psalm 34:2-3, 6-7, 18-19, 23;* Para. by John B. Foley, SJ
Tune: John B. Foley, SJ

Psalm 34 Taste and See 27

Refrain

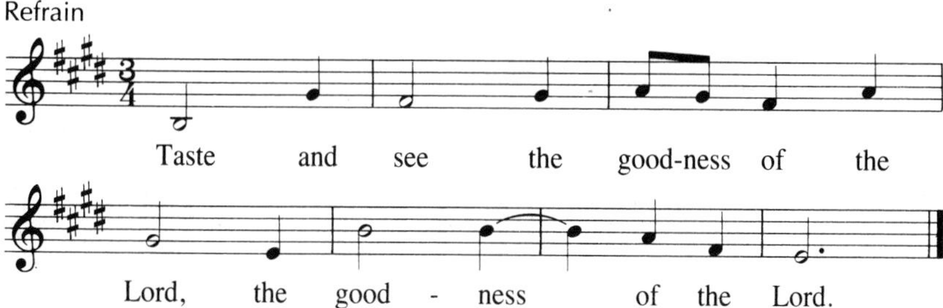
Taste and see the good-ness of the
Lord, the good - ness of the Lord.

Verses

1. I will bless the Lord; at all times,
his praise ever in my mouth.
Glory in the Lord for ever,
and the lowly will hear and be glad.

2. Glory in the Lord with me,
let us together extol his name.
I sought the Lord, and he answered me
and delivered me from all my fears.

3. Look to him that you might be radiant with joy,
and your faces free from all shame.
The Lord hears the suffering souls,
and saves them from all distress.

28 Psalm 42 Song of the Exile

Refrain

As a deer longs for run-ning streams,
so my soul longs for you, and my
heart thirsts for the God of my life.
When shall I go to see the
face of God?

Verses

1. I remember, and my soul melts within me:
   I am on my way to your wonderful tent,
   to the house of God,
   singing my songs of joy and thanksgiving.

2. I am broken, so I call to my Savior;
   as the waves roar down, sweeping over my head,
   and I call to you,
   be with me now, the God of my life.

3. In the day time may the Lord's love be with me;
   in the night your song will be still on my lips.
   I will sing to you,
   sing prayers to you, the God of my life.

Text: *Psalm 42:2-3, 5, 7-9;* Para. by Marty Haugen, b.1950
Tune: Marty Haugen, b.1950

Psalm 47 God Mounts His Throne 29

Refrain

1.
2.
God mounts his throne to shouts of
3.
joy, O sing your prais-es to the Lord!

Verses

1. All you peoples, clap your hands,
shout to God in gladness,
the Lord we must fear,
king of all the earth.

2. God goes up to shouts of joy,
sound the trumpet blast.
Sing praise to our God,
praise unto our king!

3. God is king of all the earth,
sing with all your skill
to the king of all nations,
praise him on his throne!

Text: *Psalm 47:2-3, 6-7, 8-9;* Adapt. by Marty Haugen, b.1950
Tune: Marty Haugen, b.1950

30 Psalm 51 Be Merciful, O Lord

Refrain

Be mer-ci - ful, O Lord, for we have sinned;
be mer-ci - ful, O Lord, for we have sinned.

Verses

1. Have mercy on me, God, in your kindness,
   in your compassion, blot out my offense.
   O wash me more and more from my guilt and my sorrow,
   and cleanse me from all of my sin.

2. My offenses, truly I know them,
   and my sins are always before me;
   Against you alone have I sinned, O Lord,
   what is evil in your sight I have done.

3. Create in me a clean heart, O God,
   put your steadfast spirit in my soul.
   Cast me not away from your presence, O Lord,
   and take not your spirit from me.

4. Give back to me the joy of your salvation,
   let your willing spirit bear me up
   and I shall teach your way to the ones who have wandered,
   and bring them all home to your side.

Psalm 51 Create in Me 31

Refrain

Cre-ate in me a clean heart, O God.

Verses

1. Have mercy on me, O God.
   In the greatness of your love,
   cleanse me from my sin.
   Wash me.

2. Stay close to me, O God.
   In your presence keep me safe.
   Fill me with your spirit.
   Renew me.

3. Your salvation is joy to me.
   In your wisdom show the way.
   Lead me back to you.
   Teach me.

Text: *Psalm 51: 3-4, 12-13, 14-15;* Para. by David Haas, b.1957
Tune: David Haas, b.1957

32 Psalm 62 In God Alone

Refrain

In God a - lone is my soul at rest, the God who is my help. The Lord is my rock, my strength and my hope; my for - tress, my God.

Verses

1. Only in God is my soul at rest,
   from my God comes my salvation.
   God is my rock, the salvation of my life.
   I shall not be shaken, for the Lord is my strength!

2. Only in God is my soul at rest,
   from my God comes my hope.
   God is my rock, my salvation and my song.
   I will rest in the Lord, I will not be afraid!

3. Glory and safety, God is my joy.
   God is my rock and my strength.
   God is my refuge, I trust with all my heart.
   Pour out your hearts before the Lord!

Text: *Psalm 62;* Para. by David Haas, b.1957
Tune: David Haas, b.1957

Psalm 63 As Morning Breaks 33

Refrain

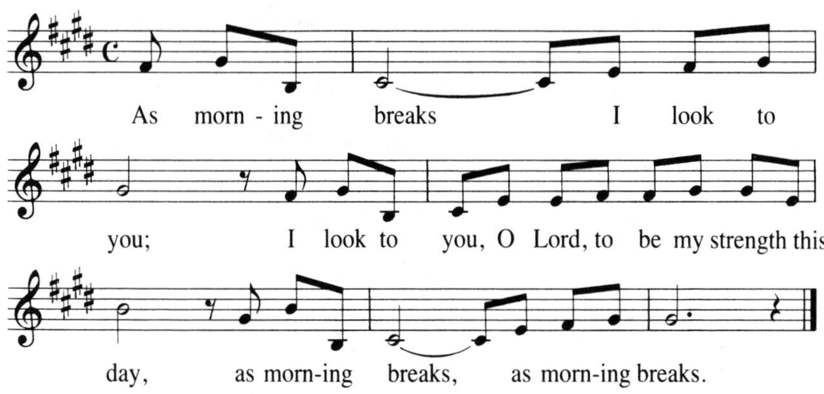
As morn - ing breaks I look to
you; I look to you, O Lord, to be my strength this
day, as morn-ing breaks, as morn-ing breaks.

Verses

1. O God, you are my God, for you I long;
   for you my soul is thirsting.
   My body pines for you
   like a dry, weary land without water.
   So I gaze on you in your holy place
   to see your strength and your glory.

2. For your love is better than life,
   my lips will speak your praise.
   So I will bless you all my life,
   in your name I will lift up my hands.
   My soul shall be filled as with a banquet,
   my mouth shall praise you with joy.

3. On my bed I remember you.
   On you I muse through the night
   for you have been my help;
   in the shadow of your wings I rejoice.
   My soul clings to you;
   your right hand holds me fast.

34 Psalm 63 My Soul Is Thirsting

Refrain

My soul is thirst - ing, my soul is thirst - ing,
my soul is thirst-ing for you, O Lord my God.

Verses

1. O God, you are my God whom I seek;
   O God, you are my God whom I seek;
   for you my flesh pines, my soul thirsts
   like the earth, parched, lifeless, without water.

2. Thus have I gazed t'ward you in your holy place
   to see your power and your glory.
   Your kindness is a greater good than life itself;
   my lips will glorify you.

3. Thus will I bless you while I live;
   Lifting up my hands I will call upon your name.
   As with a banquet shall my soul be satisfied;
   with exultant lips my mouth shall praise you.

4. For you have been my help, you have been my help;
   in the shadow of your wings I shout for joy.
   My soul clings fast to you; your right hand holds me firm;
   in the shadow of your wings I sing for joy.

Psalm 66 Let All the Earth 35

Refrain

Let all the earth cry out with joy to the Lord;

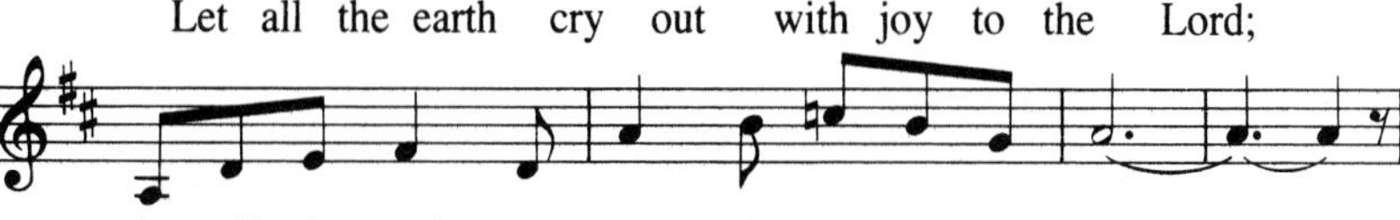
let all the earth cry out with joy to the Lord!

Verses

1. Cry out in joy to the Lord, all peoples on earth,
   sing to the praise of his name,
   proclaim him for ever,
   tremendous his deeds for us.

2. Leading his people safe through fire and water,
   bringing their souls to life;
   Come, sing of his glory,
   his love is eternal!

3. Hearken to me as I sing my love of the Lord,
   he answers the prayer of my heart,
   he leads me in safety
   from death unto life.

Text: *Psalm 66:1-3, 12, 16, 19;* Para. by Marty Haugen, b.1950
Tune: Marty Haugen, b.1950

36 Psalm 72 Every Nation on Earth

Refrain

Ev-'ry na-tion on earth will a - dore you, Lord;
ev-'ry na-tion on earth will a - dore you, Lord.

Verses

1. O God, with your judgment endow the king;
with your justice endow the King's son.
With justice he will govern your people,
your afflicted ones with right judgment.

2. Justice shall flower in his days,
lasting peace 'til the moon be no more.
May he rule from sea to sea,
from the river to the ends of the earth.

3. The kings of Tarshish and the isles offer gifts,
those from Seba and Arabia bring tribute.
All kings shall pay him their homage,
all nations shall serve him.

4. He rescues the poor when they cry out,
the afflicted with no one to help.
The lowly and poor he shall pity,
the lives of the poor he will save.

Text: *Psalm 72: 1-2, 7-8, 10-11, 12-13;* Adapt. by Michael Joncas, b.1951
Tune: Michael Joncas, b.1951

Ps. 80/85/Lk. 1 Lord, Make Us Turn to You 37

Refrain

Lord, make us turn to you, show us your
face and we shall be saved.

Verses

Psalm 80: 2-3, 15-16, 18-20

1. Shepherd of Israel, hearken from your throne and shine forth,
   O, rouse your power and come to save us.

2. We are your chosen vine, only by your care do we live,
   reach out your hand, O Lord, unto your people.

3. If you dwell with us, we shall live anew in your love,
   O, shine upon us, great Lord of life.

Psalm 85: 9-14

4. Lord, we are present here, show us your kindness and love,
   O, speak your word of peace unto your people.

5. Lord, let salvation rain, shower down your justice and peace,
   the earth shall bring forth truth, the skies your love.

6. See, Lord, we look to you, you alone can bring us to life,
   O, walk before us to light our pathways.

Luke 1:46-55

7. God has done wondrous things, holy is his name for all time,
   his mercy and his love are with his people.

8. God is my joy and song, I would have my life speak his praise,
   on me his love has shown, his blessings given.

9. He fills all hungry hearts, sending the rich empty forth,
   and holding up in love the meek and lowly.

Text: *Psalm 80: 2-3 15-16, 18-20; Psalm 85: 9-14; Luke 1: 46-55;* Para. by Marty Haugen, b.1950
Tune: Marty Haugen, b.1950

38 Psalm 84 How Lovely Is Your Dwelling Place

Refrain

How love - ly is your dwell - ing place, O Lord God of hosts!

Verses

1. My soul yearns and pines for the courts of the Lord,
   my heart and my flesh cry out;
   even the sparrow may find a home,
   the swallow a nest for her young;
   your altars, my king and my God!

2. How happy are they who may dwell in your courts,
   how happy when you are their strength;
   though they might go through the valley of death,
   they make it a place of springs.
   Your first rain will bring it to life.

3. O Lord of Hosts, hear my cry,
   and hearken, O God of Jacob;
   one day in your house is worth much more to me
   than ten thousand anywhere else;
   the Lord is my sun and my shield!

Text: *Psalm 84:2, 3-4, 5-7, 9, 11-12;* Para. by Michael Joncas, b.1951
Tune: Michael Joncas, b.1951

39 Psalm 84 Happy Are They

Refrain

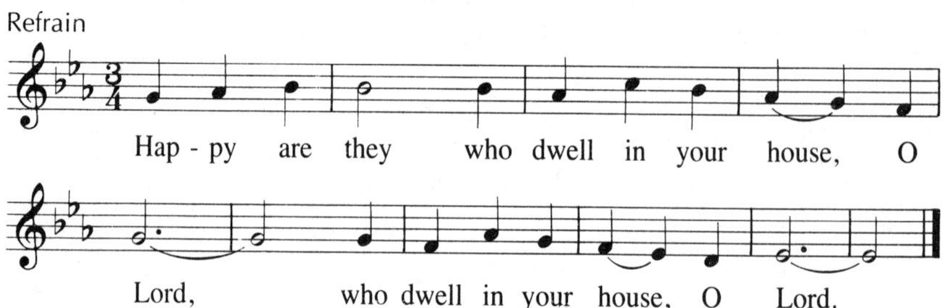
Hap - py are they who dwell in your house, O
Lord, who dwell in your house, O Lord.

Verses

1. My soul yearns and pines for the courts of the Lord.
My heart and my flesh cry to the living God.

2. The sparrow finds a home and the swallow a nest;
Your altars, O Lord, my King and my God.

3. Happy are they who abide in your house.
You are their strength, your praises they will sing.

Text: *Psalm 84:2, 3, 4, 5-6;* Para. by Thomas J. Porter, b.1958
Tune: Thomas J. Porter, b.1958

Psalm 85 Lord, Let Us See Your Kindness 40

Refrain

Lord, let us see your kind - ness;
Lord, let us see your kind - ness.

Verses

1. Let us hear what our God proclaims:
Peace to the people of God,
salvation is near to the ones who fear him.

2. Kindness and truth, justice and peace;
truth shall spring up as the water from the earth,
justice shall rain from the heavens.

3. The Lord will come and you shall know his love,
justice shall walk in his pathways,
salvation the gift that he brings.

Text: *Psalm 85:9-10, 11-12, 13-14;* Para. by Marty Haugen, b.1950 © 1983, GIA Publications, Inc.; Refrain trans. © 1969, ICEL
Tune: Marty Haugen, b.1950, © 1983, GIA Publications, Inc.

41 Psalm 89 For Ever I Will Sing

Refrain

For ev - er I will sing the good - ness of the
Lord, the good - ness of the Lord.

Verses

1. I have found David, my servant;
   with my holy oil I have annointed him,
   That my hand may ever be with him,
   and my arm make him strong.

2. My faithfulness and love shall be with you,
   in my Name your name will be exalted.

3. You shall cry to me,
   "My God, my rock of salvation, my salvation."

Text: *Psalm 89: 21-22, 25, 27;* Adapt. by Marty Haugen, b.1950, © 1987, GIA Publications, Inc.; Refrain trans. © 1969, ICEL
Tune: Marty Haugen, b.1950, © 1987, GIA Publications, Inc.

42 Psalm 91 Be with Me

Refrain

Be with me, Lord, when I am in
trou-ble, be with me, Lord, I pray.

Verses

1. You who dwell in the shelter of the Lord, Most High,
   who abide in the shadow of our God,
   say to the Lord, "My refuge and fortress,
   the God in whom I trust."

2. No evil shall befall you, no pain come near,
for his angels stand close by your side
guarding you always and bearing you gently,
watching over your life.

3. Those who cling to the Lord live secure in his love,
lifted high, those who trust in his name,
call on the Lord, he will never forsake you,
He will bring you salvation and joy.

Text: *Psalm 91: 1-2, 10-11, 14-15;* Para. by Marty Haugen, b.1950
Tune: Marty Haugen, b.1950

Psalm 95 If Today You Hear His Voice 43

Refrain

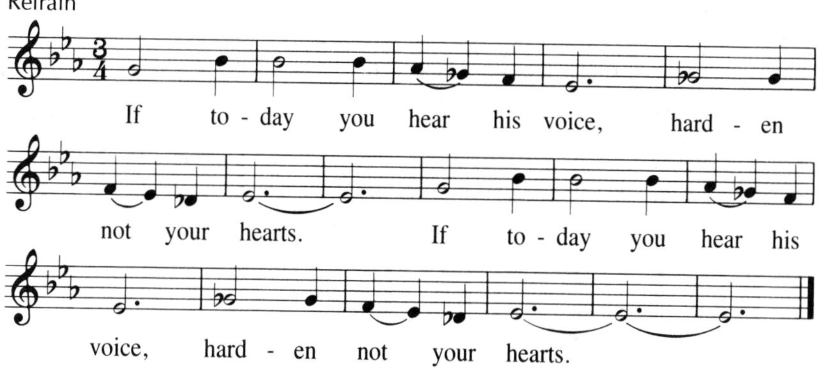
If to - day you hear his voice, hard - en
not your hearts. If to - day you hear his
voice, hard - en not your hearts.

Verses

1. Come, ring out our joy to the Lord, hail the Rock who saves us,
let us come now before him, with songs let us hail the Lord.

2. Come, let us bow and bend low, let us kneel before him who made us,
for he is our God; we his people, the flock that is led by his hand.

3. O that today you would hear his voice, "Harden not your hearts,
as on that day in the desert, when your parents put me to the test."

Text: *Psalm 95: 1-2, 6-7, 8-9;* alt.; © 1963, 1986, The Grail; Refrain trans. © 1969, ICEL
Tune: David Haas, b.1957, © 1983, GIA Publications, Inc.

44 Psalm 98 All the Ends of the Earth

Refrain

All the ends of the earth have seen the pow - er of God;
all the ends of the earth have seen the pow-er of God.

Verses

1. Sing to the Lord a new song, for he has done wondrous deeds;
his right hand has won the victory for him, his holy arm.

2. The Lord has made his salvation known, his justice revealed to all,
remembered his kindness and faithfulness to Israel.

3. All of the ends of earth have seen salvation by our God.
Joyfully sing out all you lands, break forth in song.

4. Sing to the Lord with harp and song, with trumpet and with horn.
Sing in your joy before the king, the king our Lord.

Text: *Psalm 98:1, 2-3, 3-4, 5-6;* Adapt. by David Haas, b.1957, Marty Haugen, b.1950
Tune: David Haas, b.1957, Marty Haugen, b.1950

Psalm 100 We Are His People 45

Ostinato Refrain

Melody
We are his peo - ple, the
Tenor
Alto

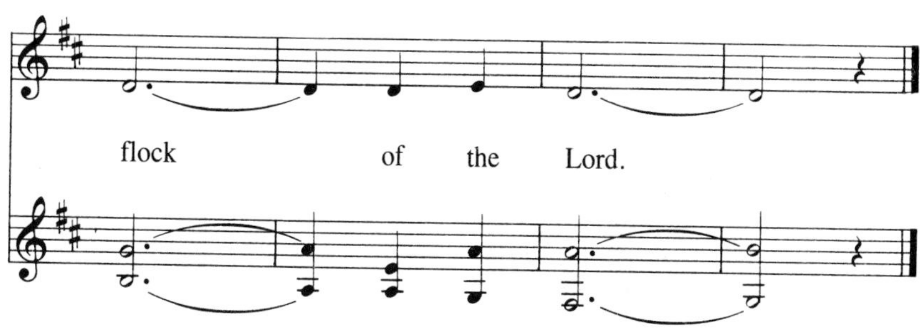
flock of the Lord.

Verses

1. Cry out with joy to the Lord, all you lands, all you lands.
   Serve the Lord now with gladness, come before him singing for joy!

2. Know that the Lord is God! Know that the Lord is God!
   He made us, we are his, his people, the sheep of his flock!

3. Go now within his gates giving thanks, giving thanks.
   Enter his courts singing praise, give him thanks and bless his name!

4. Indeed, how good is the Lord, his mercy endures for ever,
   for the Lord, he is faithful, he is faithful from age to age!

Text: *Psalm 100:1-2, 3, 4, 5;* Adapt. by David Haas, b.1957
Tune: David Haas, b.1957

46 Psalm 103 The Lord Is Kind and Merciful

Refrain

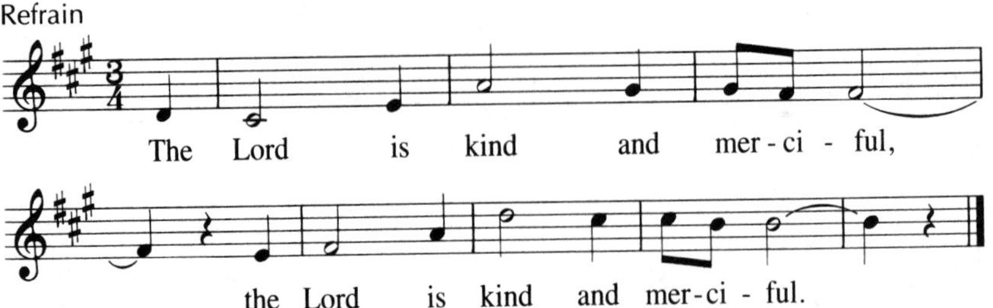
The Lord is kind and mer - ci - ful,
the Lord is kind and mer-ci - ful.

Verses

1. Bless the Lord, O my soul,
and all my being bless his name;
bless the Lord, and forget not his benefits.

2. He pardons all your iniquities,
and comforts your sorrows,
redeems your life from destruction,
and crowns you with his kindness.

3. Merciful, merciful,
and gracious is our God;
slow to anger, abounding in kindness.

Psalm 104 Lord, Send Out Your Spirit 47

Refrain

Lord, send out your Spir - it, and re- new the face of the earth!

Verses

1. Bless the Lord, O my soul;
   O Lord, my God, you are great indeed.
   How manifold are your works, O Lord!
   The earth is full of your creatures!

2. You take away their breath, they die,
   and they return to their dust.
   When you send forth your spirit of life,
   they are created in your sight!

3. May his glory last for all time;
   may the Lord be glad in his works.
   Pleasing to him will be my theme;
   I will be glad in the Lord!

48 Psalm 116 Our Blessing Cup

Refrain

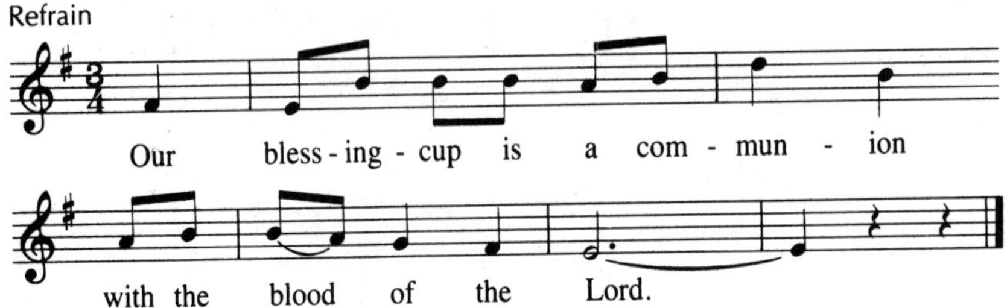
Our bless - ing - cup is a com - mun - ion
with the blood of the Lord.

Verses

1. How can I make a return to the Lord
for all he has done for me?
The cup of salvation I will take up,
I will call on the name of the Lord.

2. Precious, indeed, in the sight of the Lord
is the death of his faithful ones;
and I am your servant, your chosen one,
for you have set me free.

3. Unto your name I will offer my thanks
for the debt that I owe to you.
In the presence of all who have called on your name,
in the courts of the house of the Lord.

Text: *Psalm 116: 12-13, 15-16, 17-19;* Adapt. by Marty Haugen, b.1950
Tune: Marty Haugen, b.1950

Psalm 117 Holy is God, Holy and Strong 49

Refrain

Ho - ly is God!
Ho - ly is

Ho - ly and strong! Ho-ly is God!
God! Ho - ly! Ho - ly! Ho-ly is God!

Ho-ly and strong! Ho-ly and liv-ing for - ev - er!
Ho-ly and strong! Ho-ly and liv-ing for - ev - er!

Verses

1. O praise the Lord, all you nations,
   acclaim him, all you people!
   Strong is his love for us,
   he is faithful for evermore!

2. Give glory to the Father Almighty,
   to his Son Jesus Christ the Lord,
   to the Spirit who dwells in our hearts,
   both now and for ever. Amen.

50 Psalm 118 Let Us Rejoice

Refrain

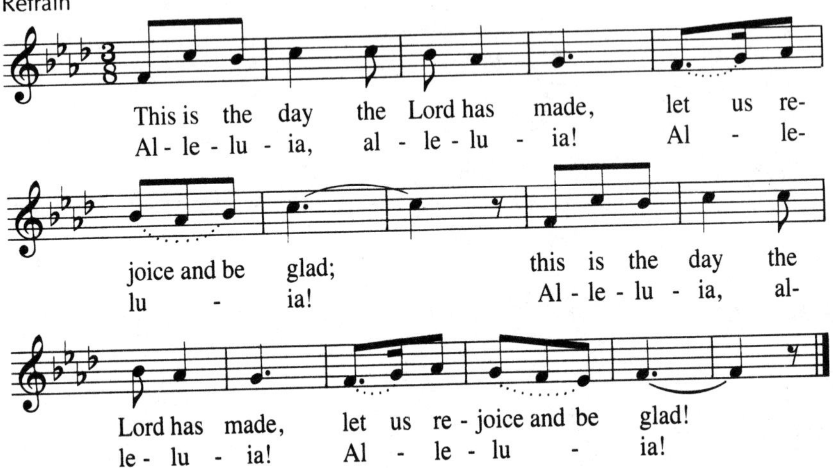
This is the day the Lord has made, let us re-joice and be glad; this is the day the Lord has made, let us re-joice and be glad!
Al-le-lu-ia, al-le-lu-ia! Al-le-lu-ia! Al-le-lu-ia, al-le-lu-ia! Al-le-lu-ia!

Verses

1. Give thanks to the Lord for he is good;
   his mercy endures for ever.
   Let the House of Israel say:
   "His mercy endures for ever."

2. The hand of the Lord has struck with power,
   his right hand is exalted,
   I shall not die, but live anew,
   declaring the works of the Lord.

3. The stone which the builders rejected
   has become the cornerstone,
   the Lord of love and mercy
   has brought wonder to our eyes.

Psalm 118 Alleluia, Alleluia 51

Refrain

Cantor:
Al - le - lu - ia! Al-le-lu-ia!
All:
Al - le - lu - ia! Al-le-lu-ia!
Cantor:
Al - le - lu - ia! Al-le - lu - ia!
All:
Al - le - lu - ia! Al-le - lu - ia!

Verses

1. This is the day the Lord has made,
   let us rejoice, be glad, and sing!
   Thanks and praise be to our God,
   for his mercy endures for ever.

2. The right hand of God has come with power,
   the Lord, our God, is lifted high!
   I shall not die, but I shall live
   and rejoice in the works of the Lord!

3. The stone which the builders once denied
   now has become the cornerstone
   by the Lord has this been done,
   it has brought wonder to our eyes!

Text: *Psalm 118:24, 1, 16-17, 22-23;* Adapt. by David Haas, b.1957
Tune: David Haas, b.1957

52 Psalm 121 Our Help Comes from the Lord

Refrain

Our help comes from the Lord, the
mak - er of heav - en and earth.

Verses

1. I lift up my eyes to the mountains:
from where shall come my help?
My help shall come from the Lord
who made heaven and earth.

2. May he never allow you to stumble!
Let him sleep not, your guard.
No, he sleeps not, nor slumbers,
He, Israel's guard.

3. The Lord is your guard and your shade:
at your right side he stands.
By day the sun shall not smite you
nor the moon in the night.

4. The Lord will guard you from evil:
he will guard your soul.
The Lord will guard your going and coming
both now and for ever.

5. Glory to the Father, and to the Son,
and to the Holy Spirit:
as it was in the beginning, is now,
and will be for ever. Amen.

Psalm 122 Let Us Go Rejoicing 53

Refrain

Let us go re - joic - ing to the
house of the Lord; let us go re-
joic - ing to the house of the Lord.

Verses

1. I rejoiced when I heard them say:
 "Let us go to the house of the Lord,"
 and now our feet are standing
 within your gates, O Jerusalem.

2. Jerusalem is a city built with unity and strength.
 It is there, it is there, that the tribes go up,
 the tribes of the Lord.

3. For Israel's law it is to praise God's name
 and there to give God thanks.
 There are set the judgment thrones for all of David's house.

4. Pray for the peace of Jerusalem!
 "May those who love you proper;
 May peace ever reign within your walls,
 and wealth within your buildings."

5. For love of my family and love of my friends,
 I pray that peace be yours.
 For love of the house of the Lord our God
 I pray for your good.

54 Psalm 128 O Blessed Are Those

Refrain

O blessed are those who fear the Lord and
walk in his ways, O blessed are those who
fear the Lord and walk in his ways.

Verses

1. O blessed are those who fear the Lord
   and walk in his ways!
   By the labor of your hands you shall eat.
   You will be happy and prosper.

2. Your wife like a fruitful vine
   in the heart of your house;
   your children like shoots of the olive
   around your table.

3. Indeed thus shall be blest
   all those who fear the Lord.
   May the Lord bless you from Zion
   all the days of your life!

Psalm 128 Blest Are Those Who Love You 55

Refrain

Blest are those who love you, hap-py those who
fol-low you, blest are those who seek you, O God.

Verses

1. Happy all those who fear the Lord,
and walk in God's pathway;
You will find what you long for –
the riches of our God.

2. Your spouse shall be like a fruitful vine
in the midst of your home,
Your children flourish like olive plants
rejoicing at your table.

3. May the blessings of God be yours
all the days of your life,
May the peace and love of God
live always in your heart.

Text: *Psalm 128: 1-2, 3, 5;* Para. by Marty Haugen, b.1950
Tune: Marty Haugen, b.1950

56 Psalm 130 With the Lord There Is Mercy

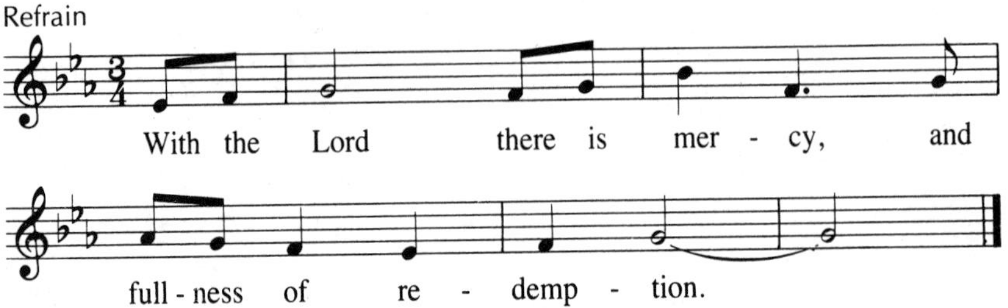
Refrain
With the Lord there is mer - cy, and
full - ness of re - demp - tion.

Verses

1. From out of the depths, I cry unto you, Lord,
   hear my voice, come hear my prayer;
   O let your ear be open to my pleading.

2. If you, O Lord, should mark your guilt,
   then who could stand within your sight?
   But in you is found forgiveness for our failings.

3. Just as those who wait for the morning light,
   even more I long for the Lord, my God,
   and his word to me shall ever be my comfort.

Text: *Psalm 130:1-2, 3-4, 5-6;* Para. by Marty Haugen, b.1950, Refrain trans.
Tune: Marty Haugen, b.1950,

Psalm 130 With the Lord There Is Mercy 57

Refrain

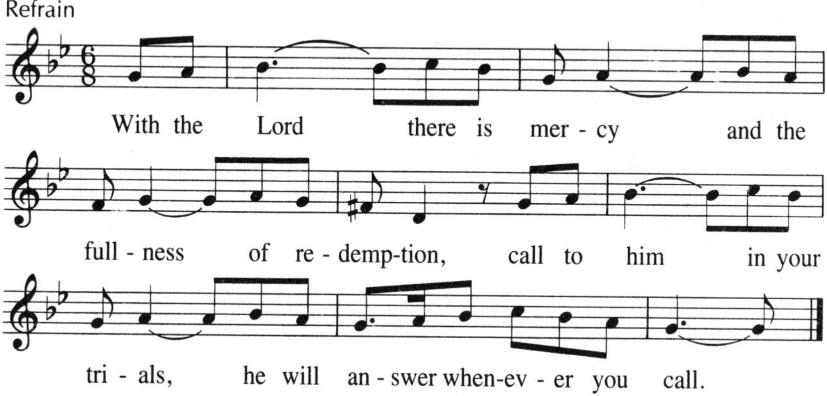
With the Lord there is mer - cy and the
full - ness of re - demp-tion, call to him in your
tri - als, he will an - swer when-ev - er you call.

Verses

1. Out of the depths I cry to you,
I cry to you, O Lord.
Lord, open your ears and hear my voice,
attend to the sound of my plea.

2. If you, O Lord, should mark our guilt,
then, Lord, who could hope to survive?
But with you is found forgiveness of sin,
and mercy that we might revere you.

3. Trust in the Lord, count on his word,
wait for the Lord, my soul.
I will wait for the Lord all the days of my life
as sentinels wait for the dawn.

4. More than the sentinels wait for the dawn,
let Israel wait for the Lord.
For kindness is his, redemption for all,
forgiveness of sins for his people.

Text: *Psalm 130: 1-2, 3-4, 5-6, 6-9;* Adapt. by Michael Joncas, b.1951
Tune: Michael Joncas, b.1951

58 Psalm 136 Love Is Never Ending

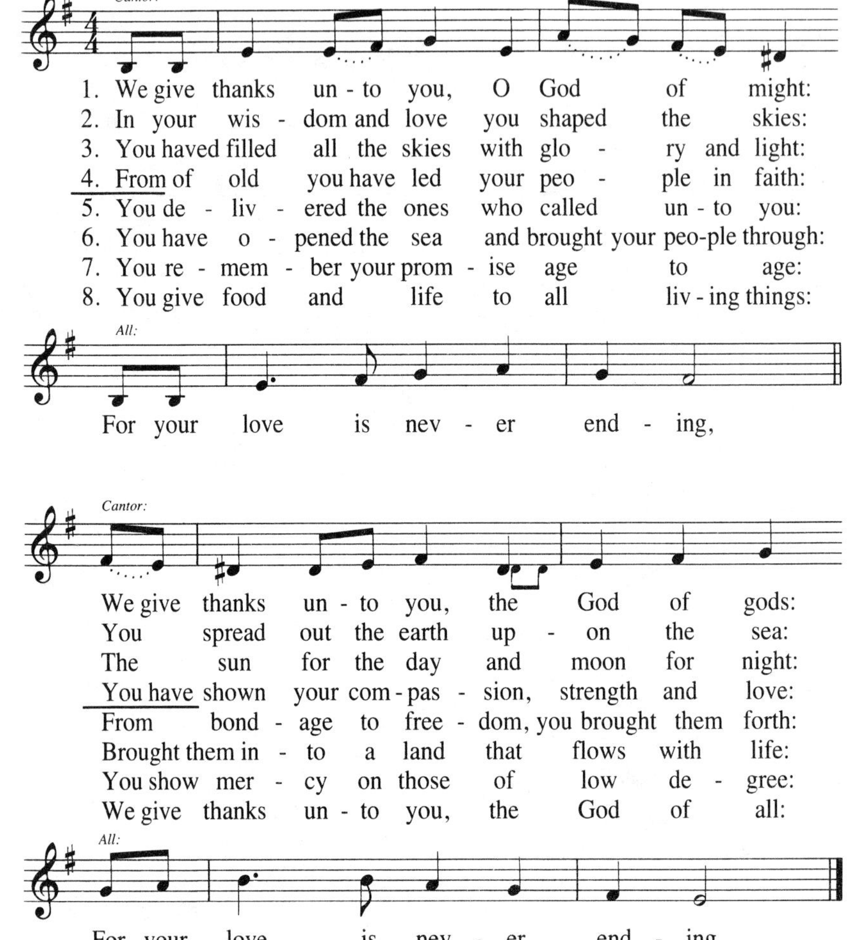
Cantor:
1. We give thanks un - to you, O God of might:
2. In your wis - dom and love you shaped the skies:
3. You haved filled all the skies with glo - ry and light:
4. From of old you have led your peo - ple in faith:
5. You de - liv - ered the ones who called un - to you:
6. You have o - pened the sea and brought your peo-ple through:
7. You re - mem - ber your prom - ise age to age:
8. You give food and life to all liv - ing things:
All:
For your love is nev - er end - ing,
Cantor:
We give thanks un - to you, the God of gods:
You spread out the earth up - on the sea:
The sun for the day and moon for night:
You have shown your com - pas - sion, strength and love:
From bond - age to free - dom, you brought them forth:
Brought them in - to a land that flows with life:
You show mer - cy on those of low de - gree:
We give thanks un - to you, the God of all:
All:
For your love is nev - er end - ing.

Text: Based on *Psalm 136;* Marty Haugen, b.1950
Tune: Marty Haugen, b.1950

Psalm 145 I Will Praise Your Name 59

Refrain

I will praise your name, my King and my God.

I will praise your name, my King and my God.

Verses

1. I will give you glory my God and King,
and I will bless your name for ever.
Every day I will bless and praise your name for ever.

2. The Lord is full of grace and mercy,
he is kind and slow to anger.
He is good in all his works and full of compassion.

3. Let all your works give you thanks, O Lord,
and let all the faithful bless you.
Let them speak of your might, O Lord, the glory of your kingdom.

4. The Lord is faithful in all his works,
and always near, his name is holy.
He lifts up all those who fall, he raises up the lowly.

Text: *Psalm 145: 1-2, 8-9, 10-11, 13b-14;* Para. by David Haas, b.1957
Tune: David Haas, b.1957

60 Psalm 146 Lord, Come and Save Us

Refrain

Lord, come and save us, Lord, come and
save us, Lord come and save us.

Verses

1. For all my life I will sing to you,
O ever faithful God.
You fill the heavens with wondrous lights,
the earth sings out your glory.

2. Put not your trust in those who rule,
the mighty of this earth.
Their breath shall fail, their power die,
there plans shall fade and vanish.

3. You give your sight to all the blind,
you raise up those bent low.
Your heart is near to the broken ones,
you welcome in the stranger.

4. Happy those who keep faith with you,
securing justice for the oppressed,
Who give your food to each hungry heart,
your freedom to each captive.

5. The weak and poor you sustain in love,
the wicked ones you bring to destruction;
For ever more shall your reign endure,
to every generation.

Text: *Psalm 146:2, 3-4, 8-9, 6b-7, 8c-10;* Para. by Marty Haugen, b.1950
Tune: Marty Haugen, b.1950

Psalm 147 Bless the Lord, My Soul 61

Refrain

Bless the Lord, my soul, who
heals the bro - ken heart - ed.

Verses

1. Praise the Lord, O Jerusalem,
chant praises to your God.
The strength of God is your fortress sure,
and blessed are your children.

2. All praise to you, O gracious God,
your goodness fills the earth.
You raise anew Jerusalem,
and gather all your lost ones.

3. You heal the hurt and the broken heart,
you bind up every wound,
You number all the stars of night
and call each one by name.

4. The peace of God shall be your hope,
God's finest wheat, your food,
The word of God fills all the earth,
as rapid as the whirlwind.

Text: *Psalm 147:12-13, 1-2, 3-4, 14-15;* Para. by Marty Haugen, b.1950
Tune: Marty Haugen, b.1950

62 Psalm 148 Praise the Lord from the Heavens

Refrain

Praise the Lord from the heav - ens, al - le - lu - ia.

Verses

1. Praise the Lord from the heavens,
   praise him in the heights.
   Praise him, all his angels,
   praise him, all his host.

2. Praise him, sun and moon,
   praise him, shining stars.
   Praise him, highest heavens
   and the waters above the heavens.

3. Let them praise the name of the Lord.
   He commanded: they were made.
   He fixed them for ever,
   gave a law which shall not pass away.

4. Praise the Lord from the earth,
   sea creatures and all oceans,
   fire and hail, snow and mist,
   stormy winds that obey his word;

5. All mountains and hills,
   all fruit trees and cedars,
   beasts, wild and tame,
   reptiles and birds on the wing.

6. All earth's kings and peoples,
   earth's princes and rulers;
   young men and maidens,
   old men together with children.

7. Let them praise the name of the Lord
   for he alone is exalted.
   The splendor of his name
   reaches beyond heaven and earth.

8. He exalts the strength of his people.
He is the praise of all his saints,
of the sons of Israel,
of the people to whom he comes close.

9. Glory to the Father, and to the Son,
and to the Holy Spirit.
As it was in the beginning,
is now and will be for ever. Amen.

63 Psalm 150 Praise God in His Holy Dwelling

Al-le - lu - ia, al - le - lu - ia, al-le - lu - ia!

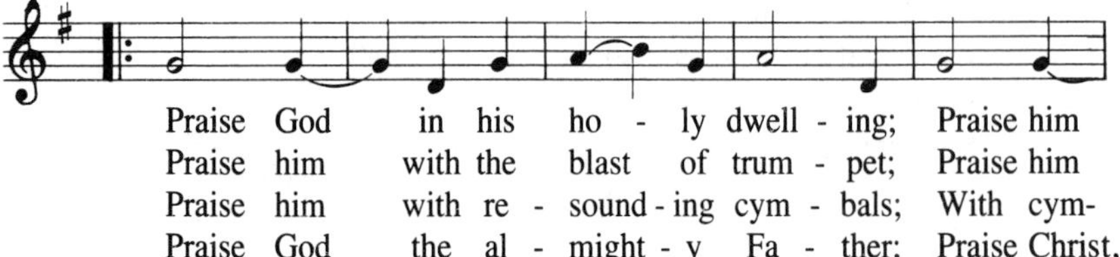
Praise God in his ho - ly dwell - ing; Praise him
Praise him with the blast of trum - pet; Praise him
Praise him with re - sound-ing cym - bals; With cym-
Praise God the al - might - y Fa - ther; Praise Christ,

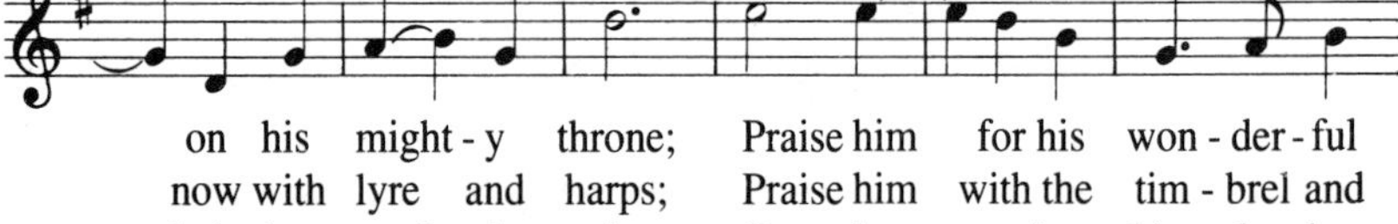
on his might-y throne; Praise him for his won-der-ful
now with lyre and harps; Praise him with the tim-brel and
bals that crash, give praise; O let ev-'ry -thing that has
his be - lov - ed Son; Give praise to the Spir - it of

deeds; Praise him for his sov-'reign maj - es - ty
dance; Praise him with the sound of string and reed.
breath, Let all liv-ing crea-tures praise the Lord.
love; For ev - er the Tri - une God be praised.

Al - le - lu - ia, al - le - lu - ia,

1.2.3.
Last time
al - le - lu - ia! lu - ia!

Text: *Psalm 150:1-2, 3-4, 5-6;* Adapt. by Omer Westendorf, b.1916
Tune: Jan M. Vermulst, b.1925

The Order of Mass

Each church gathers on the Lord's Day to listen to the scriptures, to offer 64
prayers, to give thanks and praise to God while recalling God's gifts in creation and saving deeds in Jesus, and to share in holy communion.

In these rites of word and eucharist, the church keeps Sunday as the Lord's Day, the day of creation and resurrection, the "eighth day" when the fullness of God's kingdom is anticipated. The Mass of the Christian community has rites of gathering, of word, of eucharist, of dismissal. All those who gather constitute the assembly. One member of this assembly who has been ordained to the presbyterate, the priesthood, presides by leading the opening and closing prayers and the eucharistic prayer. A member ordained to the diaconate may assist, read the gospel and preach. Other members of the assembly are chosen and trained for various ministries: These are the readers, ushers, musicians, communion ministers. All of these assist the assembly. It is the assembly itself, all those present, that does the liturgy.

The order of Mass which follows is familiar to all who regularly join in this assembly. It is learned through repetition. This order of Mass leaves many things to the local community and to the season of the liturgical year.

INTRODUCTORY RITES

The rites which precede the liturgy of the word assist the assembly to gather as a community. They prepare that community to listen to the scriptures and to celebrate the eucharist together. The procession and entrance song are ways of expressing the unity and spirit of the assembly.

GREETING

After the sign of the cross one of the greetings is given.

Presider: In the name of the Father, and of the Son, and of the Holy Spirit.

Assembly: **Amen.**

A	*Presider:*	The grace of our Lord Jesus Christ and the love of God and the fellowship of the Holy Spirit be with you all.
	Assembly:	**And also with you.**
B	*Presider:*	The grace and peace of God our Father and the Lord Jesus Christ be with you.
	Assembly:	**Blessed be God, the Father of our Lord Jesus Christ.**
		or: **And also with you.**
C	*Presider:*	The Lord be with you. (*Bishop:* Peace be with you.)
	Assembly:	**And also with you.**

65 BLESSING AND SPRINKLING OF HOLY WATER

On Sundays, instead of the penitential rite below, the blessing and sprinkling of holy water may be done. The following or another appropriate song is sung.

Refrain
"Mass of Creation"
Marty Haugen, 1984
If we have died to our-selves in Je - sus, then
we shall a - rise to new life in him. Al - le-
lu - ia, al - le - lu - ia!
Verses
1. We are fi - re and wa - ter, we are
2. In the wa - ter we seek him, in the
3. In the fi - re we seek him, in the
4. In our dy - ing and ris - ing, we shall
5. Flow-ing out of the des - ert, roll - ing
6. Rain-ing down from the heav - ens, spring-ing
7. Gift of love and of mer - cy, giv - en
sym-bol and sign of grace, we are the mys - t'ry,
well-spring of all that lives, all who are thirst - y,
hun-gers and pains we bear, hope for the hope - less,
fol - low where he has gone, pil-grims and lov - ers,
down from the moun - tain - side, up from with - in you,
up from the dri - est earth, sim - ple and ho - ly,
free - ly to all who thirst, gen - tle and yield - ing,

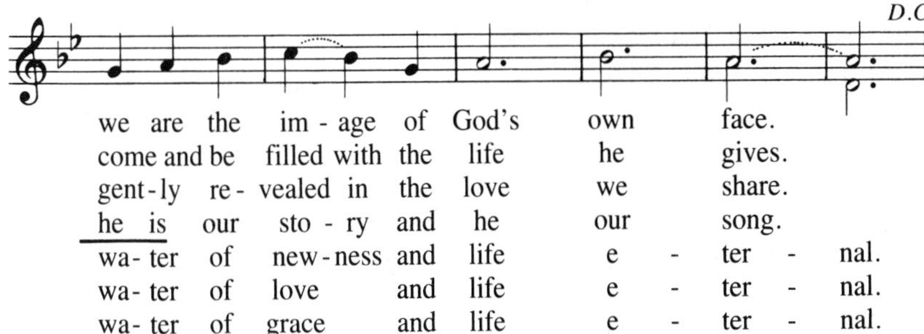
D.C.
we are the im - age of God's own face.
come and be filled with the life he gives.
gent-ly re- vealed in the love we share.
he is our sto - ry and he our song.
wa- ter of new-ness and life e - ter - nal.
wa- ter of love and life e - ter - nal.
wa- ter of grace and life e - ter - nal.

PENITENTIAL RITE 66

The presider invites all to be mindful of human sinfulness and of the great mercy of God. After a time of silence, one of the following forms is used.

A

Assembly: **I confess to almighty God,**
and to you, my brothers and sisters,
that I have sinned through my own fault
in my thoughts and in my words,
in what I have done,
and in what I have failed to do;
and I ask blessed Mary, ever virgin,
all the angels and saints,
and you, my brothers and sisters,
to pray for me to the Lord our God.

B

Presider: Lord, we have sinned against you:
Lord, have mercy.

Assembly: **Lord, have mercy.**

Presider: Lord, show us your mercy and love.

Assembly: **And grant us your salvation.**

C

The presider or another minister makes a series of invocations according to the following pattern.

Presider: (Invocation)
Lord, have mercy.

Assembly: **Lord, have mercy.**

Presider: (Invocation)
Christ, have mercy.

Assembly: **Christ, have mercy.**

Presider: (Invocation)
Lord, have mercy.

Assembly: **Lord, have mercy.**

The penitential rite always concludes:

Presider: May almighty God have mercy on us, forgive us our sins, and bring us to everlasting life.

Assembly: **Amen.**

67 **KYRIE**

Unless form C of the penitential rite has been used, the Kyrie follows.

"Mass of Creation"
Marty Haugen, 1984

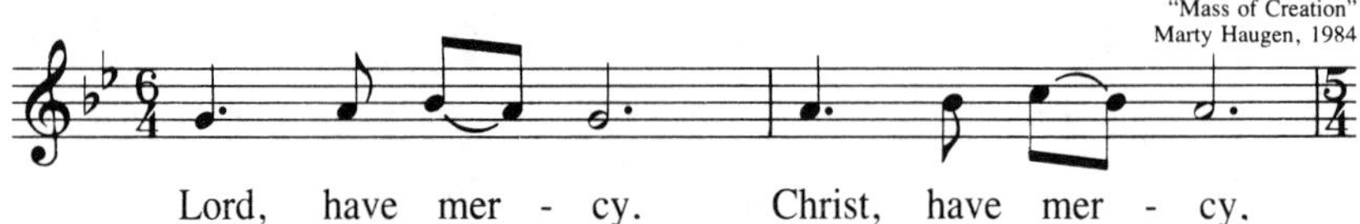
Lord, have mer - cy. Christ, have mer - cy.

Lord, have mer - cy.

68 **GLORIA**

The Gloria is omitted during Advent and Lent.

"Mass of Creation"
Marty Haugen, 1984

8
Refrain
Glo - ry to God in the high - est, and

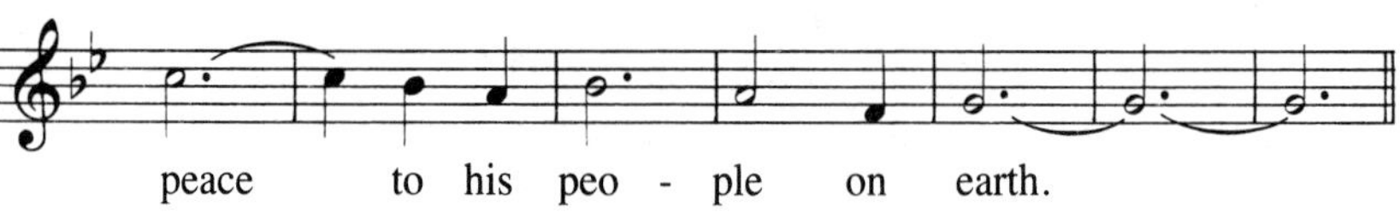
peace to his peo - ple on earth.

1. Lord God, heavenly King, almighty God and Father,
we worship you, we give you thanks,
we praise you for your glory. *Refrain*

2. Lord Jesus Christ, only Son of the Father,
Lord God, Lamb of God,
you take away the sin of the world: have mercy on us;
you are seated at the right hand of the Father:
receive our prayer. *Refrain*

3. For you alone are the Holy One,
you alone are the Lord,
you alone are the Most High, Jesus Christ,
with the Holy Spirit,
in the glory of the Father. Amen! Amen! *Refrain*

Final Refrain

Glo - ry to God in the high - est, and peace

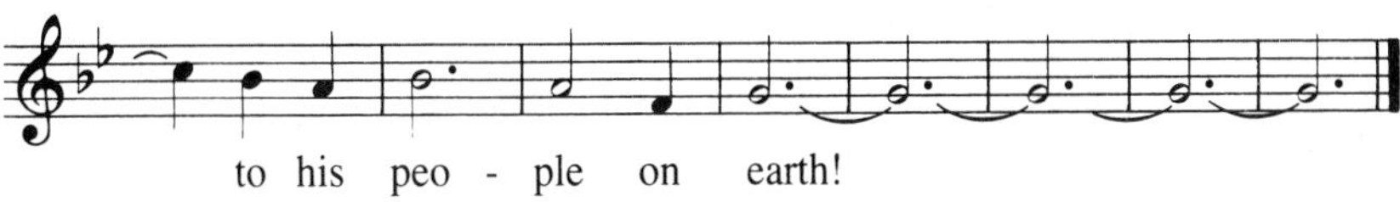
to his peo - ple on earth!

OPENING PRAYER 69

After the invitation from the presider, all pray for a while. The introductory rites conclude with the proper prayer of the day and the Amen of the assembly.

LITURGY OF THE WORD 70

When the church assembles, the book of the scriptures is opened and all listen as lectors and deacon (or presider) read from the places assigned. The first reading is normally from the Hebrew Scriptures, the second from the letters of the New Testament, and the third from the Book of Gospels. Over a three-year cycle, the church reads through the letters and gospels and a portion of the Hebrew Scriptures. During the Sundays of Ordinary Time, the letters and gospels are read in order, each Sunday continuing near the place where the previous Sunday's readings ended. During Advent/ Christmas and Lent/Easter, the readings are those which are traditional and appropriate to these seasons.

The church listens to and–through the weeks and years–is shaped by the scriptures. Those who have gathered for Sunday liturgy are to give their full attention to the words of the reader. A time of silence and reflection follows each of the first two readings. After the first reading, this reflection continues in the singing of the psalm. A homily, bringing together the scriptures and the life of the community, follows the gospel. The liturgy of the word concludes with the creed, the dismissal of the catechumens and the prayers of intercession. In the latter, the assembly continues its constant work of recalling and praying for the universal church and all those in need.

This reading and hearing of the word–simple things that they are–are the foundation of the liturgical celebration. The public reading of the scriptures and the rituals which surround this–silence and psalm and acclamation, posture and gesture, preaching and litany of intercession–gather the church generation after generation. They gather and sustain and gradually make of us the image of Christ.

READING I

In conclusion:

Reader: This is the Word of the Lord.

Assembly: **Thanks be to God.**

After a period of silence, the responsorial psalm is sung.

READING II

In conclusion:

Reader: This is the Word of the Lord.

Assembly: **Thanks be to God.**

A time of silence follows the reading.

71 GOSPEL

Before the gospel, an acclamation is sung.

"Mass of Creation"
Marty Haugen, 1984

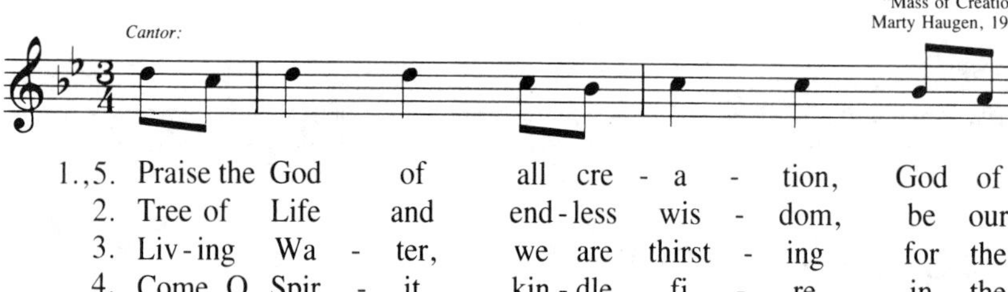
Cantor:
1.,5. Praise the God of all cre - a - tion, God of
2. Tree of Life and end-less wis - dom, be our
3. Liv-ing Wa - ter, we are thirst - ing for the
4. Come, O Spir - it, kin-dle fi - re in the

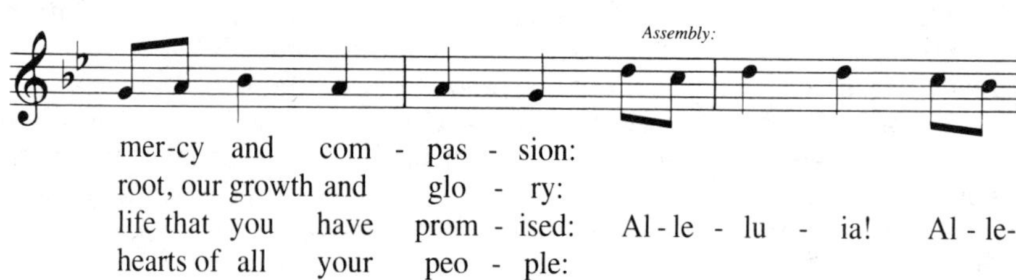
Assembly:
mer-cy and com - pas - sion:
root, our growth and glo - ry:
life that you have prom - ised: Al-le - lu - ia! Al - le-
hearts of all your peo - ple:

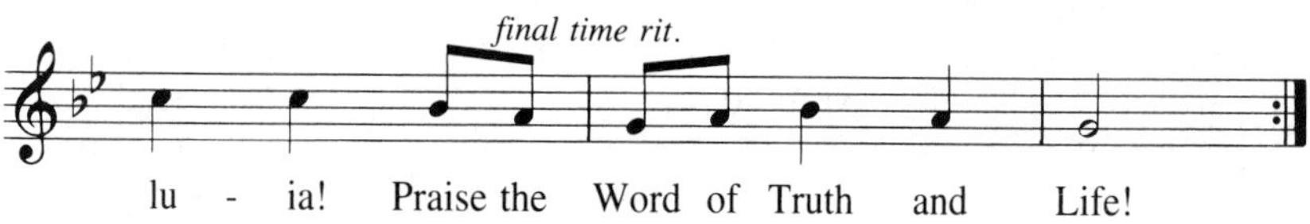
final time rit.
lu - ia! Praise the Word of Truth and Life!

During Lent one of the following acclamations replaces the alleluia.

"Mass of Creation"
Marty Haugen, 1984

A

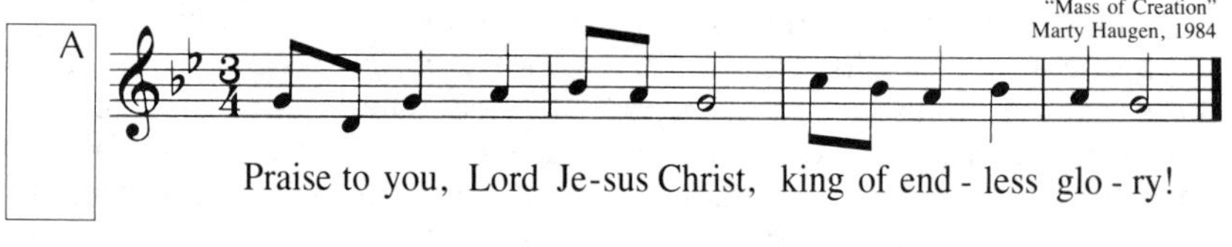
Praise to you, Lord Je-sus Christ, king of end - less glo - ry!

Or:

B **Praise and honor to you, Lord Jesus Christ!**

C **Glory and praise to you, Lord Jesus Christ!**

D **Glory to you, Word of God, Lord Jesus Christ!**

Deacon (or priest): The Lord be with you.

Assembly: **And also with you.**

Deacon: A reading from the holy gospel according to N.

Assembly: **Glory to you, Lord.**

After the reading:

Deacon: This is the gospel of the Lord.

Assembly: **Praise to you, Lord Jesus Christ.**

HOMILY

PROFESSION OF FAITH 72

**We believe in one God,
the Father, the Almighty,
maker of heaven and earth,
of all that is seen and unseen.**

**We believe in one Lord, Jesus Christ,
the only Son of God,
eternally begotten of the Father,
God from God, Light from Light,
true God from true God,
begotten, not made, one in Being with the Father.
Through him all things were made.
For us men and for our salvation he came down from heaven:**

All bow at the following words up to: and became man.

**by the power of the Holy Spirit
he was born of the Virgin Mary, and became man.
For our sake he was crucified under Pontius Pilate;
he suffered, died, and was buried.
On the third day he rose again
in fulfillment of the Scriptures;
he ascended into heaven
and is seated at the right hand of the Father.
He will come again in glory to judge the living and the dead,
and his kingdom will have no end.**

**We believe in the Holy Spirit, the Lord, the giver of life,
who proceeds from the Father and the Son.
With the Father and the Son he is worshiped and glorified.
He has spoken through the Prophets.
We believe in one holy catholic and apostolic Church.
We acknowledge one baptism for the forgiveness of sins.
We look for the resurrection of the dead,
and the life of the world to come. Amen.**

73 *At Masses with children, the Apostles' Creed may be used:*

**We believe in God, the Father almighty,
creator of heaven and earth.**

**We believe in Jesus Christ, his only Son, our Lord.
He was conceived by the power of the Holy Spirit
and born of the Virgin Mary.
He suffered under Pontius Pilate,
was crucified, died, and was buried.
He descended to the dead.
On the third day he arose again.
He ascended into heaven,
and is seated at the right hand of the Father.
He will come again to judge the living and the dead.**

**We believe in the Holy Spirit,
the holy catholic Church,
the communion of saints,
the forgiveness of sins,
the resurrection of the body,
and the life everlasting. Amen.**

74 **GENERAL INTERCESSIONS**

The people respond to each petition as follows, or according to local practice.

"Mass of Creation"
Marty Haugen, 1984

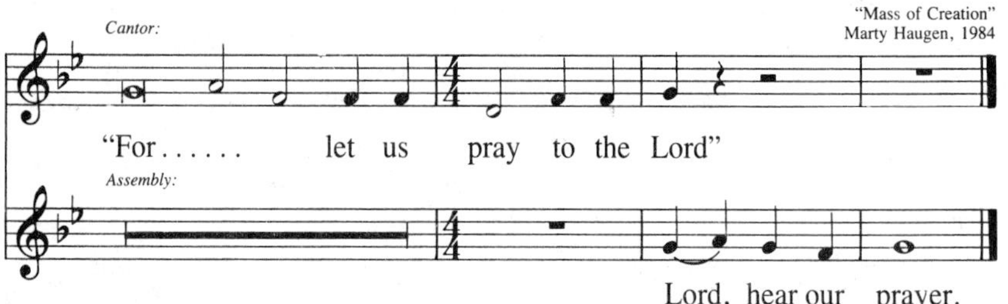
Cantor:
"For...... let us pray to the Lord"
Assembly:
Lord, hear our prayer.

75 LITURGY OF THE EUCHARIST

To do the eucharist means to give God thanks and praise. When the table has been prepared with the bread and wine, the assembly joins the presider in remembering the gracious gifts of God in creation and God's saving deeds. The center of this is the paschal mystery, the death of our Lord Jesus Christ which destroyed the power of death and his rising which brings us life. That mystery into which we were baptized we proclaim each Sunday at eucharist. It is the very shape of Christian life. We find this in the simple bread and wine which stir our remembering and draw forth our prayer of thanksgiving. "Fruit of the earth and work of human hands," the bread and wine become our holy communion in the body and blood of the Lord. We eat and drink and so proclaim that we belong to one another and to the Lord.

The members of the assembly quietly prepare themselves even as the table is prepared. The presider then invites all to lift up their hearts and join in the eucharistic prayer. All do this by giving their full attention and by singing the acclamations from the "Holy, holy" to the great "Amen." Then the assembly joins in the Lord's Prayer, the sign of peace and the "Lamb of God" litany which accompanies the breaking of bread. Ministers of communion assist the assembly to share the bread and wine. A time of silence and prayer concludes the liturgy of the eucharist.

PREPARATION OF THE ALTAR AND THE GIFTS

Bread and wine are brought to the table and the deacon or presider prepares these gifts. If there is no music, the prayers may be said aloud, and all may respond: **"Blessed be God for ever."** *The presider then invites all to pray.*

Assembly: **May the Lord accept the sacrifice at your hands**
for the praise and glory of his name,
for our good, and the good of all his church.

The presider says the prayer over the gifts and all respond: Amen.

EUCHARISTIC PRAYER 76

The central prayer of the Mass begins with this greeting and invitation between presider and assembly.

"Mass of Creation"
Marty Haugen, 1984

Presider:
Assembly:
Presider:

The Lord be with you. And al - so with you. Lift up your hearts.

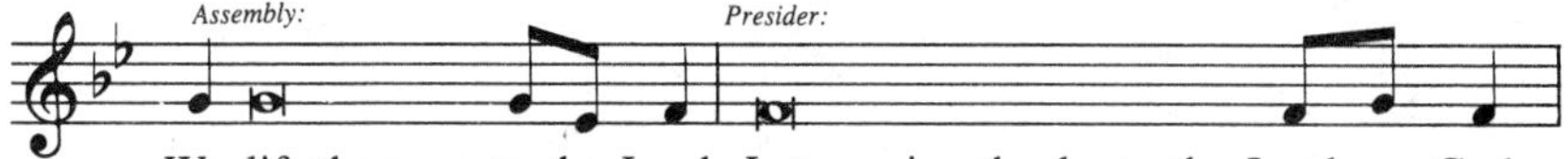
Assembly:
Presider:

We lift them up to the Lord. Let us give thanks to the Lord our God.

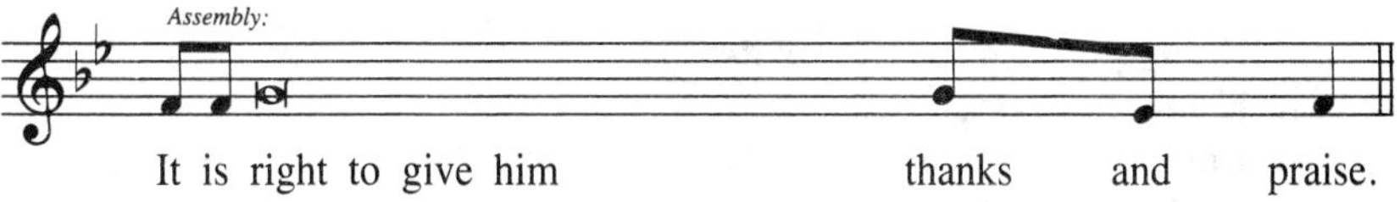
Assembly:

It is right to give him thanks and praise.

The Sanctus acclamation is sung to conclude the introduction to the eucharistic prayer.

77

"Mass of Creation"
Marty Haugen, 1984
4
Ho - ly, ho - ly, ho - ly Lord,
God of pow-er, God of might, heav-en and earth are
full of your glo - ry. Ho - san - na in the

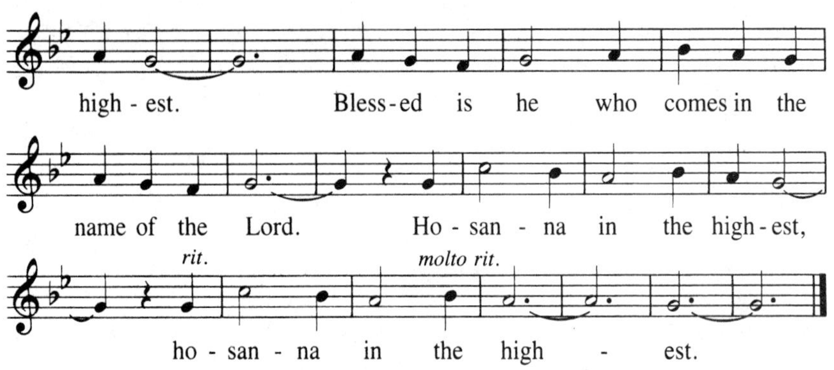
high - est. Bless-ed is he who comes in the
name of the Lord. Ho - san - na in the high-est,
rit. molto rit.
ho - san - na in the high - est.

78 *One of the following acclamations follows the deacon's or presider's invitation: "Let us proclaim the mystery of faith."*

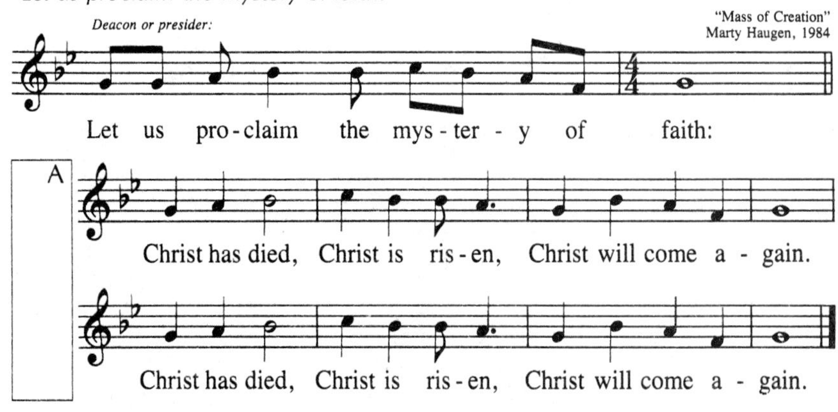
"Mass of Creation"
Marty Haugen, 1984
Deacon or presider:
Let us pro-claim the mys-ter-y of faith:
A
Christ has died, Christ is ris-en, Christ will come a - gain.
Christ has died, Christ is ris-en, Christ will come a - gain.

B **Dying you destroyed our death,**
rising you restored our life.
Lord Jesus, come in glory.

C **When we eat this bread and drink this cup,**
we proclaim your death, Lord Jesus,
until you come in glory.

D **Lord, by your cross and resurrection**
you have set us free.
You are the savior of the world.

The eucharistic prayer concludes:

79 *Presider:* Through him, with him, in him, in the unity of the Holy Spirit, all glory and honor is yours, almighty Father, for ever and ever.

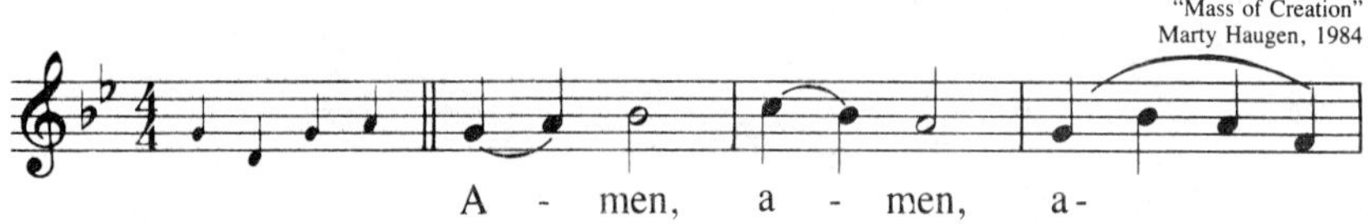
"Mass of Creation"
Marty Haugen, 1984
A - men, a - men, a-

rit.
molto rit.
men! A - men, a - men, a - men!

COMMUNION RITE

80

The presider invites all to join in the Lord's Prayer.

"Mass of Creation"
Marty Haugen, 1984

Our Fa - ther, who art in heav - en,

hal - low - ed be thy name; thy king-dom come; thy

will be done on earth as it is in heav - en.

Give us this day our dai - ly bread; and for-

poco rit.

give us our tres-pass - es as we for - give those who

a tempo

tres - pass a - gainst us; and lead us not in - to temp-

ta - tion, but de - liv - er us from e - vil.

Presider: Deliver us, Lord…
for the coming of our Savior, Jesus Christ.

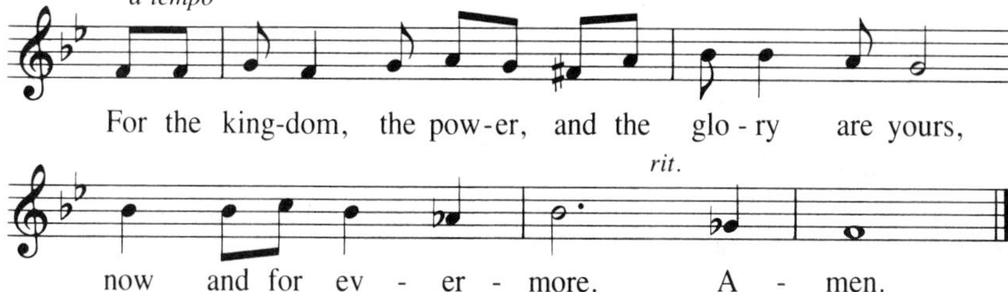
a tempo
For the king-dom, the pow-er, and the glo - ry are yours,
rit.
now and for ev - er - more. A - men.

81 *Following the prayer "Lord, Jesus Christ," the presider invites the sign of peace.*

Presider: The peace of the Lord be with you always.

Assembly: **And also with you.**

All exchange a sign of peace.

82 *Then the bread is solemnly broken and the bread and wine prepared for holy communion. The litany "Lamb of God" is sung through the breaking of the bread:*

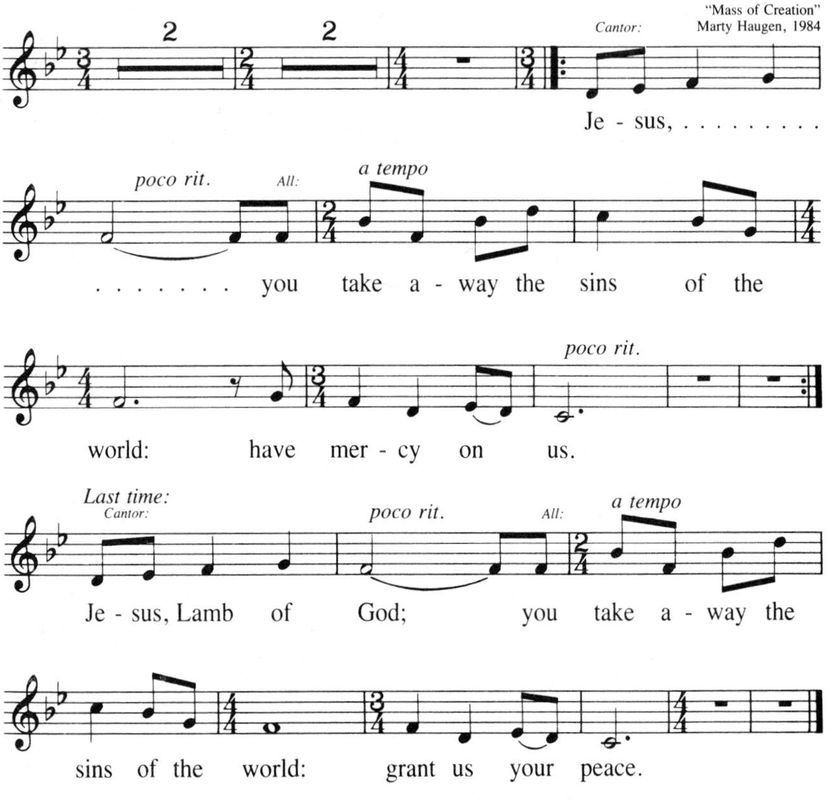
"Mass of Creation"
Marty Haugen, 1984
Cantor:
Je - sus, ...
poco rit.
All:
a tempo
. . . . you take a - way the sins of the
world: have mer - cy on us.
Last time:
Cantor:
Je - sus, Lamb of God;
poco rit.
All:
a tempo
you take a - way the
sins of the world: grant us your peace.

83 *The presider then invites all to share in the holy communion.*

Assembly: **Lord, I am not worthy to receive you,**
but only say the word and I shall be healed.

Minister of communion: The body of Christ.

Or:

The blood of Christ.

Communicant: **Amen.**

A song or psalm is ordinarily sung during communion. After communion, a time of silence is observed or a song of thanksgiving is sung. The rite concludes with the prayer after communion to which all respond: **Amen.**

CONCLUDING RITE 84

The liturgy of word and eucharist ends very simply. There may be announcements of events and concerns for the community, then the presider gives a blessing and the assembly is dismissed.

GREETING AND BLESSING

Presider: The Lord be with you.

Assembly: **And also with you.**

Optional

When the bishop blesses the people he adds the following:

Bishop: Blessed be the name of the Lord.

Assembly: **Now and for ever.**

Bishop: Our help is in the name of the Lord.

Assembly: **Who made heaven and earth.**

The blessing may be in a simple or solemn form. All respond to the blessing or to each part of the blessing: **Amen.**

DISMISSAL

Go in the peace of Christ.

or: The Mass is end - ed, go in peace. Thanks be to God.

or: Go in peace to love and serve the Lord.

Setting One

85 **KYRIE ELEISON**

"Mass of Light"
David Haas, 1987
Cantor:
All:
Ky-ri - e e - le - i - son. Ky-ri - e e - le - i - son.
Chri - ste e - le - i - son. Chri - ste e - le - i - son.
Ky-ri - e e - le - i - son. Ky-ri - e e - le - i - son.

86 **GLORIA**

Refrain
"Mass of Light"
David Haas, 1987
Glo - ry to God in the high - est,
Sing! Glo - ry to God! Glo - ry to
God in the high - est, and peace to his

peo - ple on earth!
Verses
1. Lord God, heav - en - ly King, al-
might - y God and Fa - ther,
we wor - ship you, we give you thanks,
D.C.
we praise you for your glo - ry!
2. Lord Je - sus Christ, on - ly Son of the Fa - ther,
Lord God, Lamb of God,
you take a - way the sin of the world:
have mer - cy on us;
you are seat - ed at the right hand
D.C.
of the Fa - ther: re - ceive our prayer!

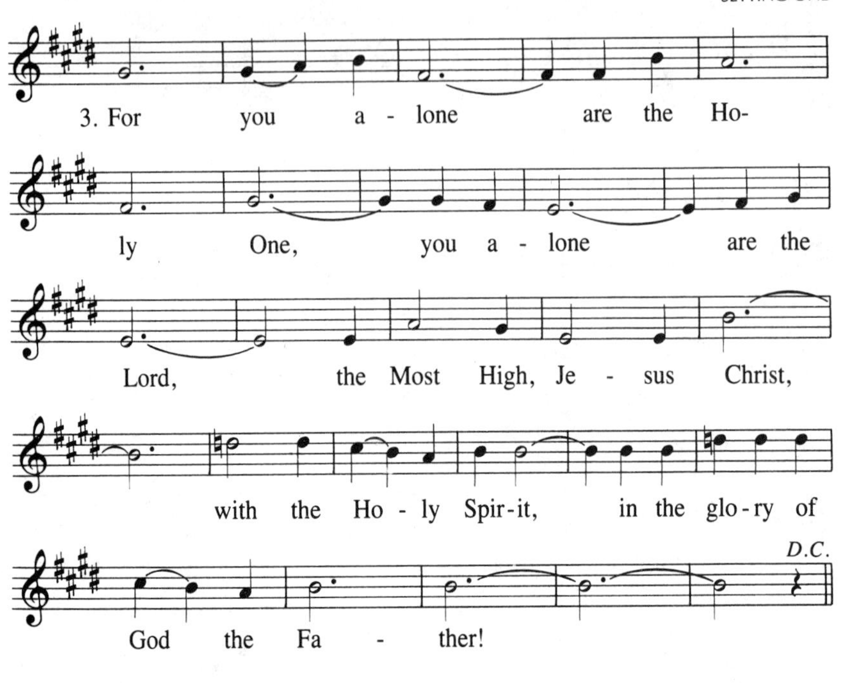
3. For you a - lone are the Ho-
ly One, you a - lone are the
Lord, the Most High, Je - sus Christ,
with the Ho - ly Spir-it, in the glo-ry of
D.C.
God the Fa - ther!

87 **ALLELUIA**

"Mass of Light"
David Haas, 1987

Cantor, then all:
Al-le-lu-ia, al-le-lu-ia, al-le-lu - ia!

88 **GOSPEL ACCLAMATION**

"Mass of Light"
David Haas, 1987

Cantor, then all:
Glo-ry to you, O Word of God, Lord Je - sus Christ.

89 **PREFACE DIALOG**

"Mass of Light"
David Haas, 1987

Presider:
The Lord be with you.
Assembly:
And al - so with you.
Presider:
Lift up your hearts.
Assembly:
We lift them up to the Lord.
Presider:
Let us give thanks to the Lord our God.

Assembly:
It is right to give him thanks and praise.

SANCTUS 90

"Mass of Light"
David Haas, 1987

Ho - ly, ho - ly, ho - ly Lord, God of pow - er,

God of might, heav-en and earth are full of your

glo - ry! Ho - san - na in the high - est!

Bless-ed is he who comes in the name of the Lord! Ho-

san - na in the high - est! Ho-

san - na in the high - est!

EUCHARISTIC ACCLAMATION I (OPTIONAL)* 91

"Mass of Light"
David Haas, 1987

Ho - san - na in the high - est!

**As in the Eucharistic Prayers for Masses with Children.*

MEMORIAL ACCLAMATION 92

"Mass of Light"
David Haas, 1987

Dy - ing you de - stroyed our death, ris - ing you re-

stored our life. Lord Je - sus come!
Lord Je - sus come in glo - ry!
93 EUCHARISTIC ACCLAMATION II (OPTIONAL)
"Mass of Light"
David Haas, 1987
Hear us, hear us. Hear us, hear us.
94 AMEN
"Mass of Light"
David Haas, 1987
A - men, a - men! A - men, a - men!
95 AGNUS DEI
"Mass of Light"
David Haas, 1987
Cantor:
All:
*Lamb of God, you take a - way the sins of the
world: have mer - cy on us.
Last time:
Cantor:
All:
Lamb of God, you take a - way the sins of the
world: grant us your peace.

** Other invocations may be substituted: Saving Cup, Hope for all, Prince of Peace, Wine of Peace, etc.*

Setting Two

KYRIE 96

"Mass of Remembrance"
Marty Haugen, 1987
Ky - ri - e e - le - i - son, Chri - ste e - le - i - son,
Ky - ri - e e - le - i - son.
GLORIA 97
Refrain
Presider or cantor:
"Mass of Remembrance"
Marty Haugen, 1987
Glo - ry to God in the high - est, and
peace to his peo - ple on earth.
All:
Glo - ry to God in the high - est, and
peace to his peo - ple on earth.

Choir: Lord God, heavenly King, almighty God and Father,
we worship you, we give you thanks,
we praise you for your glory.
All Sing Entire Refrain

Lord Jesus Christ, only Son of the Father,
Lord God, Lamb of God, you take away the sin of the world:
have mercy on us;
you are seated at the right hand of the Father:
receive our prayer.
All Sing Entire Refrain

For you alone are the Holy One, you alone are the Lord,
you alone are the Most High, Jesus Christ,
with the Holy Spirit, in the glory of God the Father. Amen.
All Sing Entire Refrain

98 ALLELUIA

"Mass of Remembrance"
Marty Haugen, 1987

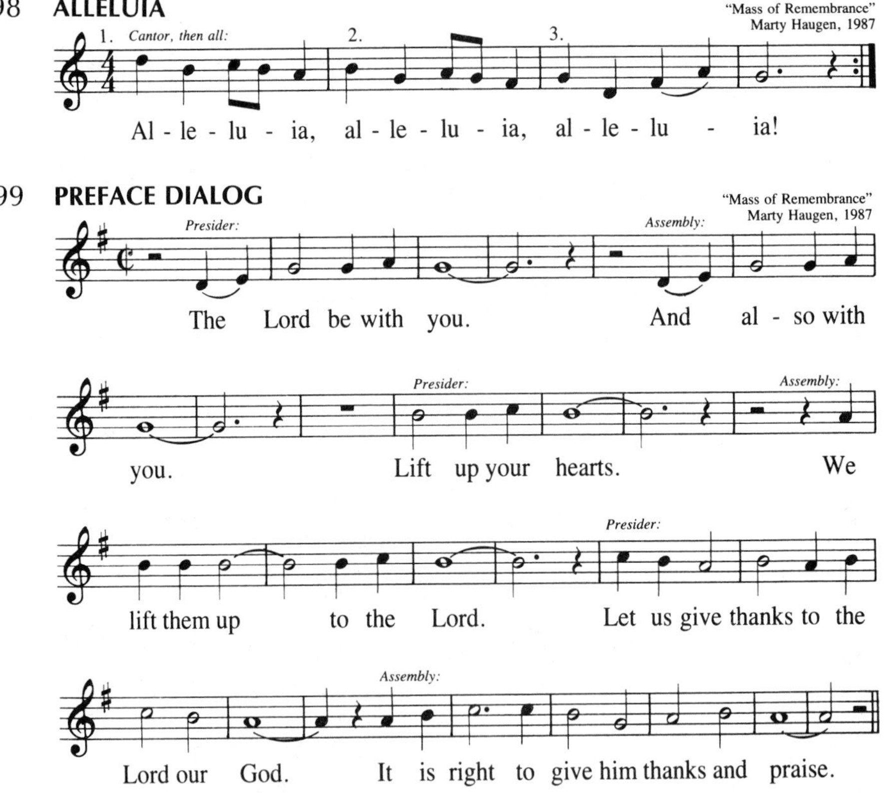
1. Cantor, then all:
2.
3.
Al - le - lu - ia, al - le - lu - ia, al - le - lu - ia!
99 PREFACE DIALOG
"Mass of Remembrance"
Marty Haugen, 1987
Presider:
The Lord be with you.
Assembly:
And also with you.
Presider:
Lift up your hearts.
Assembly:
We lift them up to the Lord.
Presider:
Let us give thanks to the Lord our God.
Assembly:
It is right to give him thanks and praise.

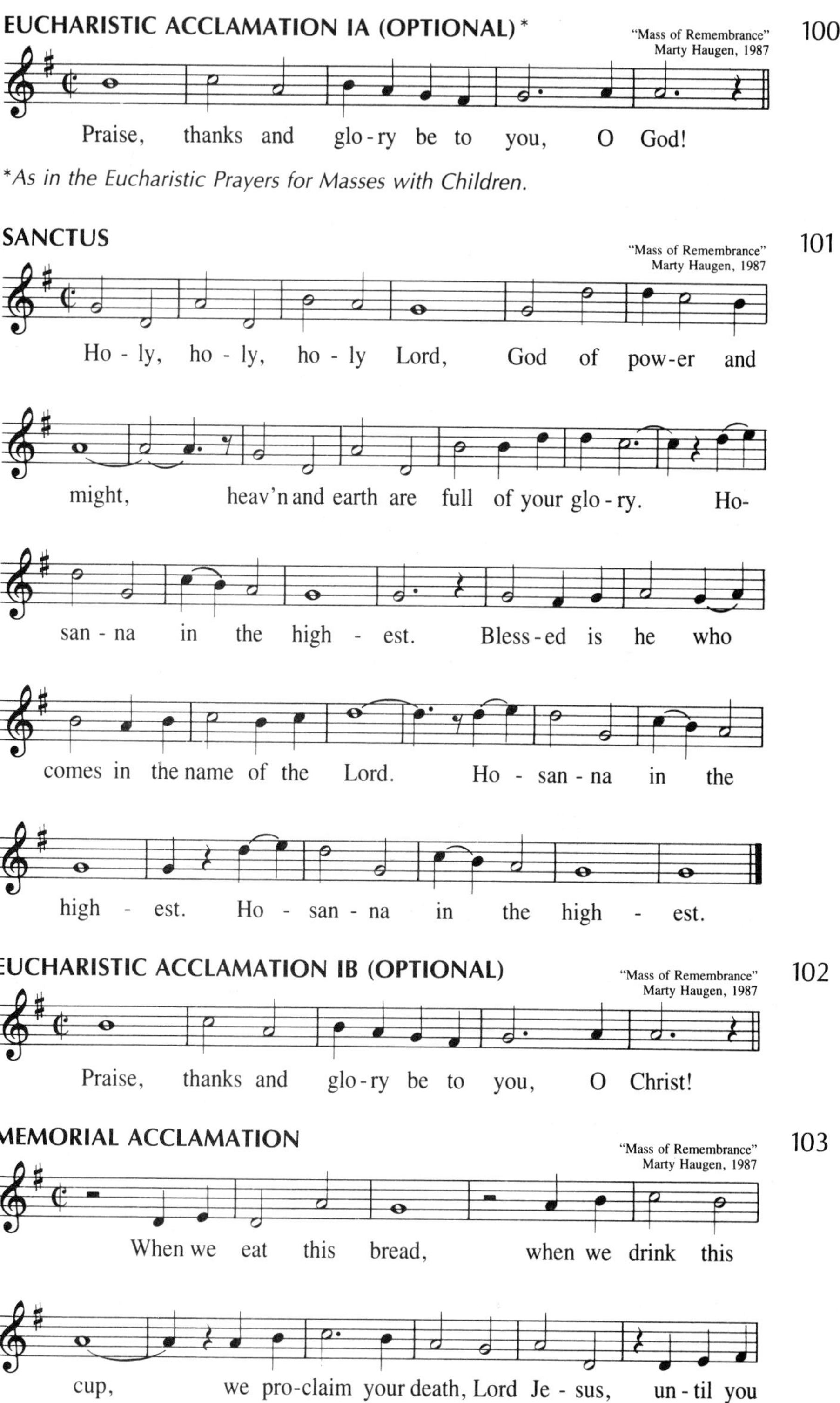
EUCHARISTIC ACCLAMATION IA (OPTIONAL)*
"Mass of Remembrance"
Marty Haugen, 1987
100
Praise, thanks and glo-ry be to you, O God!
*As in the Eucharistic Prayers for Masses with Children.
SANCTUS
"Mass of Remembrance"
Marty Haugen, 1987
101
Ho-ly, ho-ly, ho-ly Lord, God of pow-er and might, heav'n and earth are full of your glo-ry. Ho-san-na in the high-est. Bless-ed is he who comes in the name of the Lord. Ho-san-na in the high-est. Ho-san-na in the high-est.
EUCHARISTIC ACCLAMATION IB (OPTIONAL)
"Mass of Remembrance"
Marty Haugen, 1987
102
Praise, thanks and glo-ry be to you, O Christ!
MEMORIAL ACCLAMATION
"Mass of Remembrance"
Marty Haugen, 1987
103
When we eat this bread, when we drink this cup, we pro-claim your death, Lord Je-sus, un-til you

come, un - til you come in glo - ry!
104 EUCHARISTIC ACCLAMATION II (OPTIONAL)
"Mass of Remembrance"
Marty Haugen, 1987
We re - mem-ber how you loved us to your
death, and still we cel - e - brate, for you are with us
here; and we be - lieve that we will see you
when you come in your glo - ry, Lord. We re-
mem - ber, we cel - e - brate, we be - lieve.
105 EUCHARISTIC ACCLAMATION III (OPTIONAL)
"Mass of Remembrance"
Marty Haugen, 1987
Hear us, O Lord; hear us, O Lord.
106 AMEN
"Mass of Remembrance"
Marty Haugen, 1987
Al - le - lu - ia, a - men.
During Lent: Praise to you, Lord, a - men.
Al - le - lu - ia, a - men.
Praise to you, Lord, a - men.

AGNUS DEI

107

"Mass of Remembrance"
Marty Haugen, 1987

Cantor:
All:
Lamb of God, you take a - way the sins of the
To repeat
2
Last time
world: have mer - cy on us.
world:

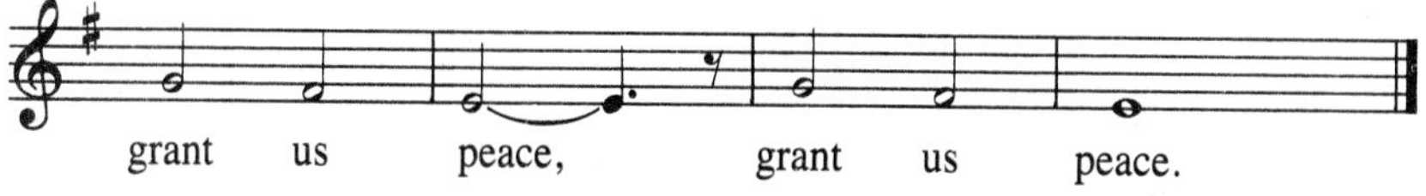
grant us peace, grant us peace.

Setting Three

108 **KYRIE**

The Psallite Mass
Michael Joncas, 1988

109 **GLORIA**

The Psallite Mass
Michael Joncas, 1988

Cantor:
All:
Lord, have mercy. Lord, have mer-cy.
Cantor:
All:
Christ, have mer - cy. Christ, have mer-cy.
Cantor:
All:
Lord, have mer-cy. Lord, have mer-cy.
Refrain I
Glo - ri - a in ex - cel - sis De - o, glo - ri - a
in ex - cel - sis De - o, glo - ri - a in ex-
cel - sis De - o, et in ter - ra pax.

Choir: Glory to God in the highest, and peace to his people on earth.
Glory to God in the highest, and peace to his people on earth.
Refrain One

Lord God, heavenly King, almighty God and Father,
we worship you, we give you thanks, we praise you for your glory.
Refrain One

Lord Jesus Christ, only Son of the Father,
Lord Jesus Christ, Lord God, Lamb of God,
Refrain Two

Refrain II
Do-mi-ne Je - su Chri-ste, Do-mi-ne Je - su Chri-ste,
mi - se - re - re no - bis, mi - se - re - re.

You take away the sin of the world: have mercy on us;
you are seated at the right hand of the Father: receive our prayer.
Refrain Two

For you alone are the Holy One, you alone are the Lord,
you alone are the Most High, Jesus Christ, *(begin Refrain One)*
with the Holy Spirit, with the Holy Spirit
in the glory of God the Father. Amen.

SANCTUS 110

The Psallite Mass
Michael Joncas, 1988

2
Ho - ly, ho - ly, ho - ly.
Lord God of pow - er and might, heav - en and earth are
Ho - ly, ho - ly, ho -
full of your glo - ry.
- ly. Ho - san - na, ho - san - na
in the high - est! Ho - ly, ho - ly, ho - ly.

Bless - ed is he, bless - ed is he,
Ho - ly, ho - ly,
blest is he who comes in the name of the Lord.
ho - ly.
Ho-san-na, ho-san-na in the high - est!

111 MEMORIAL ACCLAMATION

The Psallite Mass
Michael Joncas, 1988

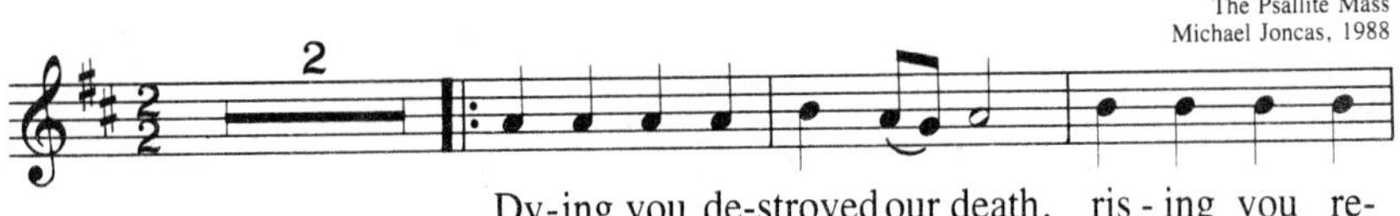
2
Dy-ing you de-stroyed our death, ris-ing you re-

stored our life. Lord Je-sus, Lord, Je-sus, come in glo - ry!

112 AMEN

The Psallite Mass
Michael Joncas, 1988

A - men, a - men, a - men.
Al-le-lu - ia, al-le-lu - ia, al-le-lu - ia!

113 AGNUS DEI

The Psallite Mass
Michael Joncas, 1988

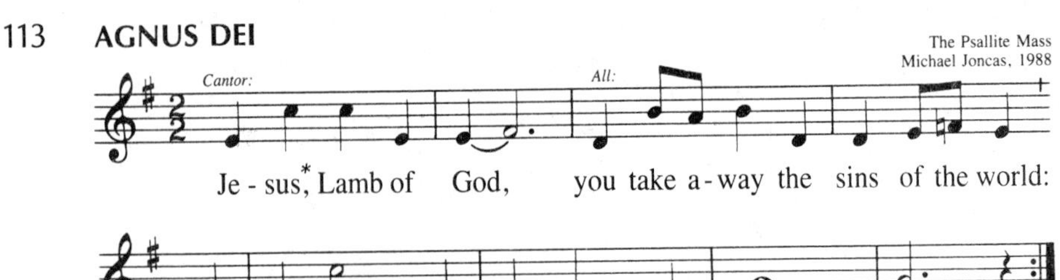
Cantor:
All:
Je - sus,* Lamb of God, you take a-way the sins of the world:
have mer - cy, have mer - cy on us.

* *Other invocations may be used: King of Kings, Prince of Peace, Bread of Life, Ancient Cup, etc.*

Last time:
Cantor:
All:
Je - sus, Lamb of God, you take a-way the sins of the world:

have mer - cy, and grant us your peace.

Service Music

114 **RITE OF SPRINKLING**

Refrain

David Haas, 1987

Wa - ter of life, Je - sus our light; jour-ney from

death to new life. Wa - ter of life,

Je - sus our light; jour-ney from death to new life.

Verses

1. Foun-tain of light, new sight for the blind, we come to the
2. Foun-tain of com-pas-sion, free-dom from fear, we come to the
3. Foun-tain of jus-tice, free all our hate, we come to the
4. Foun-tain of mer-cy, bind all our wounds, we come to the
5. Foun-tain of our fu-ture, seek out our pain, we come to the
6. Foun-tain of new life, seek out our thirst, we come to the
7. Foun-tain of mis-sion, call-ing our name, we come to the

D.C.
wa - ter, we come now to see!
wa - ter, we come to find peace!
wa - ter, we come now to love!
wa - ter, we come to be healed!
wa - ter, we come to be whole!
wa - ter, we come now to live!
wa - ter, we come now to serve!

ALLELUIA 115

Abraham Maraire

Al - le - lu - ia, al - le - lu - ia,

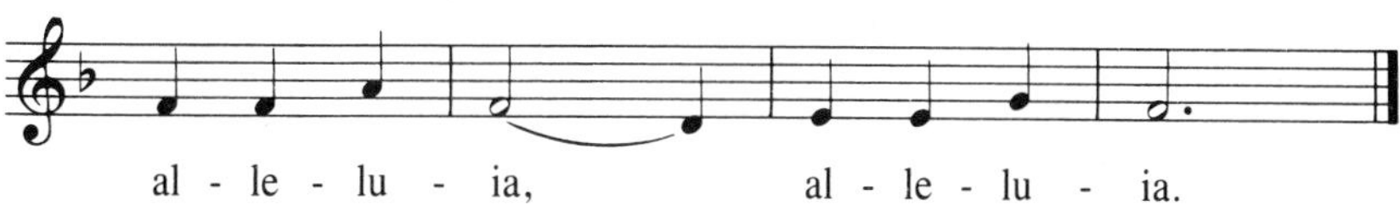
al - le - lu - ia, al - le - lu - ia.

ALLELUIA 116

Joe Wise, 1966, 1973

Al - le - lu - ia, al - le - lu - ia,

al - le - lu - ia, al-le - lu - ia, al - le - lu - ia.

Verse

We will hear your Word, one in love; we will live your Word,

D.C.
one in love; we will spread your Word, one in love.

117 ALLELUIA

Celtic Alleluia
Fintan O'Carroll, Christopher Walker

Refrain

Al - le - lu - ia, al - le - lu - ia!

Al - le - lu - ia, al - le - lu - ia!

Verses

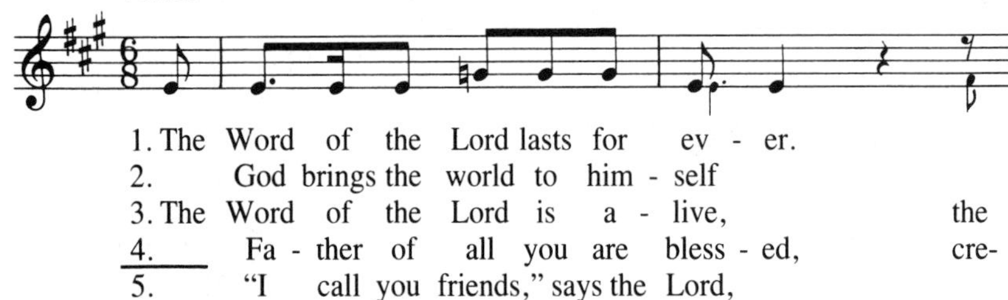
1. The Word of the Lord lasts for ev - er.
2. God brings the world to him - self
3. The Word of the Lord is a - live, the
4. Fa - ther of all you are bless - ed, cre-
5. "I call you friends," says the Lord,
6. "The sheep of my flock," says the Lord,
7. "Ev - en if you have to die
8. Stay a - wake pray at all times,

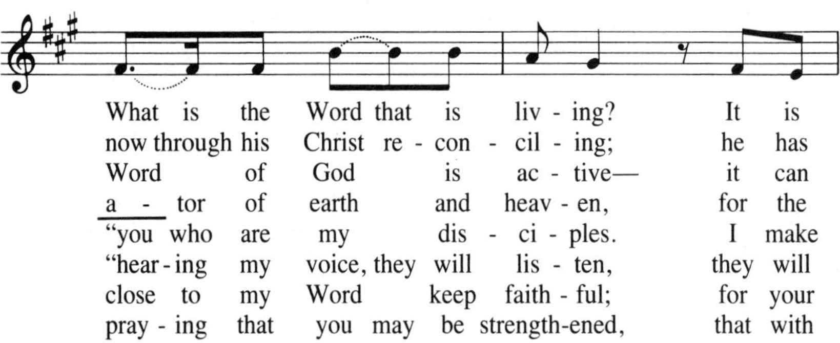
What is the Word that is liv - ing? It is
now through his Christ re - con - cil - ing; he has
Word of God is ac - tive— it can
a - tor of earth and heav - en, for the
"you who are my dis - ci - ples. I make
"hear - ing my voice, they will lis - ten, they will
close to my Word keep faith - ful; for your
pray - ing that you may be strength-ened, that with

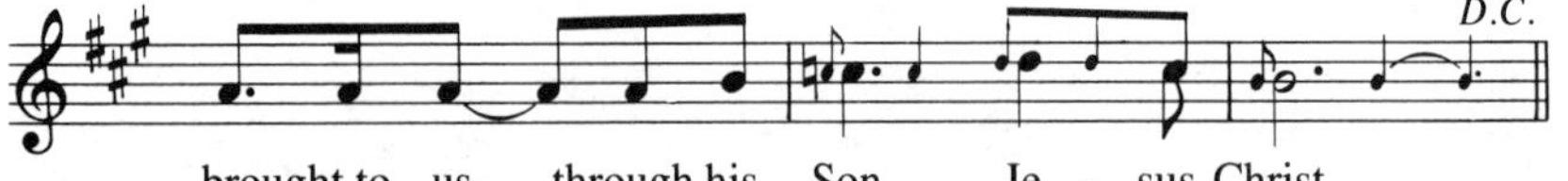
D.C.

brought to us through his Son Je - sus Christ.
trust - ed us with the news of re-deem-ing love.
judge our thoughts, bring us clos-er to the Fa - ther.
mys - ter - ies of the king-dom shown to chil - dren.
known to you all I've learned from my Fa - ther."
fol - low me, for I know them, they are mine."
faith - ful - ness I will give you the crown of life."
con - fi - dence you can meet the Son of Man.

ALLELUIA
Taizé Community
Jacques Berthier, 1984
118
Al-le - lu - ia, al-le - lu - ia, al-le - lu - ia.
Al-le - lu - ia, al-le - lu - ia, al-le - lu - ia.
ALLELUIA/LENTEN ACCLAMATION
Southern Harmony, 1835
Adapt. by M.D. Ridge, 1986
119
Al - le - lu - ia, al - le - lu - ia, al - le - lu - ia!
Praise to you, Lord Je - sus Christ, king of end - less glo - ry!
GOSPEL ACCLAMATION
Shaker Hymn
120
O the bless-ed Gos - pel, O the bless - ed Gos - pel, it
shall be mine! I will la - bor for it,
I will la - bor for it, it shall be mine.
LENTEN ACCLAMATION
Marty Haugen, 1983
121
Praise to you, Lord Je - sus, king of might and glo - ry,
Sav - ior of the world, Sav - ior of the world.

122 CREED

Joe Wise, 1979

Refrain
To verse
Last time
We be-lieve, Lord; help our un-be - lief.
un - be - lief.

1. We believe in God, the Father almighty,
   creator of heaven, the heavens and the earth.

2. We believe in Jesus Christ, his only Son, our Lord,
   who was conceived by the power of the Holy Spirit
   and born of the Virgin Mary.

3. And he suffered under Pontius Pilate, was
   crucified, died, and was buried. He descended
   to the dead. On the third day he arose again.

4. He ascended into heaven, and is seated at the
   right hand of the Father. He will come again
   judge the living and the dead.

5. We believe in the Holy Spirit, the holy catholic
   Church, the communion of saints, the forgiveness
   of sins, the resurrection of the body, and the life everlasting.

123 GENERAL INTERCESSIONS

Bob Hurd, 1984

O God, hear us; hear our prayer.

124 GENERAL INTERCESSIONS

James E. Moore, Jr., 1983

O lov - ing Fa - ther, hear us we pray.

125 GENERAL INTERCESSIONS

Taizé Community
Jacques Berthier, 1980

Ky - ri - e, Ky - ri - e e - le - i - son. (hum)

126 SANCTUS

"Jefferson"
Adapt. by M.D. Ridge, 1986

Ho - ly, ho - ly, ho - ly Lord, God of pow'r and

God of might, heav - en and earth are full of your glo - ry.
Ho - san-na in the high - est. Bless - ed is he who comes
in the name of the Lord. Ho - san - na
in the high - est. Ho - san-na in the high - est.

MEMORIAL ACCLAMATION 127

"O Waly Waly"
Adapt. by M.D. Ridge, 1986

Lord, by your cross and res - ur - rec - tion
you have set us free, you have set us free.
You are the Sav - ior of the world,
you are the Sav - ior of the world.

AMEN 128

"O Waly Waly"
Adapt. by M. D. Ridge, 1986

A - men, a - men.
A - men, a - men.

129 SANCTUS

"Land of Rest"
Adapt. by Marcia Pruner, 1980
Acc. by Richard Proulx, 1984

Ho - ly, ho - ly, ho - ly Lord,
God of pow - er and might,
heav - en and earth are full of your glo - ry. Ho-
san - na in the high - est. Bless - ed is
he who comes in the name of the
Lord. Ho - san - na in the
high - est, ho - san - na in the high - est.

130 MEMORIAL ACCLAMATION

"Land of Rest"
Adapt. by Richard Proulx, 1984

Christ has died, Christ is ris - en,
Christ will come a - gain. Christ has died,
Christ is ris - en, Christ will come a - gain.

AMEN

131

"Land of Rest"
Adapt. by Richard Proulx, 1984
A - men, a - men, a - men.

MEMORIAL ACCLAMATION

132

Joe Wise, 1970
Christ has died, al - le - lu - ia. Christ is

ris - en, al - le - lu - ia. Christ will

come a - gain, al - le - lu - ia, al - le - lu - ia.

AGNUS DEI

133

Paul Inwood, 1982
4
Cantor, then all:
1. Je-sus, Lamb of God, have mer-cy on us.
2. Je-sus, Bread of Life, have mer-cy on us.
3. Je-sus, Lamb of God have mer-cy on us.

Cantor:
Je-sus, Word made flesh, bear - er of our sins:
Je-sus, Morn-ing Star; Je - sus, Prince of Peace:
Je-sus, King of kings; Je - sus, Lord of all:

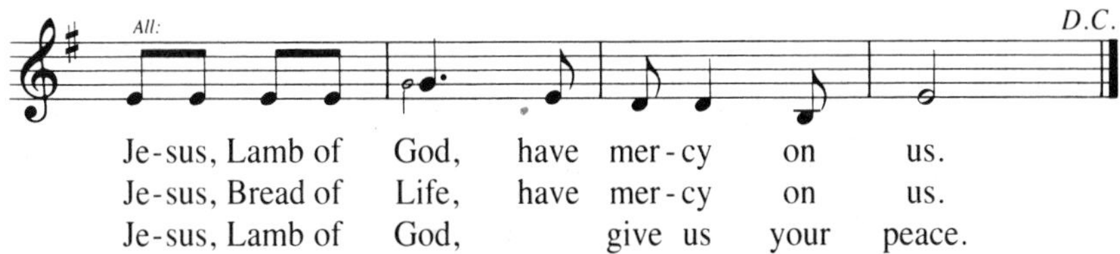
All:
D.C.
Je-sus, Lamb of God, have mer - cy on us.
Je-sus, Bread of Life, have mer - cy on us.
Je-sus, Lamb of God, give us your peace.

134 AGNUS DEI

Cantor:
All:
David Haas, 1987
*Lamb of God, you take a - way the

sins of the world: have mer - cy on us.

Last time:
Cantor:
All:
Lamb of God, you take a - way the

sins of the world: grant us your peace.

*Other invocations may be used: King of Kings, Prince of Peace, Bread of Life, Ancient Cup, etc.

135 AGNUS DEI

Trinity Mass
Becket Senchur, OSB

Lamb of God, you take a-way the sins of the world: have

mer - cy on us. Lamb of God, you take a-way the

sins of the world: grant us peace, grant us peace.

The Day Is Near 136

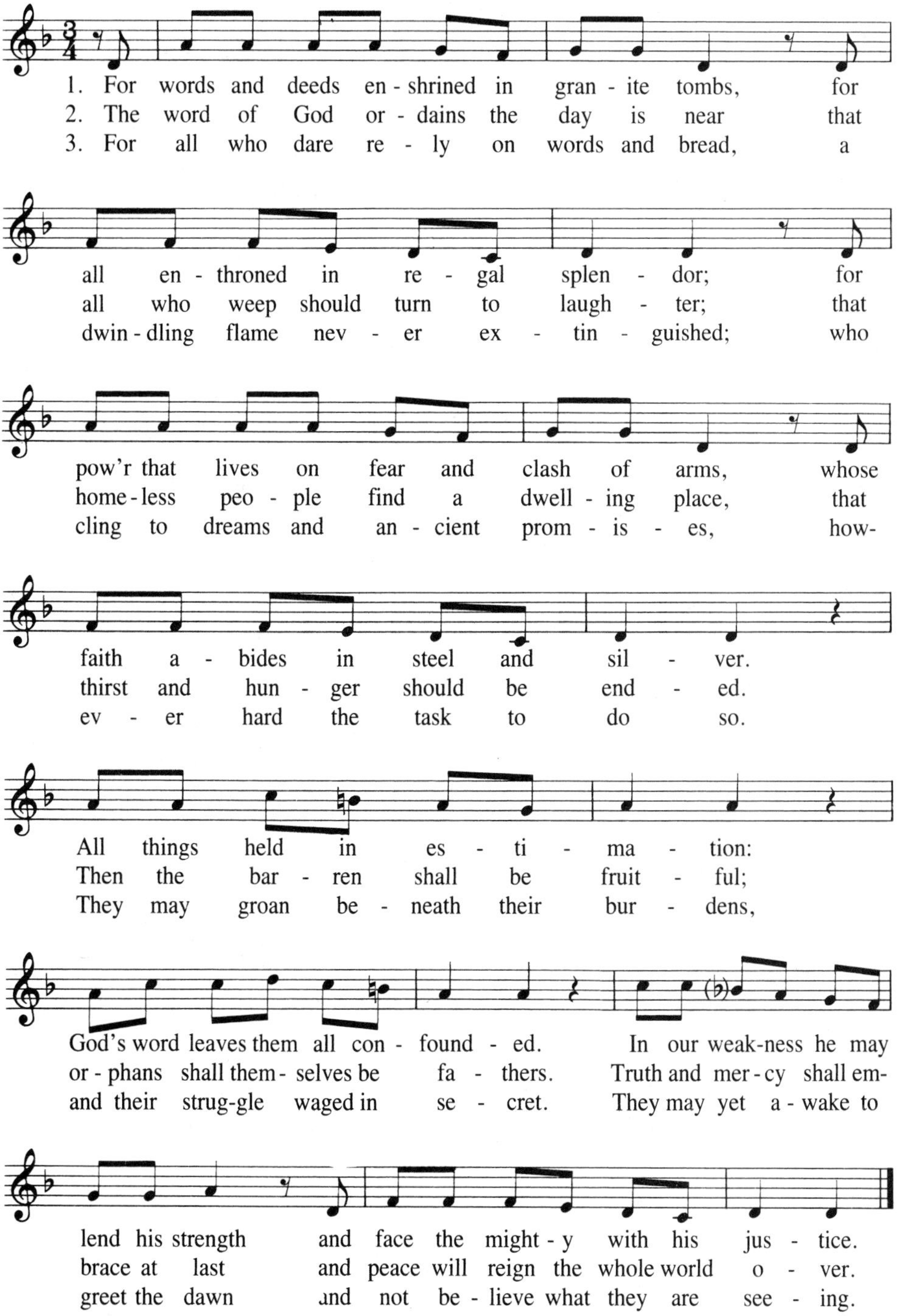

1. For words and deeds en - shrined in gran - ite tombs, for
2. The word of God or - dains the day is near that
3. For all who dare re - ly on words and bread, a

all en - throned in re - gal splen - dor; for
all who weep should turn to laugh - ter; that
dwin - dling flame nev - er ex - tin - guished; who

pow'r that lives on fear and clash of arms, whose
home - less peo - ple find a dwell - ing place, that
cling to dreams and an - cient prom - is - es, how-

faith a - bides in steel and sil - ver.
thirst and hun - ger should be end - ed.
ev - er hard the task to do so.

All things held in es - ti - ma - tion:
Then the bar - ren shall be fruit - ful;
They may groan be - neath their bur - dens,

God's word leaves them all con - found - ed. In our weak-ness he may
or - phans shall them - selves be fa - thers. Truth and mer - cy shall em-
and their strug-gle waged in se - cret. They may yet a - wake to

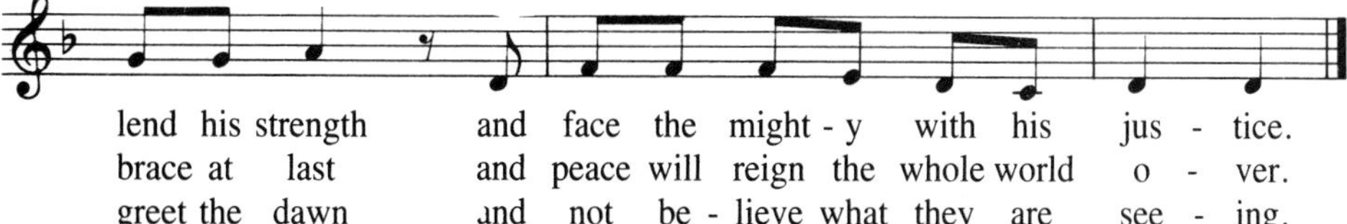
lend his strength and face the might - y with his jus - tice.
brace at last and peace will reign the whole world o - ver.
greet the dawn and not be - lieve what they are see - ing.

Text: Huub Oosterhuis, b.1933; Trans. by Tony Barr; Rev. by Tom Conry
Tune: Bernard Huijbers

137 My Soul in Stillness Waits

Refrain

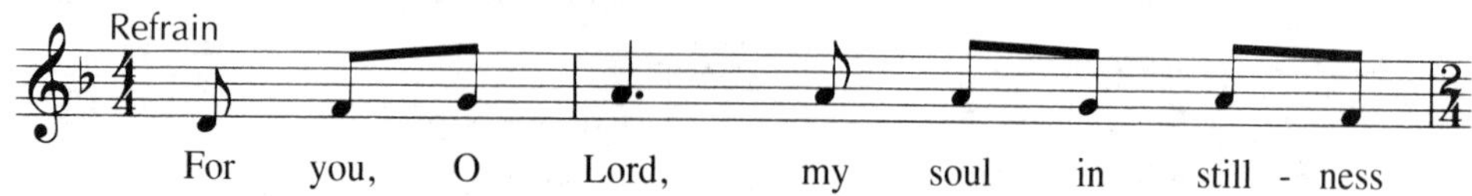
For you, O Lord, my soul in still - ness

waits, tru - ly my hope is in you.

Verses

1. O Lord of Light, our on - ly hope of
2. O Spring of Joy, rain down up - on our
3. O Root of Life, im - plant your seed with-
4. O Key of Know - ledge, guide us in our
5. Come, let us bow be - fore the God who
6. Here we shall meet the Mak - er of the

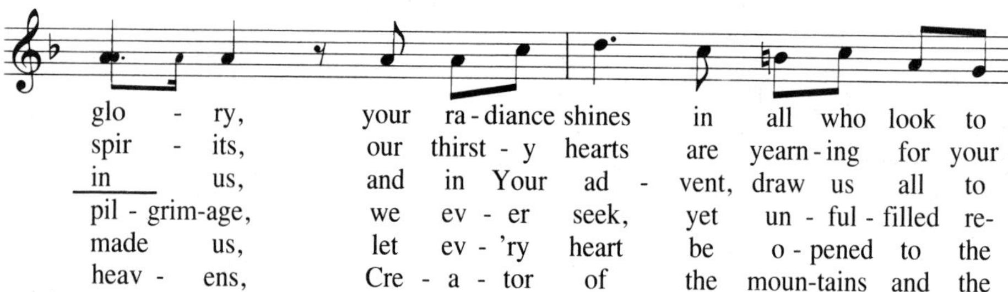
glo - ry, your ra - diance shines in all who look to
spir - its, our thirst - y hearts are yearn - ing for your
in us, and in Your ad - vent, draw us all to
pil - grim-age, we ev - er seek, yet un - ful - filled re-
made us, let ev - 'ry heart be o - pened to the
heav - ens, Cre - a - tor of the moun-tains and the

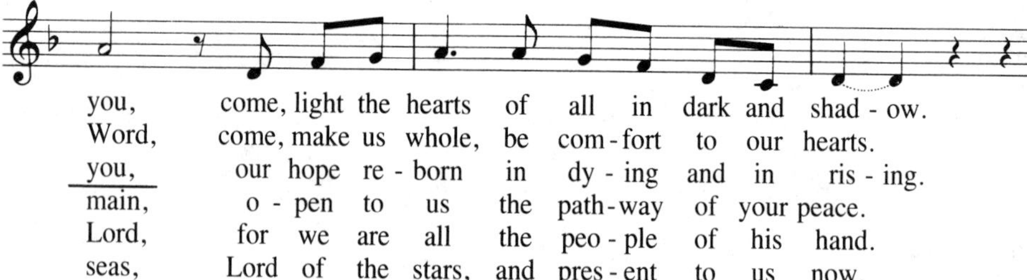
you, come, light the hearts of all in dark and shad - ow.
Word, come, make us whole, be com - fort to our hearts.
you, our hope re - born in dy - ing and in ris - ing.
main, o - pen to us the path - way of your peace.
Lord, for we are all the peo - ple of his hand.
seas, Lord of the stars, and pres - ent to us now.

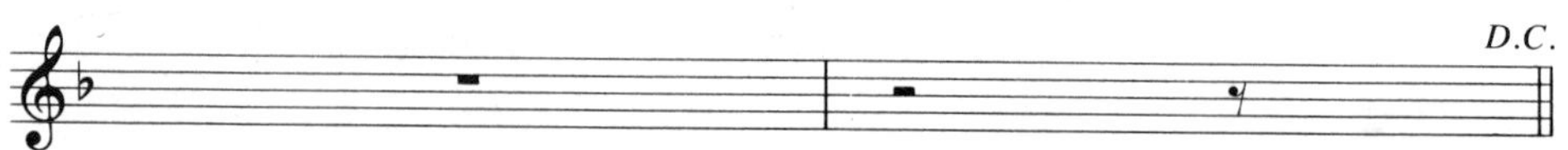
D.C.

Text: Psalm 95 and "O" Antiphons; Marty Haugen, b.1950
Tune: Marty Haugen, b.1950

Each Winter As the Year Grows Older 138

1. Each win - ter as the year grows old - er, We
2. When race and class cry out for trea - son, When
3. Yet I be - lieve be - yond be - liev - ing, That
4. So e - ven as the sun is turn - ing, To
5. O Child of ec - sta - sy and sor - rows, O
each grow old - er too. The
si - rens call for war, They
life can spring from death; That
jour - ney to the north, The
Prince of peace and pain, Bright
chill sets in a lit - tle cold - er; The
o - ver - shout the voice of rea - son, And
growth can flow - er from our griev - ing; That
liv - ing flame, in se - cret burn - ing, Can
en to - day's world by to - mor - row's, Re-
ver - i - ties we knew Seem
scream till we ig - nore All
we can catch our breath And
kin - dle on the earth, And
new our lives a - gain; Lord
shak - en and un - true.
we held dear be - fore.
turn trans - fixed by faith.
bring God's love to birth.
Je - sus, come and reign!

Text: William Gay, fl. 1969
Tune: CAROL OF HOPE, 96 966; Annabeth Gay, fl. 1969 from *A New Song 3*, © 1971, United Church Press; Acc. by Marty Haugen, b. 1950, © 1987, GIA Publications, Inc.

139 Wait for the Lord

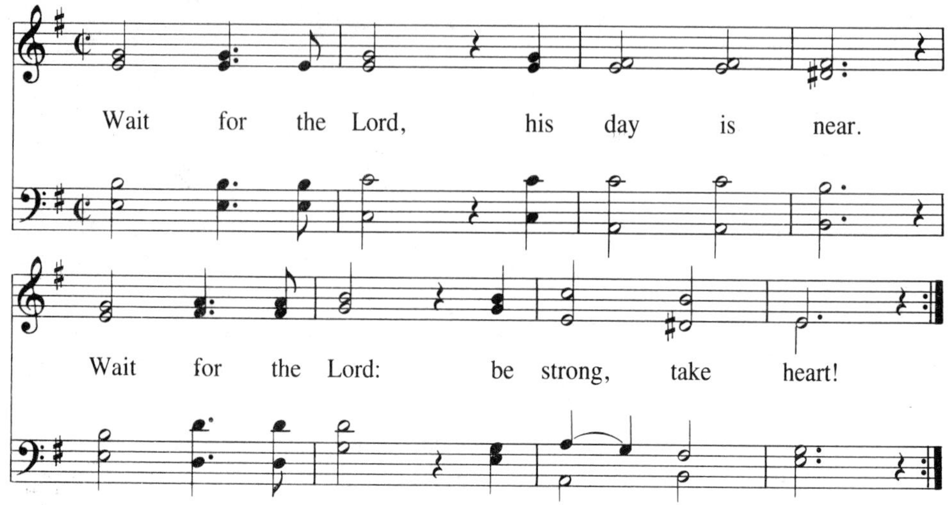
Wait for the Lord, his day is near.
Wait for the Lord: be strong, take heart!

Text: Taizé Community, 1984
Tune: Jacques Berthier, b.1923

140 People of the Night

1. We are your peo - ple of the night,
2. For in our win - ter we are dead,
3. You wait for us, you are our choice,
4. Give us new faith, give us the joy,
We long to see your new born light,
Lead us in hope to see a - head, The
The liv - ing word; the sav - ing voice.
As we a - wait your Son the Lord.
Dis - tant glim - mer; ris - ing from a - far.
spring-time and the gift that is to come.
Break the si - lence, lis - ten to our call.
In our pres - ence, child born of your breath,

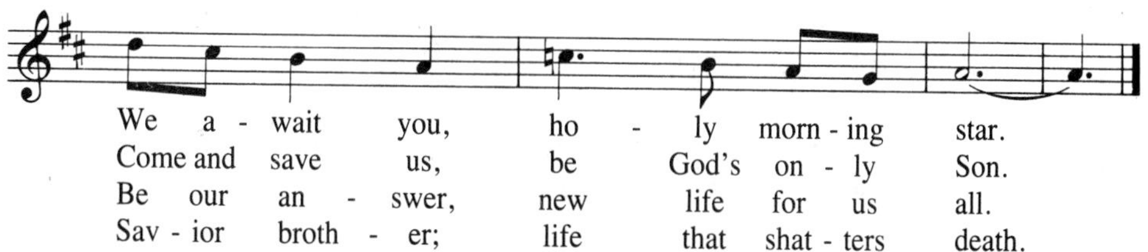
We a - wait you, ho - ly morn - ing star.
Come and save us, be God's on - ly Son.
Be our an - swer, new life for us all.
Sav - ior broth - er; life that shat - ters death.

Text: David Haas, b.1957
Tune: SHEPHERD'S SONG, 88 99; David Haas, b.1957

Maranatha 141

Refrain

Come, O Lord, and set us free. Ma - ra - na - tha.

Verses

1. Des - ert and dry land will grow green in praise;
2. Strength-en the hearts of the fear - ful and weak;
3. We have been wait - ing and long - ing for light;
4. Give us a star in the sky day and night;

clay will re - joice with full bloom.
be strong; fear not, God is near.
watch - ing for signs of the Lord.
sign of your prom - ise to save.

Show - ers of flow - ers giv'n birth in dead earth; in
Com - ing in pow - er and loos - ing our bonds;
"Prom-ised of a - ges," "Mes - si - ah to come,"
O - ver the moun - tains we fol - low its light

col - ors they ech - o his song.
set - ting the cap - tives free.
hear us, we beg you: "Come, save!"
hop - ing for sign of your life.

D.C.

Text: Isaiah 35, Romans 13, James 5; Tim Schoenbachler
Tune: Tim Schoenbachler

142 Come to Set us Free

Refrain
Come to set us free, come to make us your own.

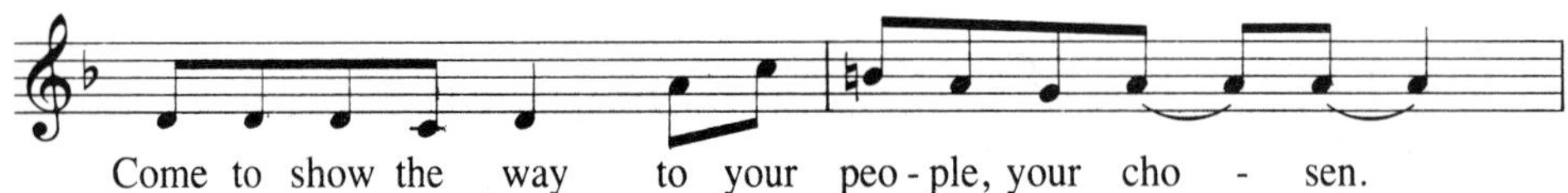
Come to show the way to your peo - ple, your cho - sen.

O - pen our lives to the light of your prom - ise.

Come to our hearts with heal - ing, come to our minds with pow - er,

come to us and bring us your life.

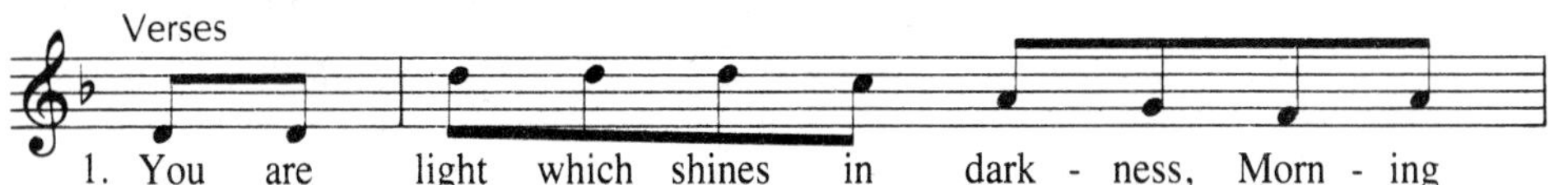
Verses
1. You are light which shines in dark - ness, Morn - ing
2. You are hope which brings us cour - age, you are
3. You are prom - ise of sal - va - tion, you are

Star which nev - er sets. O - pen our eyes which
strength which nev - er fails. O - pen our minds to
God who lives with men. Bring to our world of

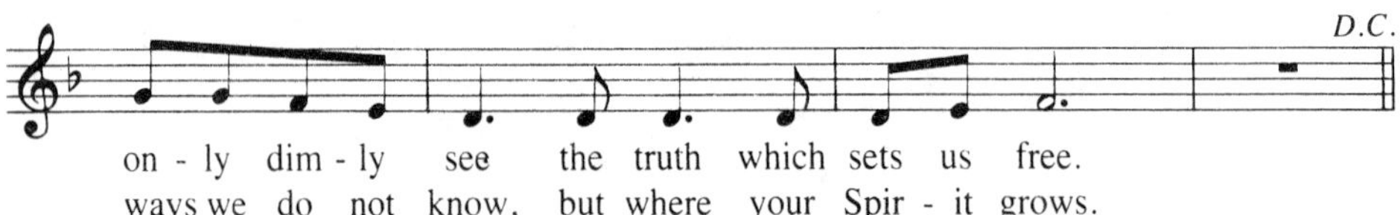
D.C.
on - ly dim - ly see the truth which sets us free.
ways we do not know, but where your Spir - it grows.
emp - ti - ness and fear the Word we long to hear.

Text: Bernadette Farrell
Tune: Bernadette Farrell

God of All People 143

1. God of all plac - es: pres - ent, un - seen;
2. God of all dream - ing, near and yet far.
3. God of all peo - ple, dust and the clay.
Voice in our si - lence, song in our midst.
Vi - sion un - heard of, wake us to rest.
Breath of a new wind, fire in our hearts.
We are your peo - ple, know - ing, un - sure.
We are your pres - ence, sent forth a - fraid.
Light born of heav - en, peace on the earth.
Come, Lord Je - sus, come!
3.
Come! Come, Lord Je - sus, come!

Text: David Haas, b.1957
Tune: KINGDOM 9.9.9.6; David Haas, b.1957

144 Born of Peace

Verse 1: When all the earth was cruelly held in ancient winter's grasp.
When hope was old and faded, or strewn like shattered glass:
A universe of promises, stretched deep across the sky,
And death begun to die.

Refrain

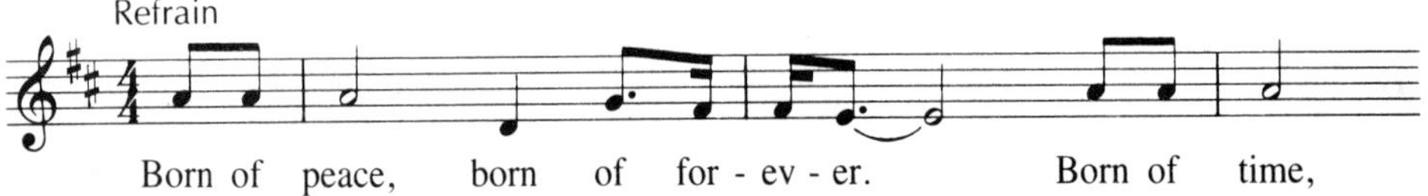
Born of peace, born of for - ev - er. Born of time,

born here to - day. Born of fire, born of light, in the

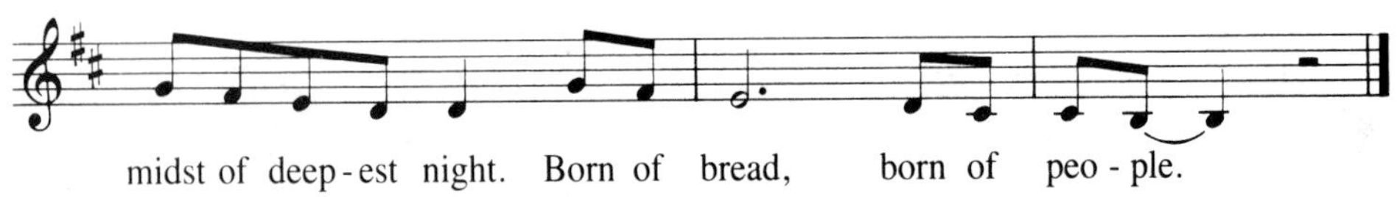
midst of deep-est night. Born of bread, born of peo - ple.

Verse 2: Restless and uncertain, we journeyed through the night,
led by common dreaming and a single wand'ring light.
Fed upon our traveling by singing from afar;
Hidden in our stars (Refrain)

Verse 3: Through night-time's speechless carnival, and windblown crystal sun,
We carried what we had and what we needed to become.
Our murdered dreams behind us, weathered, parched and tossed,
Starry-eyed and lost. (Refrain)

Verse 4: From foreign lands and alien gods and fixed unwav'ring skies,
Whose buried secret chaos holds all prisoners inside;
Beyond the restless longing where our desp'rate hopes belong,
Nearer to our song. (Refrain)

Text: Tom Conry
Tune: Tom Conry; Acc. by Patrick Loomis

Verse 5: Who has cupped in hand the waters of the sea?
Who has bound the sky and weighed the mountains?
Who has opened rivers from atop the barren heights?
Who has heard the crying of God's own?
Have you not seen? Have you not heard?
Stories told long before rememb'ring;
Sheltered on our way, and passed among us all,
Singing in the midst of darkling silence. (Final Refrain sung twice)

Song of the Stable 145

1. Chill of the night - fall, Lamps in the win - dows,
2. Si - lence of mid - night, Voi - ces of an - gels,
3. Splen-dor of star - light High in the hill - side,
4. Glo - ry of day - break! Sor - rows and shad - ows,
Let - ting their light fall Clear on the snow;
Sing - ing to bid night Yield to the dawn;
Faint is the far light Burn - ing be - low;
Sud - den - ly they break Forth in - to morn;
Bit - ter De - cem - ber Bids us re - mem - ber
Dark-ness is end - ed, Sin - ners be - friend - ed,
Kneel-ing be - fore him Shep-herds a - dore him,
Sing out and tell now All shall be well now;
Christ in the sta - ble Long, long a - go.
Where in the sta - ble Je - sus is born.
Christ in the sta - ble Long,long a - go.
For in the sta - ble Je - sus is born!

Text: *Chill of the Nightfall*, Timothy Dudley-Smith, b.1926, © 1980, Hope Publishing Company
Tune: PRIOR LAKE, 5 5 5 4 D; David Haas, b.1957, © 1985, GIA Publications, Inc.

146 Night of Silence

1. Cold are the peo - ple, win - ter of life, We
2. Voice in the dis - tance, call in the night, On
3. Spir - it a - mong us, shine like the star, Your

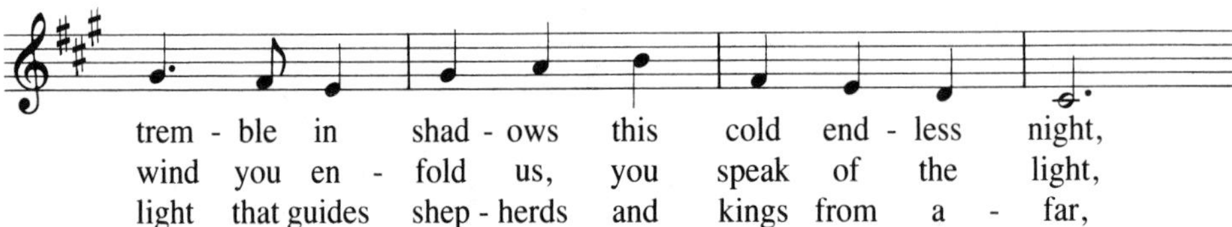
trem - ble in shad - ows this cold end - less night,
wind you en - fold us, you speak of the light,
light that guides shep - herds and kings from a - far,

Fro-zen in the snow lie ros - es sleep - ing,
Gen-tle on the ear you whis - per soft - ly,
Shim-mer in the sky so emp - ty, lone - ly,

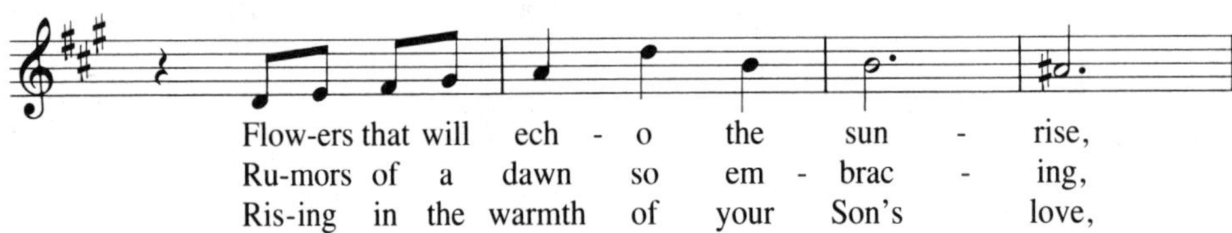
Flow-ers that will ech - o the sun - rise,
Ru-mors of a dawn so em - brac - ing,
Ris-ing in the warmth of your Son's love,

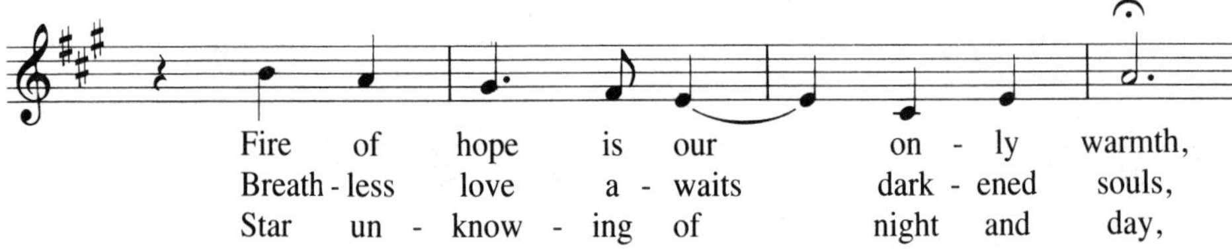
Fire of hope is our on - ly warmth,
Breath - less love a - waits dark - ened souls,
Star un - know - ing of night and day,

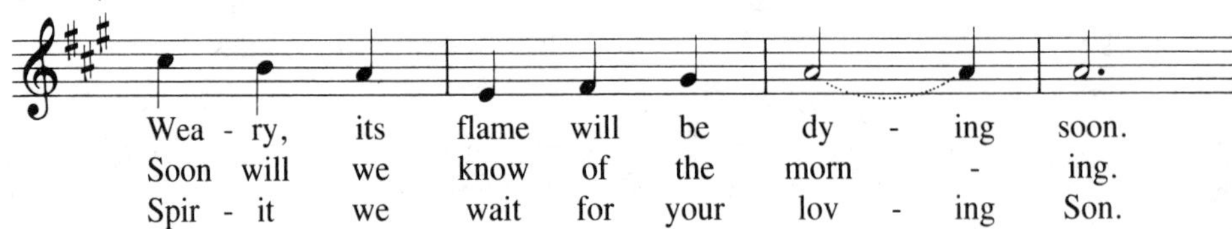
Wea - ry, its flame will be dy - ing soon.
Soon will we know of the morn - ing.
Spir - it we wait for your lov - ing Son.

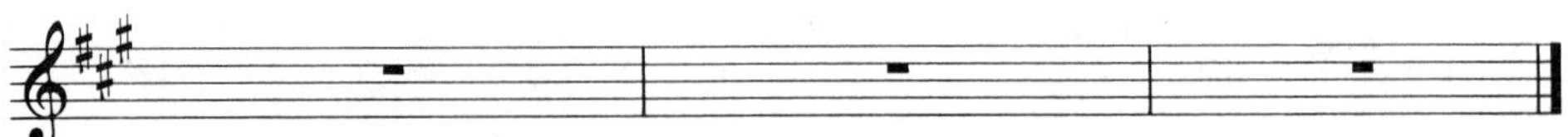

Text: Daniel Kantor
Tune: Daniel Kantor

1. Si - lent night, ho - ly night, All is calm, all is bright
2. Si - lent night, ho - ly night, Shep-herds quake at the sight;
3. Si - lent night, ho - ly night, Son of God, love's pure light

Round yon Vir - gin Moth-er and Child, Ho - ly In-fant, so ten-der and mild,
Glo - ries stream from heav-en a - far, Heav'n-ly hosts sing al - le - lu - ia;
Ra - diant beams from thy ho-ly face, With the dawn of re-deem - ing grace,

Sleep in heav-en - ly peace, Sleep in heav - en - ly peace.
Christ, the Sav-ior, is born! Christ, the Sav - ior, is born!
Je - sus, Lord, at thy birth, Je - sus, Lord, at thy birth.

Silent Night *and* Night of Silence *(146) can be sung simultaneously.*

Text: *Stille Nacht, heilige Nacht;* Joseph Mohr, 1792-1849; Trans. by John F. Young, 1820-1885
Tune: STILLE NACHT, 66 89 66; Franz X. Gruber, 1787-1863

148 Let the Heavens Be Glad

1.
2.
3.
Let the heav - ens be glad and the earth re - joice be-

fore the Lord, for he comes, for he comes.
For he comes.

1. and 2. hold last note of round until round is completed; then all sing respective parts on final cadence.

Text: Joe Wise
Tune: Joe Wise, © 1968; Acc. by Saul Stirks, © 1968

149 Gloria, Gloria

Canon

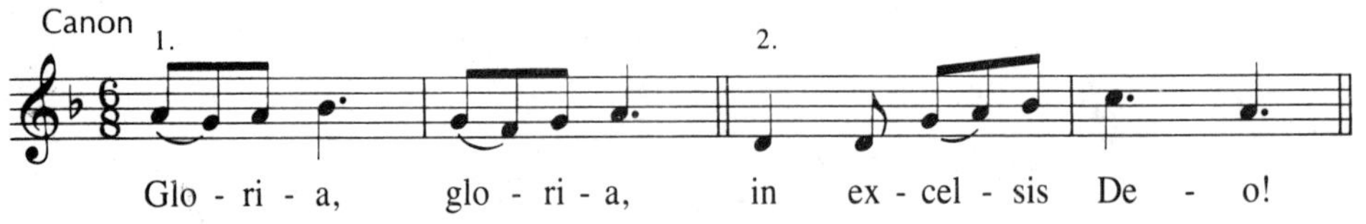
1.
2.
Glo - ri - a, glo - ri - a, in ex - cel - sis De - o!

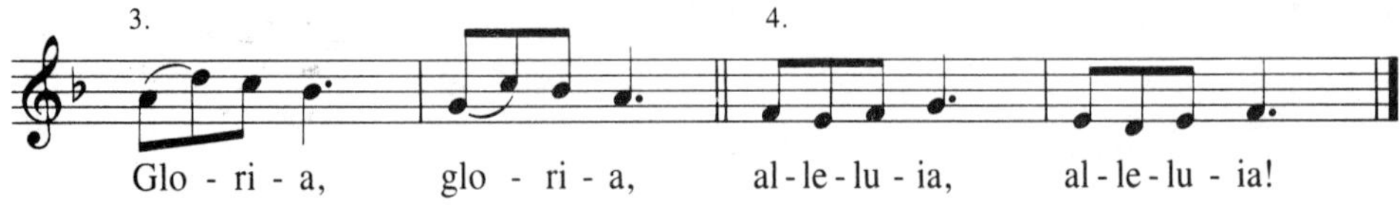
3.
4.
Glo - ri - a, glo - ri - a, al - le - lu - ia, al - le - lu - ia!

Text: Luke 2:14; *Glory to God in the highest;* Taizé Community, 1978
Tune: Jacques Berthier, b.1923

A Dulcimer Carol 150

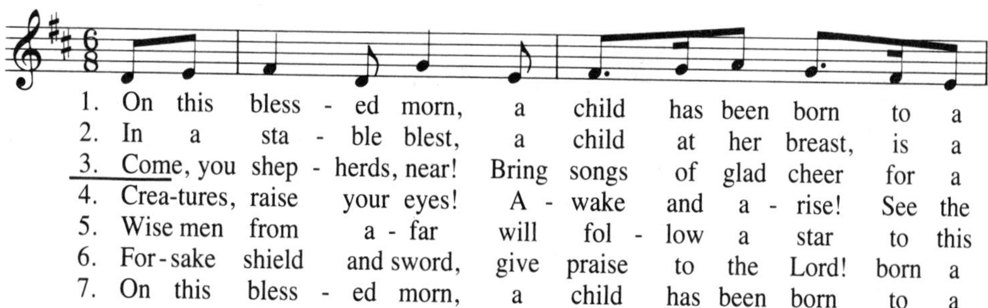
1. On this bless - ed morn, a child has been born to a
2. In a sta - ble blest, a child at her breast, is a
3. Come, you shep - herds, near! Bring songs of glad cheer for a
4. Crea-tures, raise your eyes! A - wake and a - rise! See the
5. Wise men from a - far will fol - low a star to this
6. For-sake shield and sword, give praise to the Lord! born a
7. On this bless - ed morn, a child has been born to a

Vir - gin in Beth - le - hem! Tell all who will
Vir - gin in Beth - le - hem! So sweet - ly to
ba - by in Beth - le - hem! Now, frag - ile and
Sav - ior in Beth - le - hem! Come forth and be-
sta - ble in Beth - le - hem! Fine gifts will they
Sav - ior in Beth - le - hem! No more mor - tal
Vir - gin in Beth - le - hem! Tell all who will

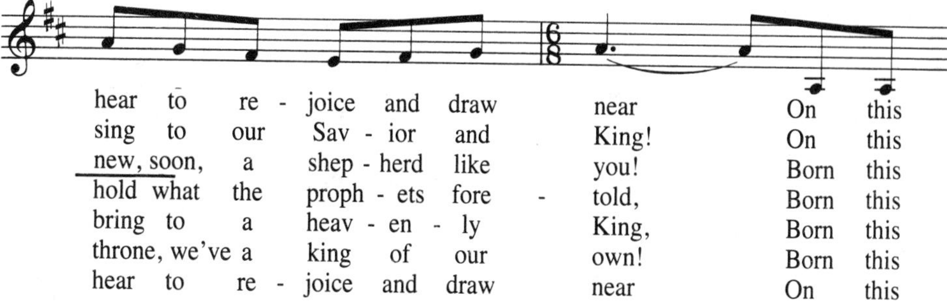
hear to re - joice and draw near On this
sing to our Sav - ior and King! On this
new, soon, a shep - herd like you! Born this
hold what the proph - ets fore - told, Born this
bring to a heav - en - ly King, Born this
throne, we've a king of our own! Born this
hear to re - joice and draw near On this

bless - ed Christ - mas morn - ing! On this

bless - ed Christ - mas morn - ing!

Text: Martin Willett
Tune: Martin Willett

151 Awake, Awake and Greet the New Morn

1. A - wake! a - wake, and greet the new morn, For
2. To us, to all in sor - row and fear, Em-
3. In dark - est night his com - ing shall be, When
4. Re - joice, re - joice, take heart in the night, Though
an - gels her - ald its dawn - ing, Sing out your joy, for
man-u - el comes a - sing - ing, His hum - ble song is
all the world is de - spair - ing, As morn - ing light so
dark the win - ter and cheer - less, The ris - ing sun shall
now he is born, Be - hold! the Child of our long - ing.
qui - et and near, Yet fills the earth with its ring - ing;
qui - et and free, So warm and gen - tle and car - ing.
crown you with light, Be strong and lov - ing and fear - less;
Come as a ba - by weak and poor, To bring all hearts to-
Mu - sic to heal the bro - ken soul And hymns of lov - ing
Then shall the mute break forth in song, The lame shall leap in
Love be our song and love our prayer, And love, our end - less
geth - er, He o - pens wide the heav - n'ly door And
kind - ness, The thun - der of his an - thems roll To
won - der, The weak be raised a - bove the strong, And
sto - ry, May God fill ev - 'ry day we share, And
lives now in - side us for ev - er.
shat - ter all ha - tred and blind - ness.
weap-ons be bro - ken a - sun - der.
bring us at last in - to glo - ry.

Text: Marty Haugen, b.1950
Tune: REJOICE, REJOICE, 9 8 9 8 8 7 8 9; Marty Haugen, b.1950

Carol at the Manger 152

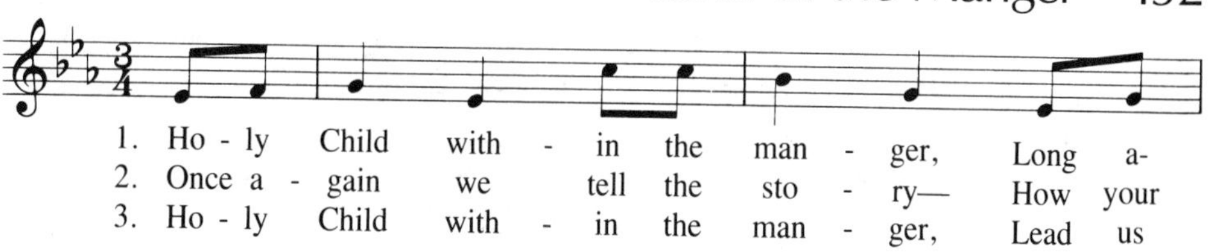
1. Ho - ly Child with - in the man - ger, Long a-
2. Once a - gain we tell the sto - ry— How your
3. Ho - ly Child with - in the man - ger, Lead us

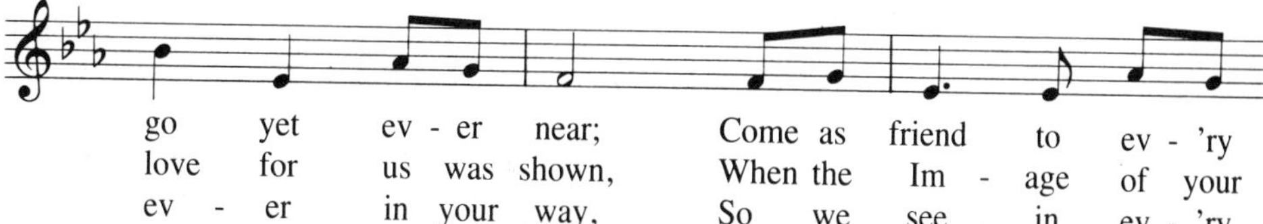
go yet ev - er near; Come as friend to ev - 'ry
love for us was shown, When the Im - age of your
ev - er in your way, So we see in ev - 'ry

stran - ger, Come as hope for ev - 'ry fear. As you
glo - ry Wore an im - age like our own. Come, en-
stran - ger How you come to us to - day. In our

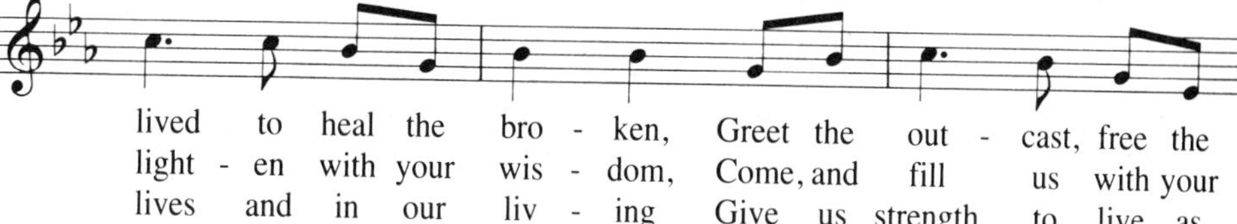
lived to heal the bro - ken, Greet the out - cast, free the
light - en with your wis - dom, Come, and fill us with your
lives and in our liv - ing Give us strength to live as

bound, As you taught us love un - spo - ken,
grace, May the fire of your com - pas - sion
you, That our hearts might be for - giv - ing

Teach us now where you are found.
Kin - dle ev - 'ry land and race.
And our spir - its strong and true.

Text: Marty Haugen, b.1950
Tune: JOYOUS LIGHT, 87 87 D; Marty Haugen, b.1950

153 Once in Royal David's City

1. Once in roy - al Da - vid's cit - y Stood a low - ly cat - tle shed,
2. He came down to earth from heav - en Who is God and Lord of all,
3. And through all his won - drous child-hood He would hon - or and o - bey,
4. For he is our child - hood's pat-tern, Day by day like us he grew;
5. And our eyes at last shall see him, Thru his own re - deem - ing love;

Where a moth - er laid her ba - by In a man - ger for his bed.
And his shel - ter was a sta - ble, And his cra - dle was a stall.
Love and watch the low - ly maid - en In whose gen - tle arms he lay.
He was lit - tle, weak, and help-less, Tears and smiles like us he knew:
For that child so dear and gen - tle Is our Lord in heav'n a - bove:

Mar-y was that moth-er mild, Je - sus Christ her lit - tle Child.
With the poor and mean and low - ly Lived on earth our Sav - ior ho - ly.
Chris-tian chil - dren all should be Kind, o - be - dient, good as he.
And he feels for all our sad-ness, And he shares in all our glad-ness.
And he leads his chil-dren on To the place where he has gone.

Text: Cecil Frances Alexander, 1818-1895
Tune: IRBY, 8 7 8 7 77; Henry J. Gauntlett, 1805-1876; Harm. by Robert J. Batastini, b.1942,

154 Song of God among Us

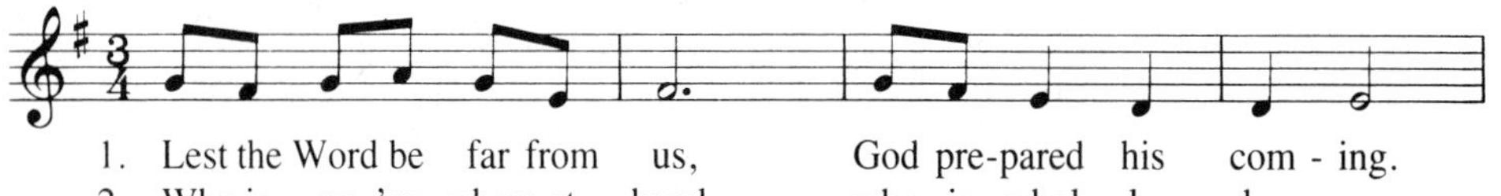

1. Lest the Word be far from us, God pre-pared his com - ing.
2. Who is ev - 'ry -where at hand, who is whol - ly hu - man,

One who longed to share our fate made with us his dwell - ing.
one who goes un - rec - og - nized si - lent, nev - er spo - ken.

In the midst of you is One you do not know.
In the midst of you is One you do not know.
3. God from God and light from light, hope of earth's sad cry - ing,
face to face with hu-man-kind, speaks of love and dy - ing.
4. Then let pa-tience be your guide, walk in ways of jus - tice;
show each oth - er at all time ev - 'ry kind of good - ness.
In the midst of you is One you do not know.
5. Now be care-free, full of joy: God a - lone, who calls us,
touch-es all who live on earth, makes a home a - mong us.

Text: Huub Oosterhuis, b.1933; Trans. by Tony Barr and Tom Conry, © 1984, TEAM Publications
Tune: Marty Haugen, b.1950, © 1986, GIA Publications, Inc.

155 Arise, Shine

Refrain
A - rise, shine! Your light has come: the light that shat-ters the dark-ness, and the
glo - ry of God is ris - en up - on you!
Verses
1. The peo - ple who stum-bled in the dark - ness,
2. The yoke of your suf - f'ring shall be lift - ed,
the peo - ple have seen the light of hope;
the rod of op - pres-sion's weight shall break;
the peo - ple who dwelt be - neath death's shad-ow,
the weap - ons of ha - tred shall be shat - tered,
on them the light has shown!
and wars shall be no more!
D.C.
3. For un - to us a child is born, the Ho - ly One is
giv - en to be light for all the peo - ple in night,

Cantor:
All:
1. to be hope for our hearts: Won - der - ful
2. to be strength for our lives: Might - y
3. to be peace for our souls: God of all
4. to be wis - dom and joy: Light for the
5. to be hope for the poor: God of all
6. to be God for all time: Prince of
7. to be love that re - news: Lov - er and
8. to be light for our eyes: Spir - it of

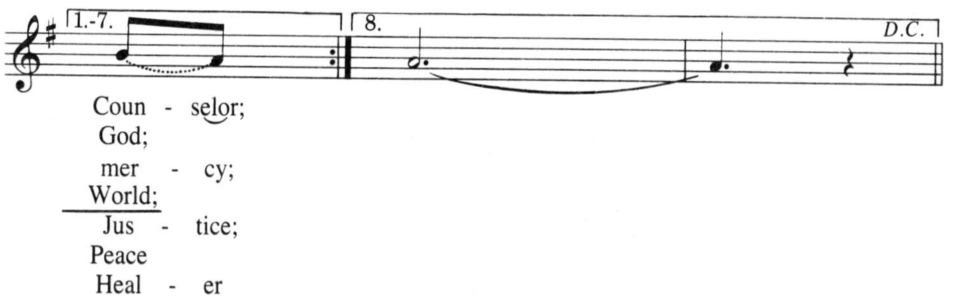
1.-7.
8.
D.C.
Coun - selor;
God;
mer - cy;
World;
Jus - tice;
Peace
Heal - er

Truth.

Text: Isaiah 9, 60; Marty Haugen, b.1950
Tune: Marty Haugen, b.1950

156 Brightest and Best

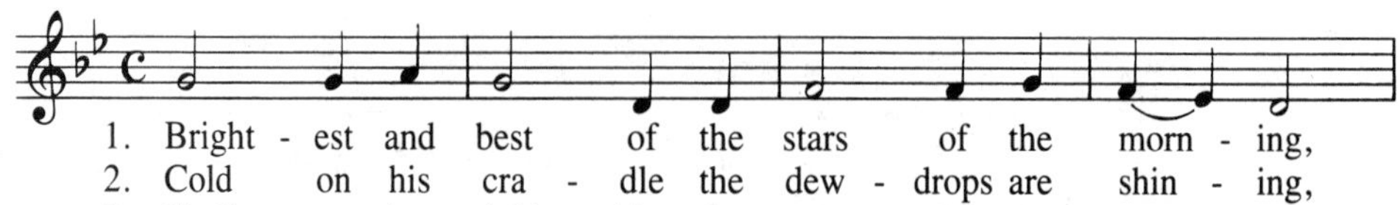

1. Bright - est and best of the stars of the morn - ing,
2. Cold on his cra - dle the dew - drops are shin - ing,
3. Shall we then yield him, in cost - ly de - vo - tion,
4. Vain - ly we of - fer each am - ple o - bla - tion,
5. Bright - est and best of the stars of the morn - ing,

Dawn on our dark - ness, and lend us thine aid;
Low lies his head with the beasts of the stall;
O - dors of E - dom, and of - f'rings di - vine,
Vain - ly with gifts would his fa - vor se - cure,
Dawn on our dark - ness, and lend us thine aid;

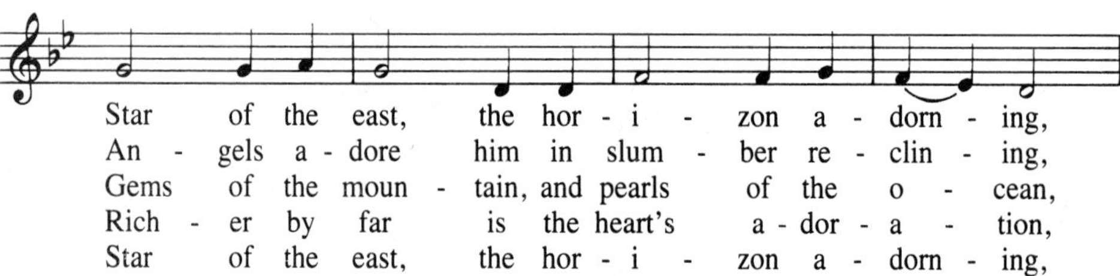

Star of the east, the hor - i - zon a - dorn - ing,
An - gels a - dore him in slum - ber re - clin - ing,
Gems of the moun - tain, and pearls of the o - cean,
Rich - er by far is the heart's a - dor - a - tion,
Star of the east, the hor - i - zon a - dorn - ing,

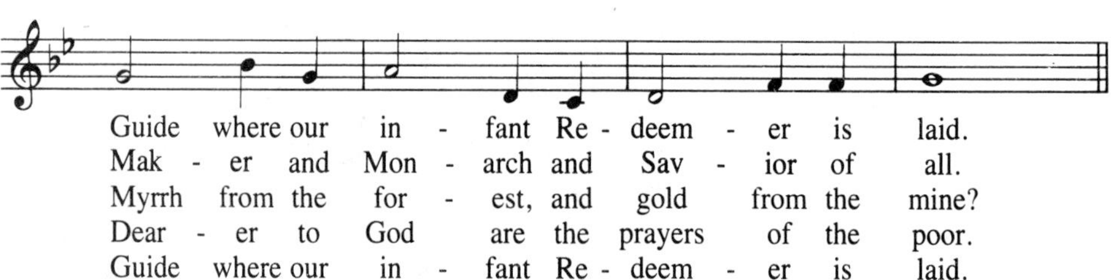

Guide where our in - fant Re - deem - er is laid.
Mak - er and Mon - arch and Sav - ior of all.
Myrrh from the for - est, and gold from the mine?
Dear - er to God are the prayers of the poor.
Guide where our in - fant Re - deem - er is laid.

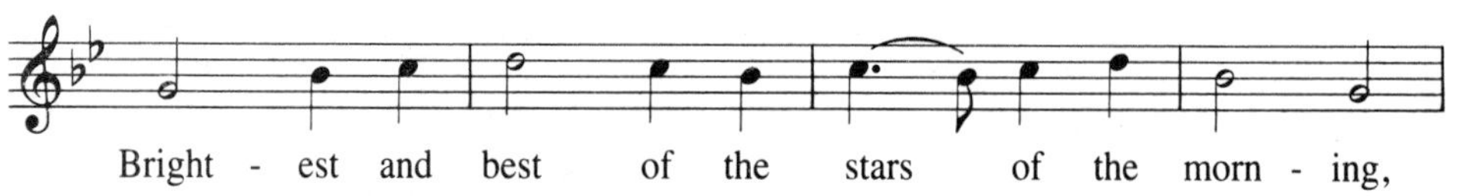

Bright - est and best of the stars of the morn - ing,

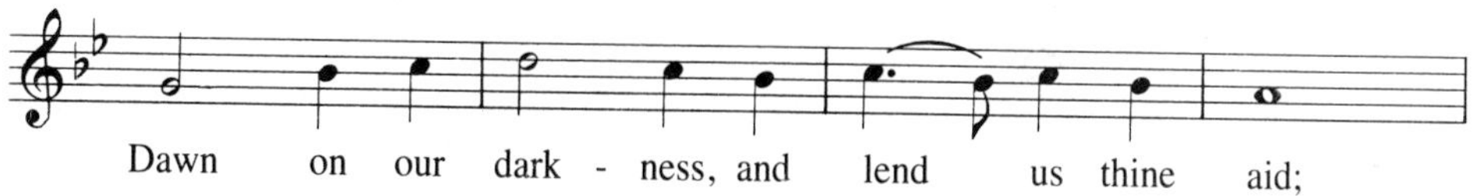
Dawn on our dark - ness, and lend us thine aid;

Star of the east, the hor - i - zon a - dorn - ing,

Guide where our in - fant Re - deem - er is laid.

Text: Reginald Heber, 1783-1826, alt.
Tune: STAR IN THE EAST, 11 10 11 10 with refrain; *Southern Harmony*, 1835; Harm. by Marty Haugen, b. 1950,

157 Lord, Today

Refrain
Lord, to - day we have seen your glo - ry, dawn fol - lows the night. We, your peo - ple who walked in dark - ness now have seen a great light.
Verses
1. A child is born, a Son giv - en us, on him do - min - ion shall rest. His name shall be Won - der - ful God, Coun - sel - or, Prince of Peace.
2. The Lord is king, the na - tions re- joice, let all of Zi - on be glad. The heav - ens pro - claim jus - tice for all. Glo - ry has filled the land.
3. O Beth - le - hem, you are from of old, too small a - mong Ju - dah's clans. From you shall come a rul - er this day, shep - herd to guide the land.
4. The days will come, the Lord prom - ised us, when he would raise up a shoot to rule the land, reign as a king, his name is Lord the Just.
5. New light has dawned up - on all the just, glad - ness for up - right of heart. Re- joice in the Lord, you faith - ful ones. Give thanks to his great name.
D.C.

Text: Mike Balhoff
Tune: Darryl Ducote, Gary Daigle

Remember Your Love 158

Refrain
Re - mem - ber your love and your faith - ful - ness, O Lord.
Re - mem - ber your peo - ple and have mer - cy on us, Lord.
Verses
1. The Lord is my light and my sal- va - tion, whom should I fear?
2. If you dwelt, O Lord, up - on our sin - ful - ness, then who could stand?
3. O Lord, hear the sound of my call and an - swer me.
4. As watch - man who waits up - on the day - light, wait for the Lord.
5. Be - fore all the moun - tains were be- got - ten and earth took shape,
The Lord is my life and my ref - uge, when I call he hears.
But with you there is mer - cy and for- give - ness and a guid - ing hand.
My heart cries out for your pres - ence; it is you I seek.
I trust in his kind - ness and re- demp - tion; and his faith - ful word.
e- ven then, O Lord, you were our ref - uge through - out ev - 'ry age.
D.C.

Text: Mike Balhoff
Tune: Darryl Ducote and Gary Daigle

159 Deep Within

Refrain
Deep within I will plant my law,
not on stone, but in your heart.
Follow me, I will bring you back, you will
be my own, and I will be your God.
Verses
1. I will give you a new heart, a new spirit within you, for I will be your strength.
D.C.
2. Seek my face, and see your God, for I will be your hope.
3. Return to me, with all your heart, and I will bring you back.
D.C.

Text: Jeremiah 31:33, Ezekiel 36:26, Joel 2:12; David Haas, b.1957
Tune: David Haas, b.1957

Eternal Lord of Love 160

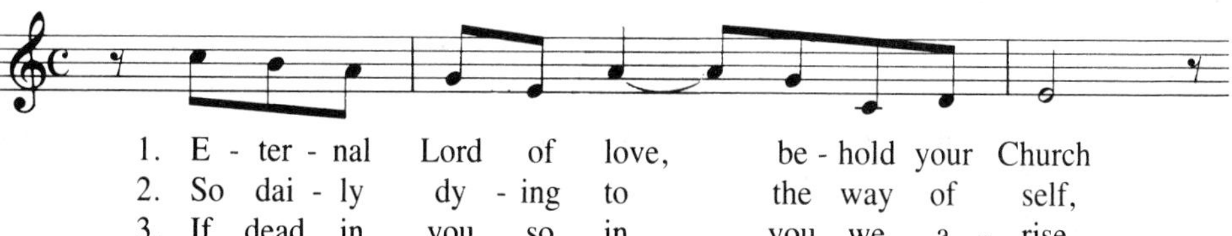
1. E - ter - nal Lord of love, be - hold your Church
2. So dai - ly dy - ing to the way of self,
3. If dead in you, so in you we a - rise,

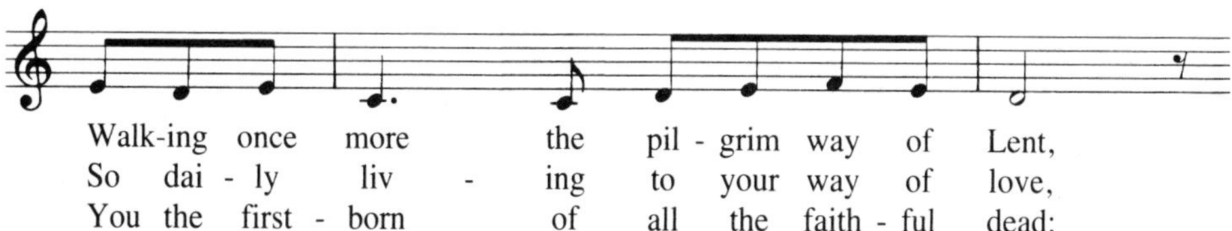
Walk-ing once more the pil - grim way of Lent,
So dai - ly liv - ing to your way of love,
You the first - born of all the faith - ful dead;

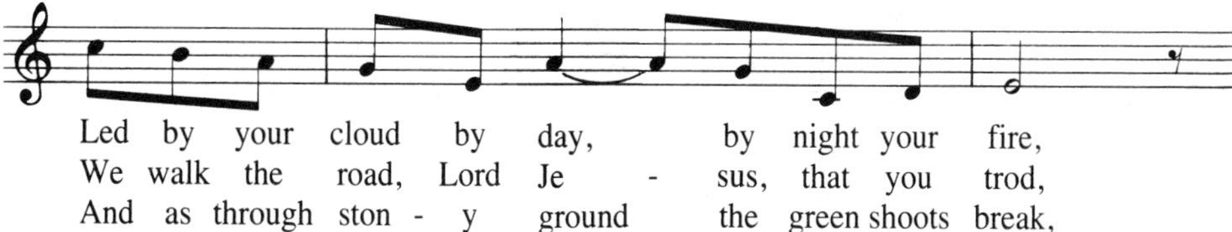
Led by your cloud by day, by night your fire,
We walk the road, Lord Je - sus, that you trod,
And as through ston - y ground the green shoots break,

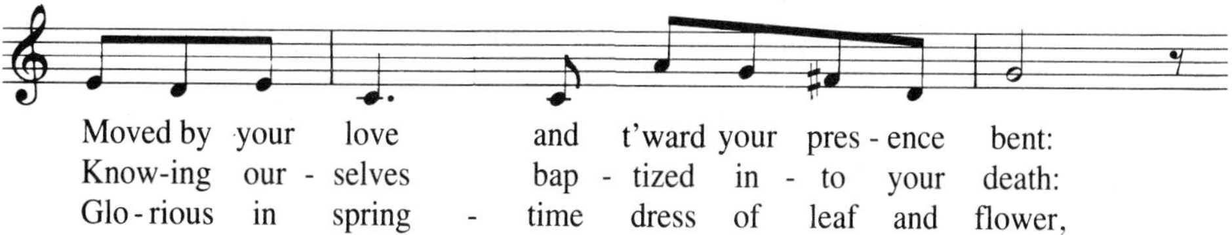
Moved by your love and t'ward your pres - ence bent:
Know-ing our - selves bap - tized in - to your death:
Glo - rious in spring - time dress of leaf and flower,

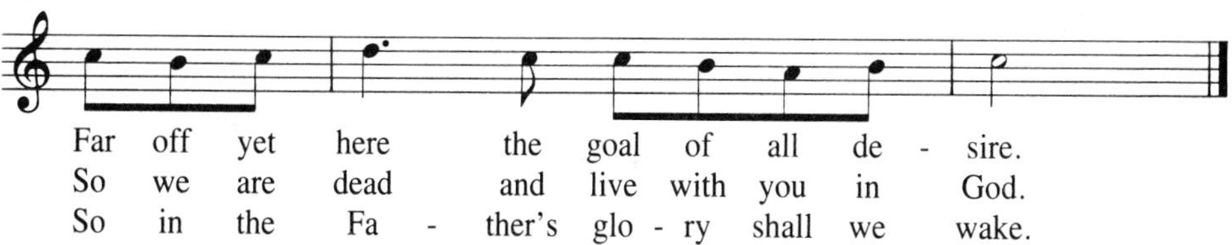
Far off yet here the goal of all de - sire.
So we are dead and live with you in God.
So in the Fa - ther's glo - ry shall we wake.

Text: Thomas H. Cain, b.1931, © 1982
Tune: FENN HOUSE, 10 10 10 10 10; Michael Joncas, b.1951, © 1988, GIA Publications, Inc.

161 Song of the Lord's Supper

1. We re - mem - ber one who loved us well,
2. We re - mem - ber how he spoke of you,
3. On the night be - fore he suf - fered death,
4. As they sat at ta - ble he took bread,
5. Now we take these gifts of field and vine,
Shared our life, its joy and sor - row,
Taught us to be - lieve your prom - ise,
Je - sus gath - ered his dis - ci - ples,
Blest it, broke it, gave it free - ly:
Bless and share them in his mem - 'ry:
Walked a - mong us as the least of all,
Showed us all what you are real - ly like—
Knelt be - fore them as a ser - vant might,
"Take this bread and eat it, all of you;
Bread of life and cup of cov - e - nant,
Gave him - self in - to our keep - ing.
Faith - ful, ten - der, God of peo - ple:
Washed their feet and bid them wel - come:
Take and eat, this is my bod - y."
King - dom - feast in pledge and prom - ise.
He is light that dawns for blind - ed eyes,
Not a God to break the wound - ed heart,
"Do you know what I have done for you,
Then he took the cup and passed it round:
When we eat this bread and drink this cup
He is hope for the de - spair - ing;
Not the thun - der of the might - y,
I who am your Lord and Mas - ter?
"Take and drink, this is my life - blood,
We pro - claim the death of Je - sus,

All on earth can find a place with him,
But a God that wel - comes sin - ners home,
If I bend to you and wash your feet,
Shed for you and for all hu - man - kind,
Taste his pres - ence, liv - ing in our midst,
Saint and sin - ner at his ta - ble.
Meets the low - ly with com - pas - sion.
So must you for one an - oth - er."
Shed that sins may be for - giv - en."
Look for him to come in glo - ry.

Text: Michael Joncas, b.1951
Tune: Michael Joncas, b.1951

Now Let Us All with One Accord 162

1. Now let us all with one accord, In com-pa-ny with a-ges past, Keep vig-il with our heav'n-ly Lord In his temp-ta-tion and his fast.

2. The cov-e-nant, so long re-vealed To those of faith in for-mer time, Christ by his own ex-am-ple sealed, The Lord of love, in love sub-lime.

3. Your love, O Lord, our sin-ful race Has not re-turned, but fal-si-fied; Au-thor of mer-cy, turn your face And grant re-pent-ance for our pride.

4. Re-mem-ber, Lord, though frail we be, In your own im-age were we made; Help us, lest in anx-i-e-ty, We cause your Name to be be-trayed.

5. There-fore, we pray you, Lord, for-give; So when our wan-d'rings here shall cease, We may with you for ev-er live, In love and u-ni-ty and peace.

Text: Attr. Gregory the Great, 540-604; Trans. *Praise the Lord,* 1972, James Quinn, SJ, b.1919, © Geoffrey Chapman
Tune: BOURBON, LM, Attr. Freeman Lewis, 1780-1859; Harm. by John Leon Hooker, b.1944, © 1984, The Church Pension Fund

163 Tree of Life

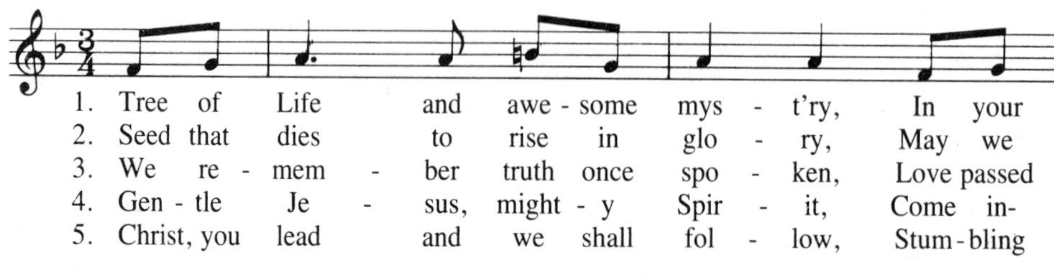
1. Tree of Life and awe - some mys - t'ry, In your
2. Seed that dies to rise in glo - ry, May we
3. We re - mem - ber truth once spo - ken, Love passed
4. Gen - tle Je - sus, might - y Spir - it, Come in-
5. Christ, you lead and we shall fol - low, Stum - bling

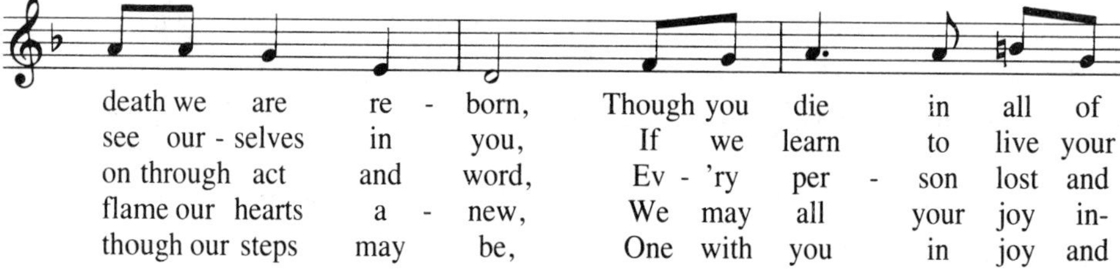
death we are re - born, Though you die in all of
see our - selves in you, If we learn to live your
on through act and word, Ev - 'ry per - son lost and
flame our hearts a - new, We may all your joy in-
though our steps may be, One with you in joy and

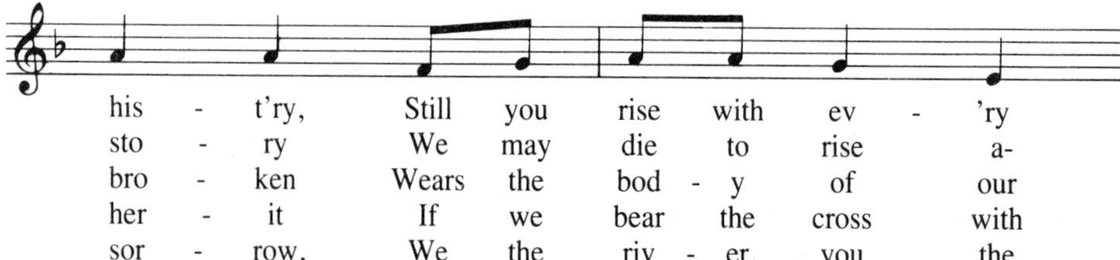
his - t'ry, Still you rise with ev - 'ry
sto - ry We may die to rise a-
bro - ken Wears the bod - y of our
her - it If we bear the cross with
sor - row, We the riv - er, you the

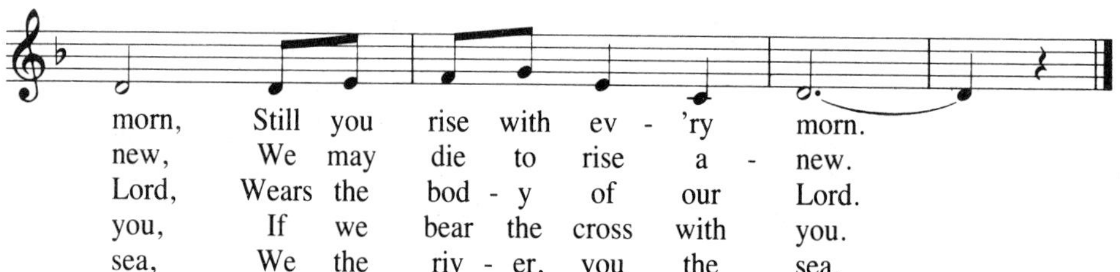
morn, Still you rise with ev - 'ry morn.
new, We may die to rise a - new.
Lord, Wears the bod - y of our Lord.
you, If we bear the cross with you.
sea, We the riv - er, you the sea.

Lenten Verses:

General: Light of life beyond conceiving, Mighty Spirit of our Lord;
Give new strength to our believing, Give us faith to live your word.

1st Sunday: From the dawning of creation you have loved us as your own;
Stay with us through all temptation, Make us turn to you alone.

2nd Sunday: In our call to be a blessing, May we be a blessing true;
May we live and die confessing Christ as Lord of all we do.

3rd Sunday: Living Water of salvation, Be the fountain of each soul;
Springing up in new creation, Flow in us and make us whole.

4th Sunday: Give us eyes to see you clearly, Make us children of your light;
Give us hearts to live more nearly As your gospel shining bright.

5th Sunday: God of all our fear and sorrow, God who lives beyond our death;
Hold us close through each tomorrow, Love as near as every breath.

Text: Marty Haugen, b.1950
Tune: THOMAS, 87 87 7; Marty Haugen, b.1950

Adoramus Te Christe 164

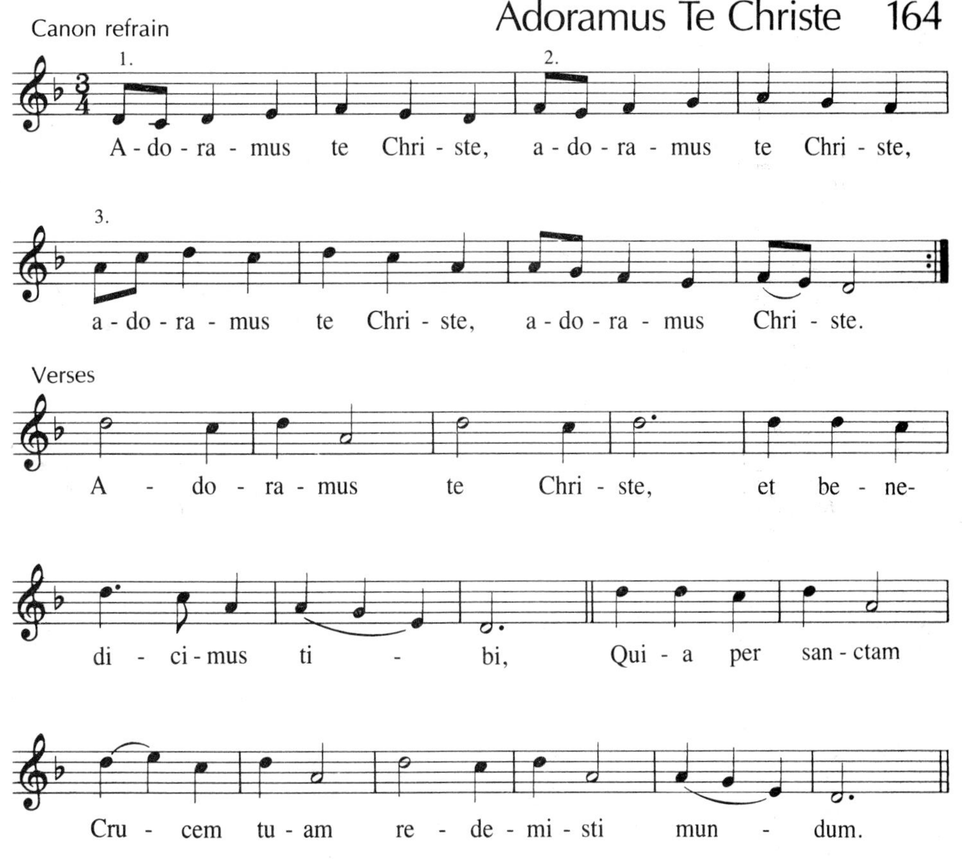
Canon refrain
1.
A - do - ra - mus te Chri - ste,
2.
a - do - ra - mus te Chri - ste,
3.
a - do - ra - mus te Chri - ste, a - do - ra - mus Chri - ste.
Verses
A - do - ra - mus te Chri - ste, et be - ne-
di - ci - mus ti - bi, Qui - a per san - ctam
Cru - cem tu - am re - de - mi - sti mun - dum.

Text: Antiphon from Good Friday Liturgy: *We adore you, O Christ, and we bless you, because by your holy cross you have redeemed the world.*
Tune: Marty Haugen, b.1950,

165 Hosanna

Refrain

Ho - san - na, ho - san - na, ho - san-

na! Ho - san - na, ho - san-

na, ho - san - na!

Verses

1. Bless - ed is he, bless - ed is he who comes in the

name of the Lord! Bless - ed is he, bless - ed is

he who comes in the name of the Lord!

D.C.

2. Bless - ed is the reign, of our Fa - ther

Da - vid. Bless - ed is the reign of our

Fa - ther Da - vid to come!

D.C.

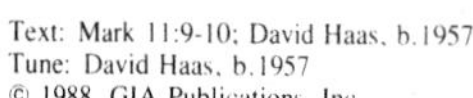

Text: Mark 11:9-10; David Haas, b.1957
Tune: David Haas, b.1957

Stay Here and Keep Watch 166

Stay here and keep watch with me. The hour has
come. Stay here and keep watch with me. Watch and pray.

Text: from Matthew 26; Taizé Community, 1984
Tune: Jacques Berthier, b.1923

Jesus, Remember Me 167

Je - sus, re-mem-ber me when you come in-to your King-dom.
Je - sus, re-mem-ber me when you come in-to your King - dom.

Text: Luke 23:42; Taizé Community, 1981
Tune: Jacques Berthier, b.1923

168 Jesu, Jesu

Refrain

Je - su, Je - su, fill us with your love, show us how to serve the neigh-bors we have from you.

Verses

1. Kneels at the feet of his friends, Si - lent - ly wash - es their feet, Mas - ter who pours out him - self for them.
2. Neigh-bors are rich and poor, Neigh-bors are black and white, Neigh - bors are near and far a - way.
3. These are the ones we should serve, These are the ones we should love. All are neigh-bors to us and you.
4. Kneel at the feet of our friends, Si - lent - ly wash - ing their feet, This is the way we should live with you.

D.C.

Text: John 13:3-5; Ghana Folk Song; Trans. by Tom Colvin, b.1925
Tune: CHEREPONI, Irregular; Ghana Folk Song; Adapt. by Tom Colvin, b.1925, Acc. by Jane Marshall, b.1924, © 1982, Hope Publishing Co.

169 Ride On, Jesus, Ride

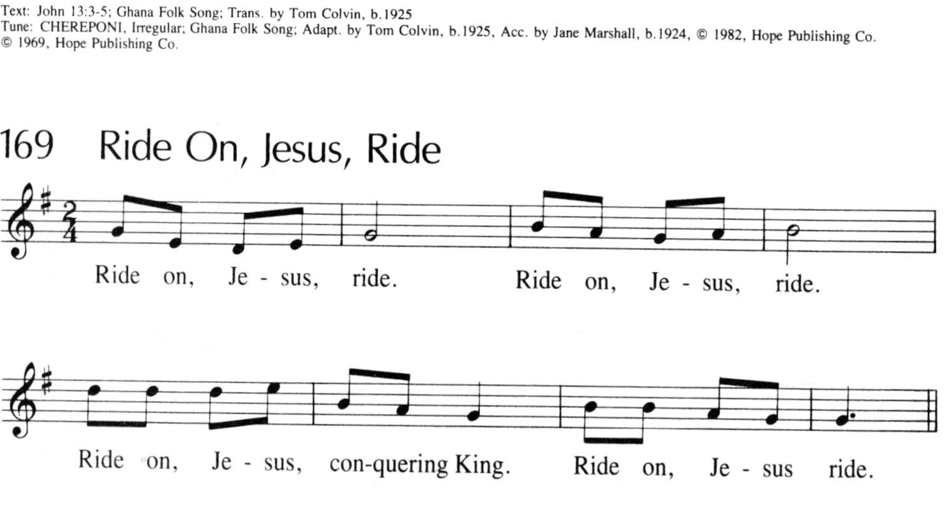
Ride on, Je - sus, ride. Ride on, Je - sus, ride.
Ride on, Je - sus, con-quering King. Ride on, Je - sus ride.

1. King Je - sus rides on a milk white horse. Ride on, Je - sus,
2. My Je - sus lift - ed his throne a - bove. Ride on, Je - sus,

ride. The riv - er Jor - dan he did cross. Ride on, Je - sus,
ride. See his mer - cy and his love. Ride on, Je - sus,

ride. Ride on, Je - sus, con-quering King. Ride on, Je - sus ride.
ride. Ride on, Je - sus, con-quering King. Ride on, Je - sus ride.

Text: Afro-American Spiritual
Tune: Afro-American Spiritual; Harm. by Barbara Jackson Martin, © 1987, GIA Publications, Inc.

Stay with Me 170

Stay with me, re - main here with me, watch and
pray watch and pray.

Text: from Matthew 26; Taizé Community, 1984
Tune: Jaques Berthier, b.1923
© 1984, Les Presses de Taizé

171 Were You There

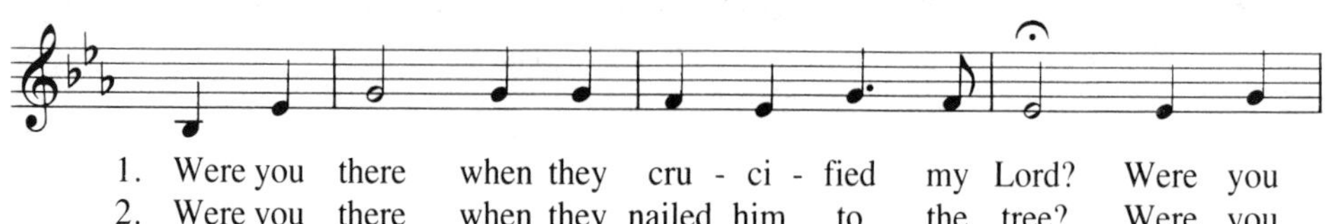

1. Were you there when they cru - ci - fied my Lord? Were you
2. Were you there when they nailed him to the tree? Were you
3. Were you there when they pierced him in the side? Were you
4. Were you there when the sun re - fused to shine? Were you

there when they cru - ci - fied my Lord? O!
there when they nailed him to the tree? O!
there when they pierced him in the side? O!
there when the sun re - fused to shine? O!

Some-times it caus - es me to trem-ble, trem-ble, trem-ble,
Some-times it caus - es me to trem-ble, trem-ble, trem-ble,
Some-times it caus - es me to trem-ble, trem-ble, trem-ble,
Some-times it caus - es me to trem-ble, trem-ble, trem-ble,

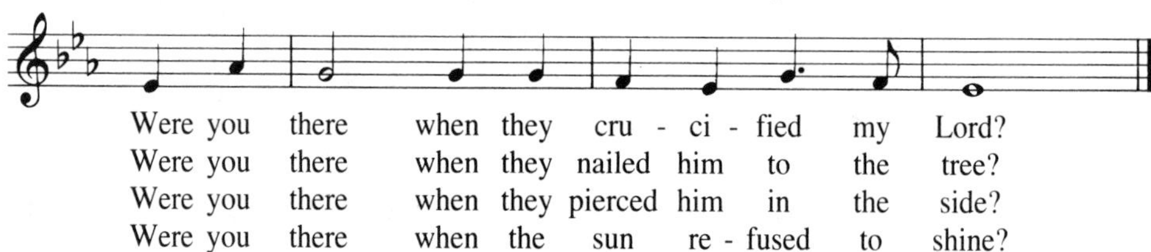

Were you there when they cru - ci - fied my Lord?
Were you there when they nailed him to the tree?
Were you there when they pierced him in the side?
Were you there when the sun re - fused to shine?

5. Were you there when they laid him in the tomb?
Were you there when they laid him in the tomb?
O! Sometimes it causes me to tremble, tremble, tremble,
Were you there when they laid him in the tomb?

6. Were you there when they rolled the stone away?
Were you there when they rolled the stone away?
O! Sometimes it causes me to tremble, tremble, tremble,
Were you there when they rolled the stone away?

Text: Afro-American Spiritual
Tune: WERE YOU THERE, 10 10 with refrain; Afro-American Spiritual; Harm. by Robert J. Batastini, b. 1942,

Calvary 172

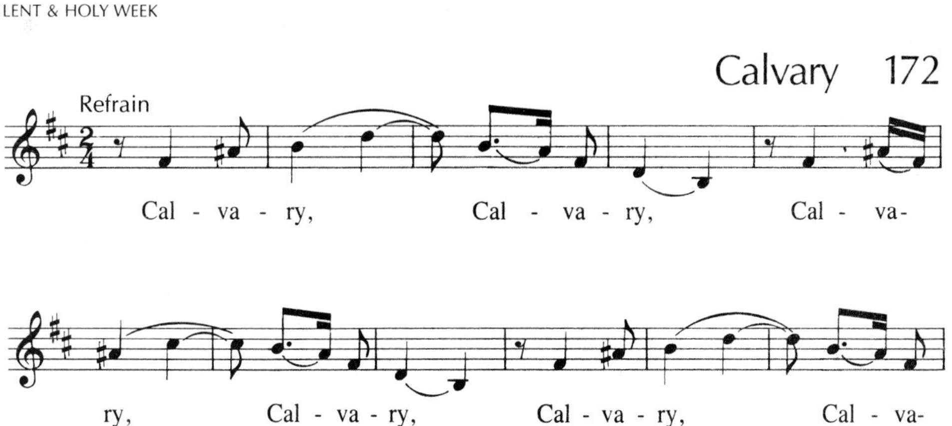
Refrain
Cal - va - ry, Cal - va - ry, Cal - va-
ry, Cal - va - ry, Cal - va - ry, Cal - va-

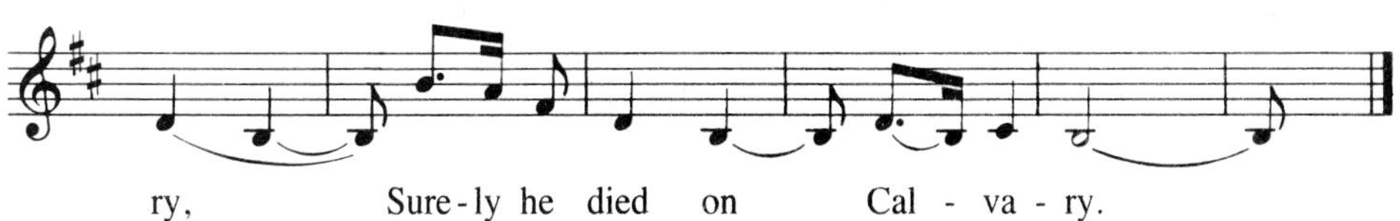
ry, Sure-ly he died on Cal - va - ry.

Verses
1. Ev - 'ry time I think a-bout Je - sus, Ev - 'ry
2. Sin - ner, do you love my Je - sus? Sin - ner,
3. We are climb - ing Ja - cob's lad - der, We are
4. Ev - 'ry round goes high - er and high - er, Ev - 'ry

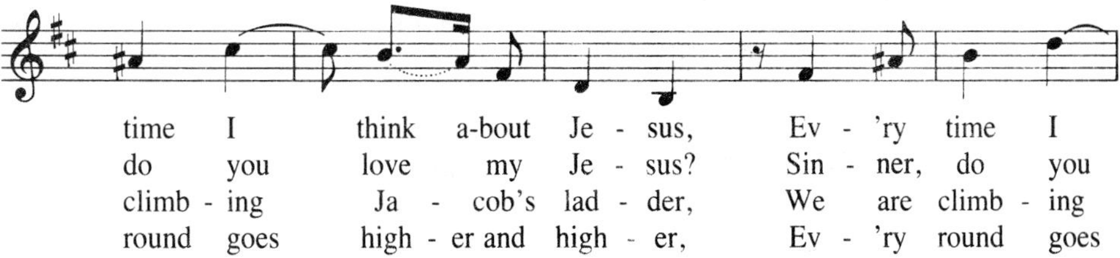
time I think a-bout Je - sus, Ev - 'ry time I
do you love my Je - sus? Sin - ner, do you
climb - ing Ja - cob's lad - der, We are climb - ing
round goes high - er and high - er, Ev - 'ry round goes

D.C.
think a-bout Je - sus,
love my Je - sus?
Ja - cob's lad - der,
high-er and high - er,
Sure-ly he died on Cal- va - ry.

Text: Afro-American Spiritual
Tune: Afro-American Spiritual

173 Ashes

1. We rise a - gain from ash - es, from the good we've failed to
2. We of - fer you our fail - ures, we of - fer you at-
3. Then rise a - gain from ash - es, let heal - ing come to
4. Thanks be to the Fa - ther, who made us like him-

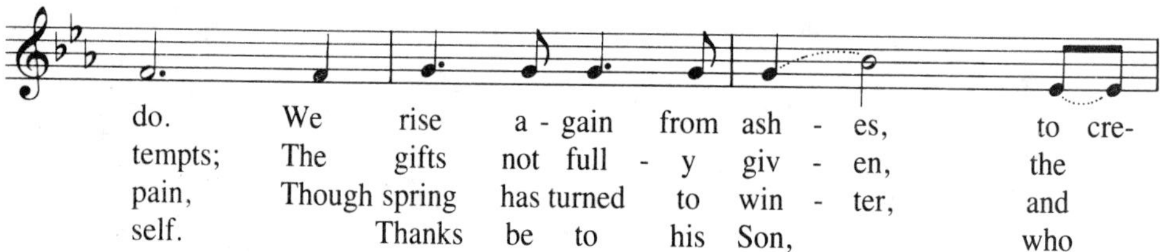

do. We rise a - gain from ash - es, to cre-
tempts; The gifts not full - y giv - en, the
pain, Though spring has turned to win - ter, and
self. Thanks be to his Son, who

ate our - selves a - new. If all our world is
dreams not full - y dreamt. Give our stum - bl - ings di-
sun - shine turned to rain. The rain we'll use for
saved us by his death. Thanks be to the

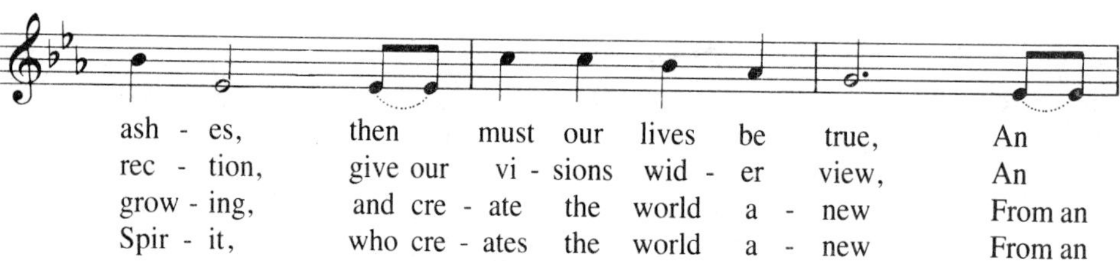

ash - es, then must our lives be true, An
rec - tion, give our vi - sions wid - er view, An
grow - ing, and cre - ate the world a - new From an
Spir - it, who cre - ates the world a - new From an

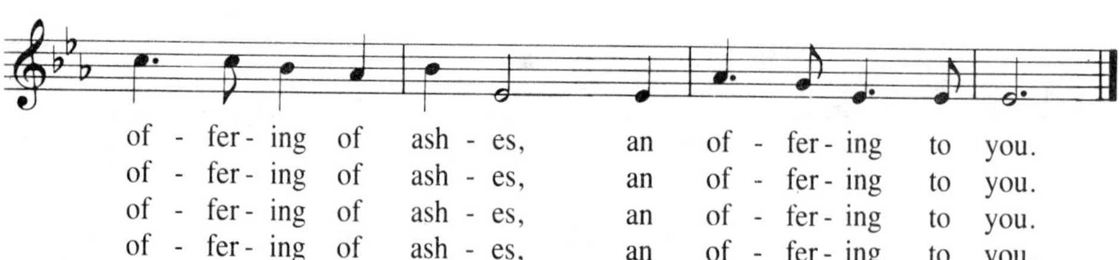

of - fer - ing of ash - es, an of - fer - ing to you.
of - fer - ing of ash - es, an of - fer - ing to you.
of - fer - ing of ash - es, an of - fer - ing to you.
of - fer - ing of ash - es, an of - fer - ing to you.

Text: Tom Conry
Tune: Tom Conry

Wherever You Go 174

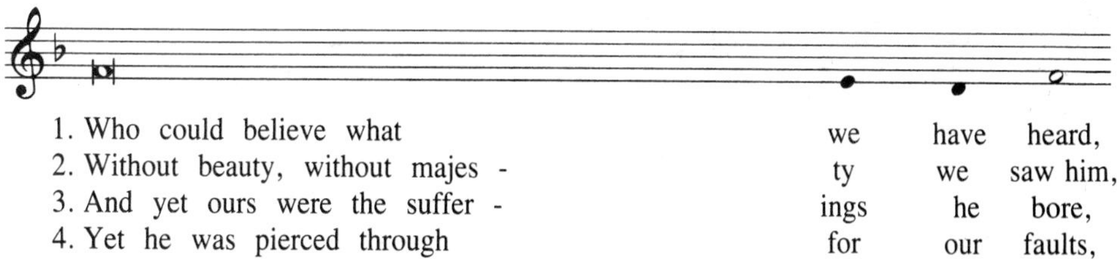
1. Who could believe what we have heard,
2. Without beauty, without majes - ty we saw him,
3. And yet ours were the suffer - ings he bore,
4. Yet he was pierced through for our faults,

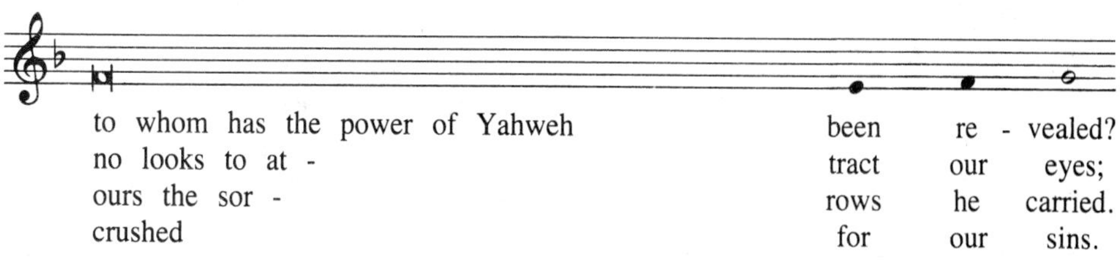
to whom has the power of Yahweh been re - vealed?
no looks to at - tract our eyes;
ours the sor - rows he carried.
crushed for our sins.

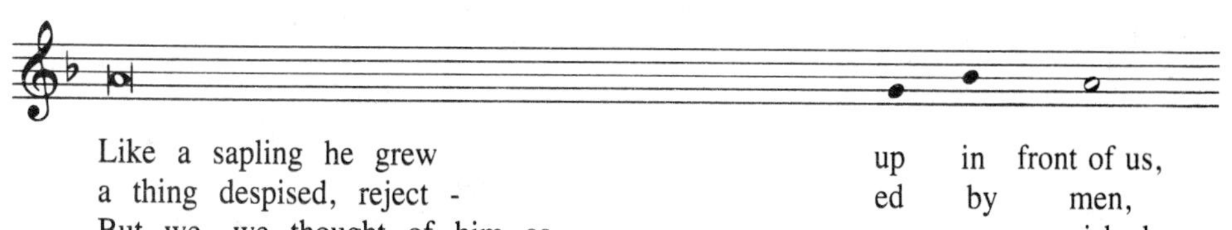
Like a sapling he grew up in front of us,
a thing despised, reject - ed by men,
But we, we thought of him as some - one punished,
On him lies a punishment that brings us peace,

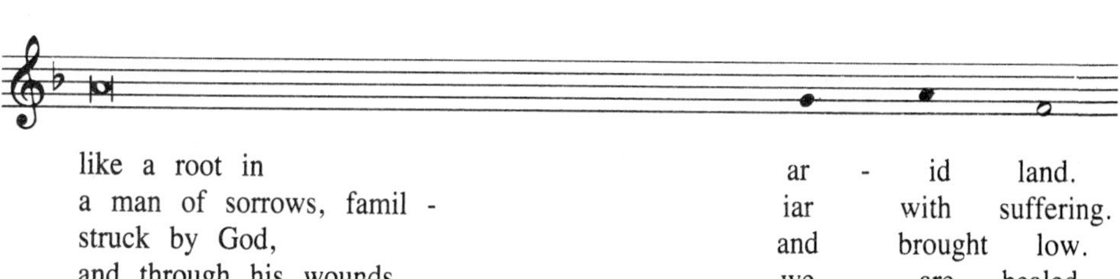
like a root in ar - id land.
a man of sorrows, famil - iar with suffering.
struck by God, and brought low.
and through his wounds we are healed.

Wher-ev - er you go, I will go, wher-ev - er you live, I will live.

Text: Ruth 1:16; Jeremiah 53:1-5; © 1966, The Jerusalem Bible
Tune: Fr. Columba Kelly, OSB, Fr. Tobias Colgan, OSB, © 1979, St. Meinrad Archabbey

175 Now the Green Blade Rises

1. Now the green blade ris - es from the bur - ied grain,
2. In the grave they laid him, love by ha - tred slain,
3. Forth he came at East - er, like the ris - en grain,
4. When our hearts are win - try, griev - ing or in pain,

Wheat that in dark earth man - y days has lain;
Think - ing that he would nev - er wake a - gain,
He that for three days in the grave had lain;
Your touch can call us back to life a - gain,

Love lives a - gain, that with the dead has been;
Laid in the earth like grain that sleeps un - seen;
Raised from the dead, my liv - ing Lord is seen;
Fields of our hearts that dead and bare have been;

Love is come a - gain like wheat a - ris - ing green.

Text: John M. C. Crum, 1872-1958, *Oxford Book of Carols*, © Oxford University Press
Tune: NOËL NOUVELET, 11 10 11 10; French Carol; Acc. by Marty Haugen, b. 1950, © 1987, GIA Publications, Inc.

176 Surrexit Dominus Vere II

Canon
1.
Sur - re - xit Do - mi - nus ve - re.
2.
Al - le - lu - ia, al - le - lu - ia.

3.
Sur - re - xit Chri - stus ho - di - e,
4.
Al - le - lu - ia, al - le - lu - ia.

Text: *The Lord is truly risen! Christ is risen today!* Taizé Community, 1978
Tune: Jacques Berthier, 1923

Psallite Deo 177

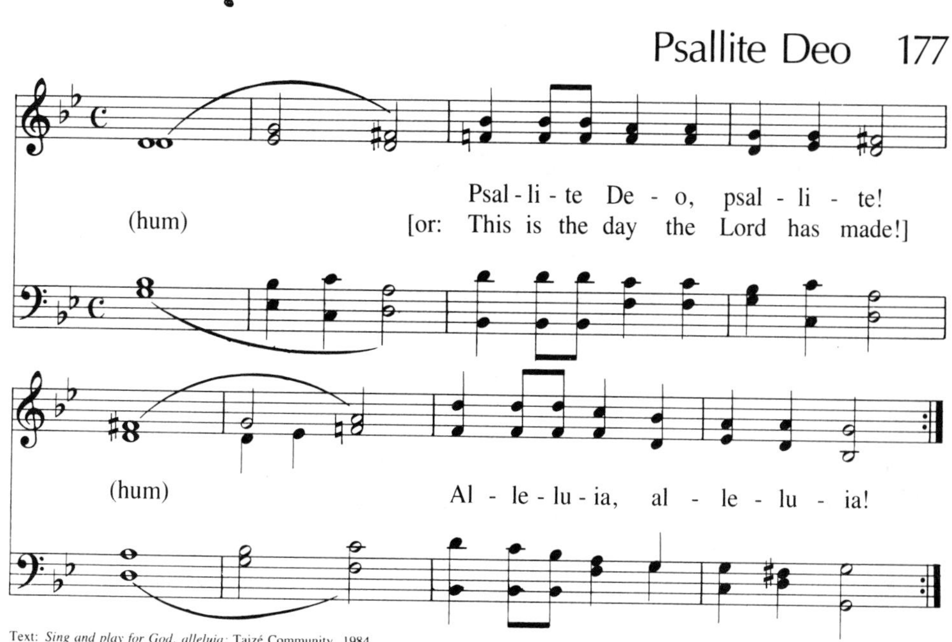
(hum)
Psal - li - te De - o, psal - li - te!
[or: This is the day the Lord has made!]
(hum)
Al - le - lu - ia, al - le - lu - ia!

Text: *Sing and play for God, alleluia;* Taizé Community, 1984
Tune: Jacques Berthier, b.1923

178 Light of Christ/Exsultet

Cantor:
All:
This is the light of Christ; Thanks be to God.
Cantor:
All:
You are the light of Christ; Thanks be to God.
Cantor:
All:
Live in the light of Christ. He is our life.
Refrain
The light of Christ sur - rounds us, the love of Christ en - folds us, the pow'r of Christ pro - tects us, the pres - ence of Christ watch - es o - ver us.
To verses
Coda - after last refrain
for ev - er and ev - er, for ev - er and ev - er. A - men!
Verses
1. All the earth is a - blaze with the glo - ry of
2. Let us fill ev - 'ry space with the sound of our
3. As this can - dle shines out through the dark - ness of

D.S.

God, for the Light has come to burn a - way the dark-ness.
joy, prais-ing Christ, who is liv - ing now a - mong us.
night, may the love of Christ burn ev - er in our hearts.

4. In the east, the Morn-ing Star ris - es bright up - on you,

D.S.

in its peace-ful light shines the glo - ry of the Lord.

Text: Based on a prayer by James Dillet Freeman and the *Exsultet;* Marty Haugen, b.1950
Tune: Marty Haugen, b.1950

I Am the Resurrection 179

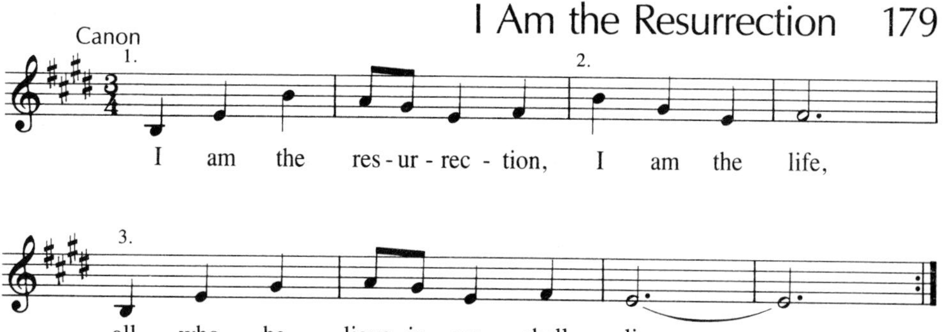
Canon
1.
I am the res - ur - rec - tion,
2.
I am the life,
3.
all who be - lieve in me shall live.

Text: John 11:26; David Haas, b.1957
Tune: David Haas, b.1957

180 Easter Alleluia

Refrain
Al - le - lu - ia, al - le - lu - ia, al - le - lu - ia.

Verses

1. Glo - ry to God who does won - drous things, let all God's
2. See how sal - va - tion for all has been won, up from the
3. Now in our pres - ence the Lord will ap - pear, shine in the
4. Call us, Good Shep-herd, we lis - ten for you, want - ing to
5. Lord, we are o - pen to all that you say, read - y to
6. If we have love, then we dwell in the Lord, God will pro-

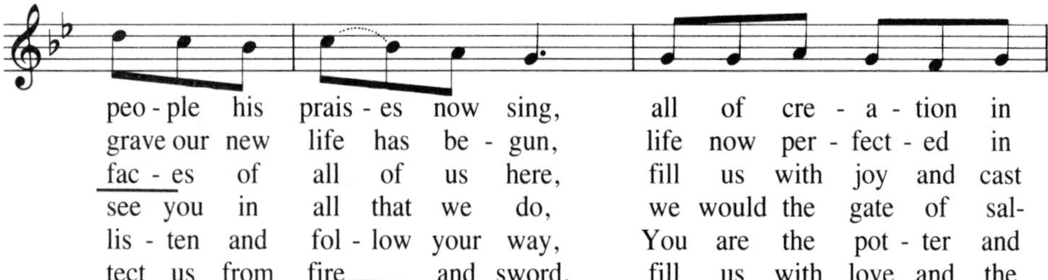
peo - ple his prais - es now sing, all of cre - a - tion in
grave our new life has be - gun, life now per - fect - ed in
fac - es of all of us here, fill us with joy and cast
see you in all that we do, we would the gate of sal-
lis - ten and fol - low your way, You are the pot - ter and
tect us from fire and sword, fill us with love and the

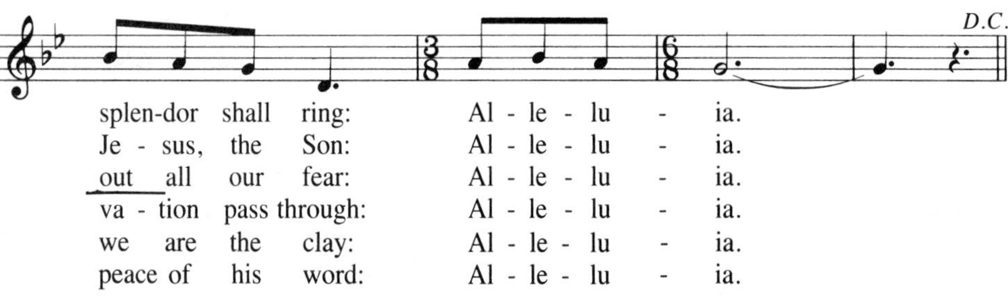
D.C.
splen-dor shall ring: Al - le - lu - ia.
Je - sus, the Son: Al - le - lu - ia.
out all our fear: Al - le - lu - ia.
va - tion pass through: Al - le - lu - ia.
we are the clay: Al - le - lu - ia.
peace of his word: Al - le - lu - ia.

Text: Marty Haugen, b.1950
Tune: O FILLII ET FILIAE; 10 10 10 with alleluias; Adapt. by Marty Haugen, b.1950

Song of the Risen One 181
Refrain
Why do you look for the liv - ing a - mong the dead?
He is not here: he has been raised to new
life! Al - le - lu - ia, al - le - lu - ia!
Verses
1. Come and see! the one whom you
2. Ev - 'ry tear will be driv - en a-
3. Strength to the weak! New sight for the
seek is no long - er here: Who is ris - en a-
way no more pain; no more weep - ing and
blind: Je - sus a - live! Go and tell all the
mong you, who goes now be - fore you a-
mourn - ing, "Be - hold I make all things
na - tions the won - drous deeds of our
live! Al - le - lu - ia, al - le - lu - ia!
new!" Al - le - lu - ia, al - le - lu - ia!
God! Al - le - lu - ia, al - le - lu - ia!
D.C.

Text: David Haas, b.1957
Tune: David Haas, b.1957

182 Hilariter

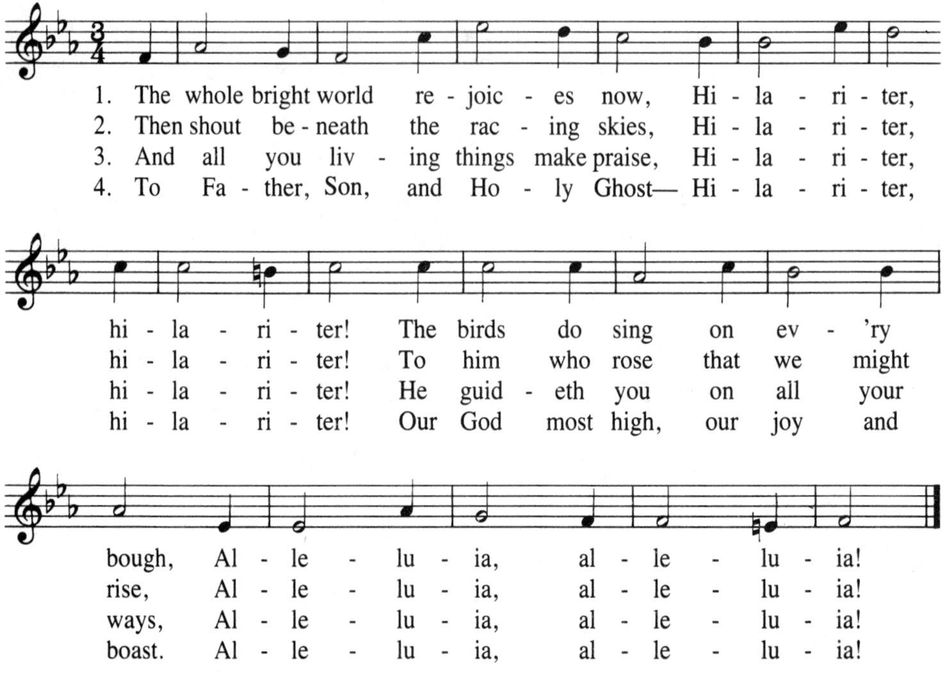
1. The whole bright world re - joic - es now, Hi - la - ri - ter,
2. Then shout be - neath the rac - ing skies, Hi - la - ri - ter,
3. And all you liv - ing things make praise, Hi - la - ri - ter,
4. To Fa - ther, Son, and Ho - ly Ghost— Hi - la - ri - ter,
hi - la - ri - ter! The birds do sing on ev - 'ry
hi - la - ri - ter! To him who rose that we might
hi - la - ri - ter! He guid - eth you on all your
hi - la - ri - ter! Our God most high, our joy and
bough, Al - le - lu - ia, al - le - lu - ia!
rise, Al - le - lu - ia, al - le - lu - ia!
ways, Al - le - lu - ia, al - le - lu - ia!
boast. Al - le - lu - ia, al - le - lu - ia!

Text: *Die ganze Welt,* from *Kirchengesäng,* 1623; Friedrich von Spee, 1592-1635; Trans. by Percy Dearmer, 1867-1936
Tune: HILARITER, LM; German, 1623; Harm. by Martin Shaw, 1875-1958, *Book of Carols* © Oxford University Press

183 Christ Is Alive

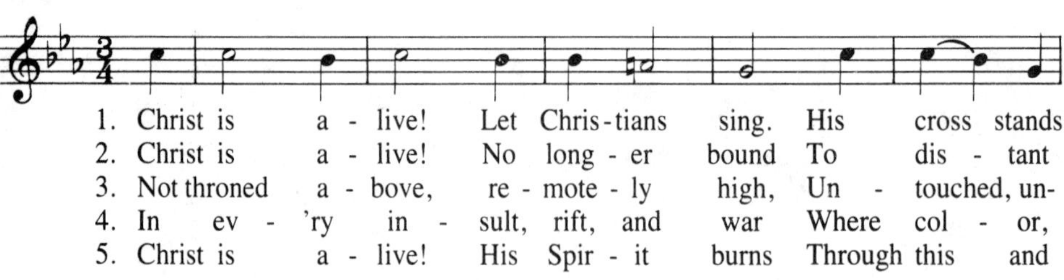
1. Christ is a - live! Let Chris - tians sing. His cross stands
2. Christ is a - live! No long - er bound To dis - tant
3. Not throned a - bove, re - mote - ly high, Un - touched, un-
4. In ev - 'ry in - sult, rift, and war Where col - or,
5. Christ is a - live! His Spir - it burns Through this and

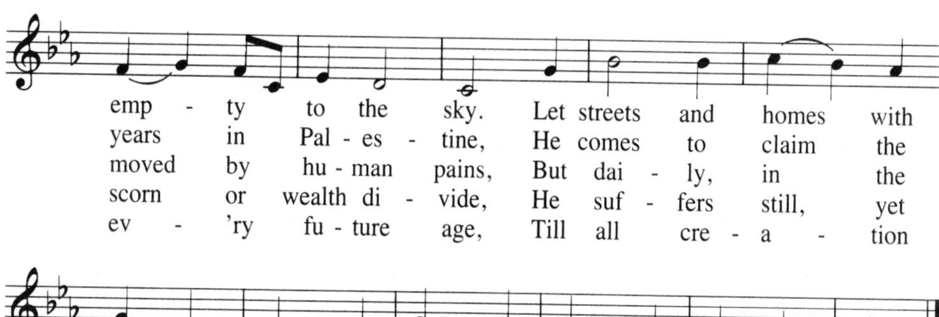
emp - ty to the sky. Let streets and homes with
years in Pal - es - tine, He comes to claim the
moved by hu - man pains, But dai - ly, in the
scorn or wealth di - vide, He suf - fers still, yet
ev - 'ry fu - ture age, Till all cre - a - tion

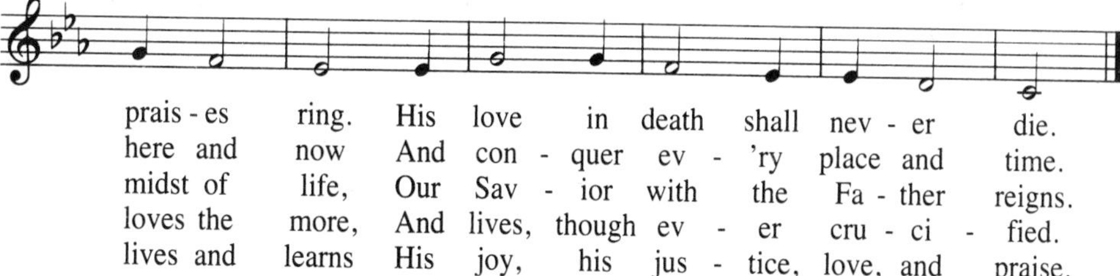
prais - es ring. His love in death shall nev - er die.
here and now And con - quer ev - 'ry place and time.
midst of life, Our Sav - ior with the Fa - ther reigns.
loves the more, And lives, though ev - er cru - ci - fied.
lives and learns His joy, his jus - tice, love, and praise.

Text: Brian Wren, b.1936, alt., © 1975, Hope Publishing Co.
Tune: AGINCOURT; *The Agincourt Song,* 15th C.; Acc. Marty Haugen, b. 1950, © 1987, GIA Publications, Inc.

Good Christians All 184

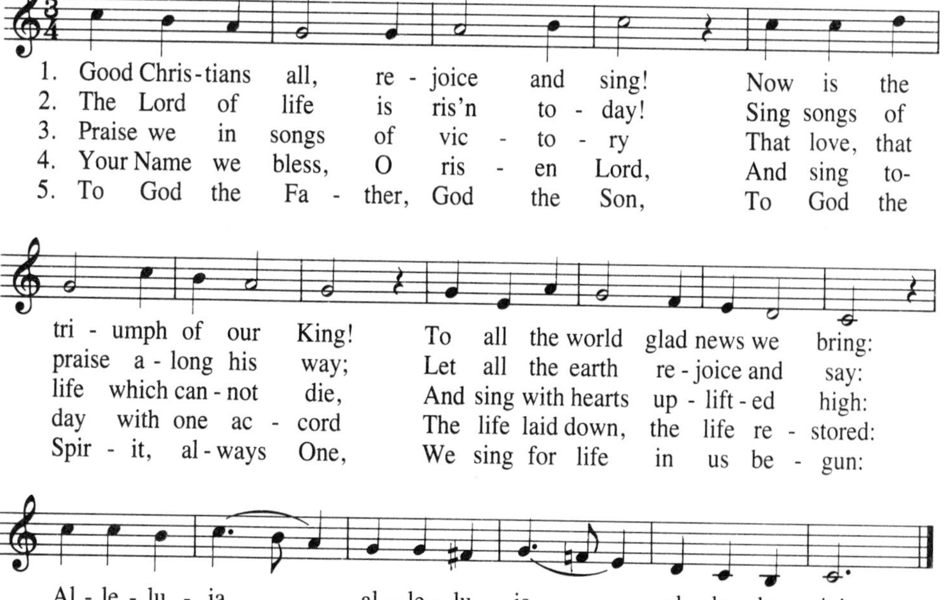
1. Good Chris - tians all, re - joice and sing! Now is the
2. The Lord of life is ris'n to - day! Sing songs of
3. Praise we in songs of vic - to - ry That love, that
4. Your Name we bless, O ris - en Lord, And sing to-
5. To God the Fa - ther, God the Son, To God the
tri - umph of our King! To all the world glad news we bring:
praise a - long his way; Let all the earth re - joice and say:
life which can - not die, And sing with hearts up - lift - ed high:
day with one ac - cord The life laid down, the life re - stored:
Spir - it, al - ways One, We sing for life in us be - gun:
Al - le - lu - ia, al - le - lu - ia, al - le - lu - ia!

Text: Cyril A. Alington, 1872-1955, alt., © 1956, Hymns Ancient and Modern Limited; St. 5, Norman Mealy, b. 1923, © 1971, Walton Music Corporation
Tune: *Gelobt sei Gott,* 888 with alleluias; Melchior Vulpius, c.1560-1616; Acc. Robert J. Batastini, b.1942, © 1987, GIA Publications, Inc.

185 Come Away to the Skies

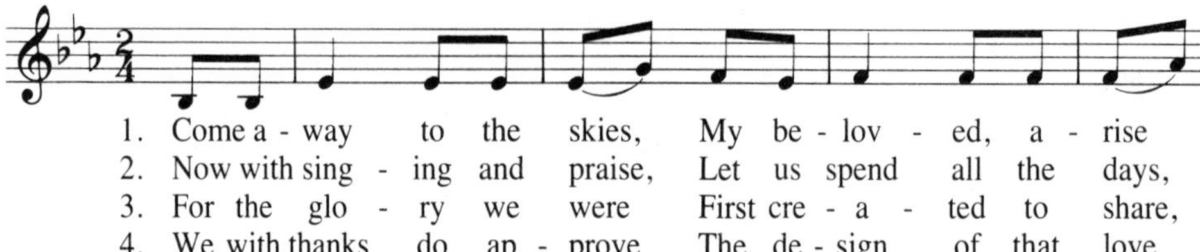
1. Come a - way to the skies, My be - lov - ed, a - rise
2. Now with sing - ing and praise, Let us spend all the days,
3. For the glo - ry we were First cre - a - ted to share,
4. We with thanks do ap - prove The de - sign of that love
5. Hal - le - lu - jah we sing, To our Fa - ther and King,

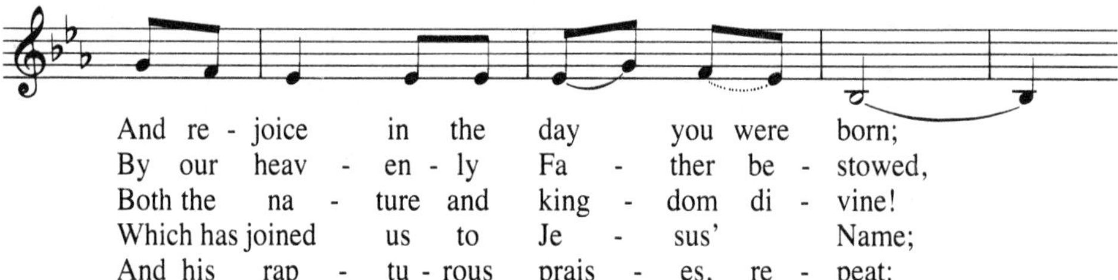
And re - joice in the day you were born;
By our heav - en - ly Fa - ther be - stowed,
Both the na - ture and king - dom di - vine!
Which has joined us to Je - sus' Name;
And his rap - tu - rous prais - es, re - peat:

On this fes - ti - val day, Come ex - ult - ing a - way,
While his grace we re - ceive From his boun - ty, and live
Now cre - a - ted a - gain That our lives may re - main,
So u - nit - ed in heart, Let us nev - er - more part,
To the Lamb that was slain, Hal - le - lu - jah a - gain,

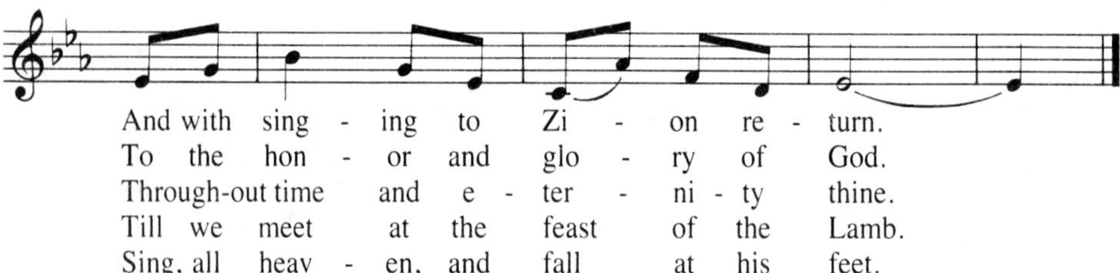
And with sing - ing to Zi - on re - turn.
To the hon - or and glo - ry of God.
Through-out time and e - ter - ni - ty thine.
Till we meet at the feast of the Lamb.
Sing, all heav - en, and fall at his feet.

Text: Anonymous, *Southern Harmony*, 1835, alt.
Tune: MIDDLEBURY, 669 669; *Southern Harmony*, 1835; Harm. by Jack W. Burnham, b.1946, © 1984

Surrexit Christus 186

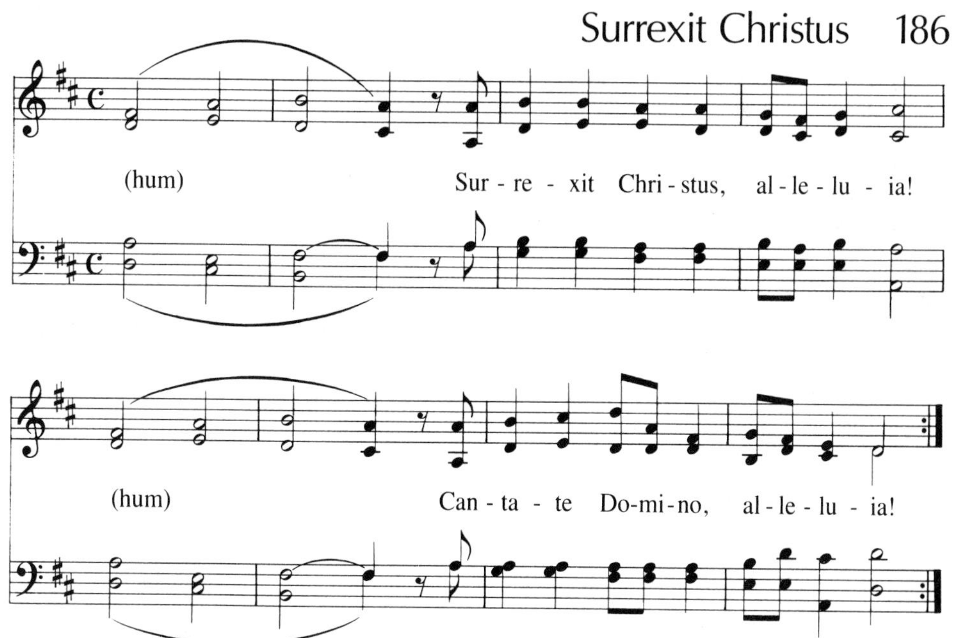
(hum)
Sur - re - xit Chri - stus, al - le - lu - ia!
(hum)
Can - ta - te Do-mi-no, al - le - lu - ia!

Text: *Christ is risen, sing to the Lord;* Daniel 3, Psalm 118; Taizé Community, 1984
Tune: Jacques Berthier, b.1923

187 Song to Jesus Christ

1. You have passed by, you came like fire that lights the skies,
2. You have passed by, as brief as foot-prints on the sea;
3. You have passed by, a strange and yet fa - mil - iar face,

Sparks fall - ing from your name glow in our hearts like eyes.
Why did you go so far? You went too far for me.
A frag - ment of our being, a flick-'ring light, a trace.

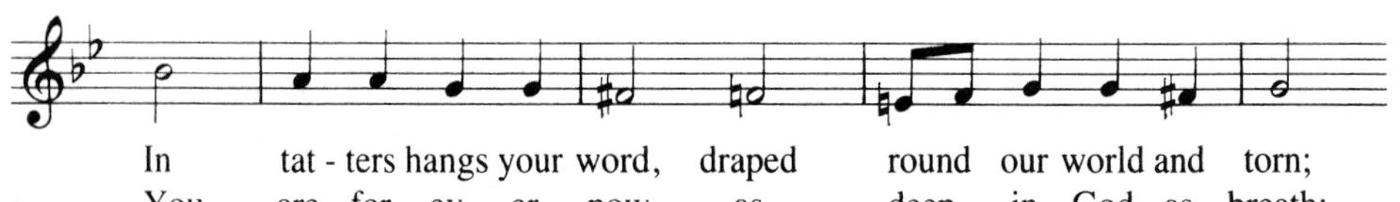

In tat - ters hangs your word, draped round our world and torn;
You are for ev - er now as deep in God as breath;
Your light is in my blood, my bod - y is your day;

Now we shall live in you; like cloth - ing you are worn.
No still - ness cap - tures you, un - think - a - ble your death.
I hope my whole life long to meet you on the way.

Text: Huub Oosterhuis, b.1933; Trans. by Redmond McGoldrick
Tune: J. Tabourot; Harm. by Bernard Huijbers

I Will Be with You 188

Refrain
"I will be with you!" That is my prom-ise.
"I will be with you for ev - er - more."
Trust in my love.
Bring me all your cares, for I will be with you for ev - er - more.
Verses
1. You are my peo - ple, and I am your God.
2. You have re-ceived me, now go and spread my word.
I made you a prom - ise, to be with you al - ways,
You are with - in me and I am in you,
be-cause I real - ly love you. I real - ly love you, and I will be with you for ev - er - more.
D.C.

Text: James E. Moore, Jr.
Tune: James E. Moore, Jr.

189 Send Us Your Spirit

Refrain

Come Lord Je - sus, send us your Spir - it, re - new the

face of the earth. Come Lord Je - sus, send us your

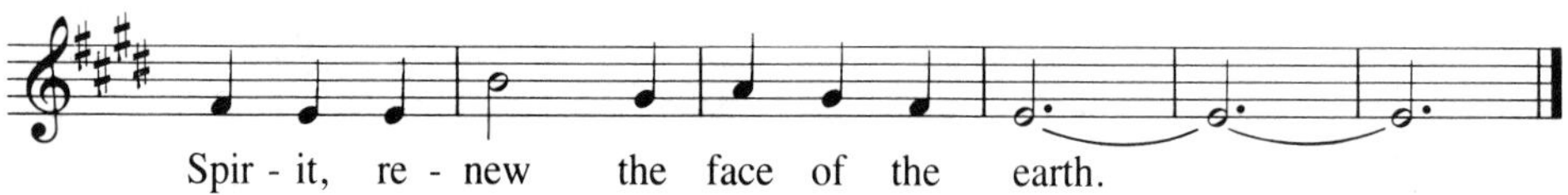
Spir - it, re - new the face of the earth.

Verses

1. Come to us, Spir - it of God, breathe in us
2. Fill us with the fire of your love, burn in us
3. Send us the wings of new birth, fill all the

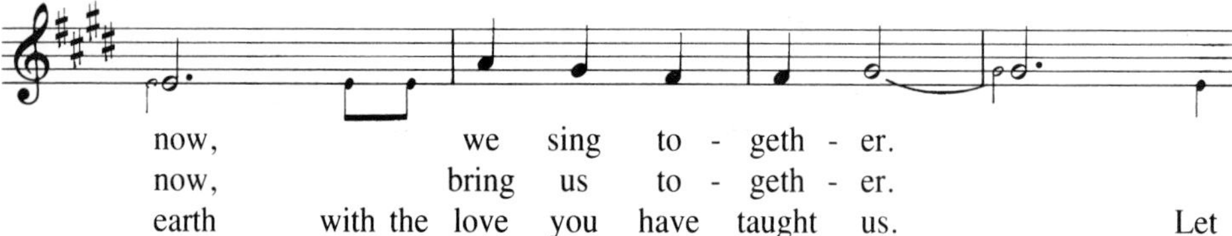
now, we sing to - geth - er.
now, bring us to - geth - er.
earth with the love you have taught us. Let

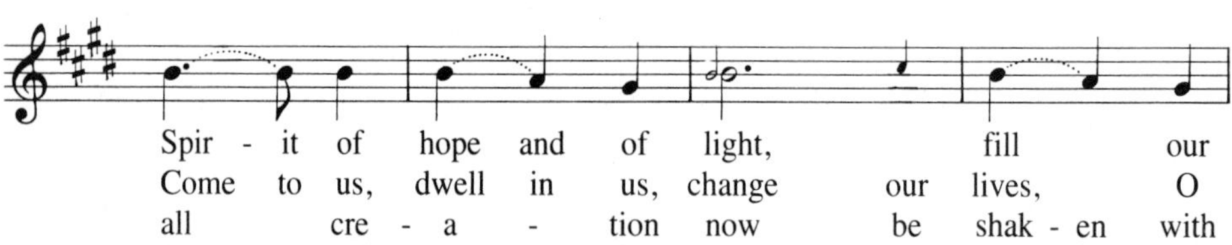
Spir - it of hope and of light, fill our
Come to us, dwell in us, change our lives, O
all cre - a - tion now be shak - en with

D.C.
lives, come to us, Spir - it of God.
Lord, come to us, Spir - it of God.
love, come to us, Spir - it of God.

Text: David Haas, b.1957
Tune: David Haas, b.1957; Acc. by Jeanne Cotter

Spirit of God within Me 190

1. Spir - it of God with - in me, pos - sess my hu - man frame.
2. Spir - it of truth with - in me, pos - sess my thought and mind;
3. Spir - it of love with - in me, pos - sess my hands and heart;
4. Spir - it of life with - in me, pos - sess this life of mine;

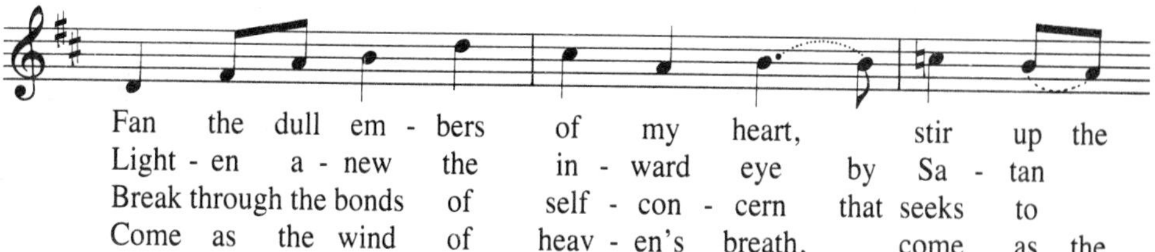
Fan the dull em - bers of my heart, stir up the
Light - en a - new the in - ward eye by Sa - tan
Break through the bonds of self - con - cern that seeks to
Come as the wind of heav - en's breath, come as the

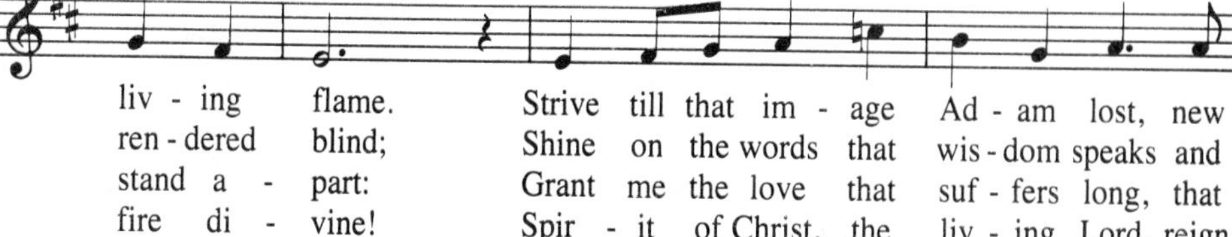
liv - ing flame. Strive till that im - age Ad - am lost, new
ren - dered blind; Shine on the words that wis - dom speaks and
stand a - part: Grant me the love that suf - fers long, that
fire di - vine! Spir - it of Christ, the liv - ing Lord, reign

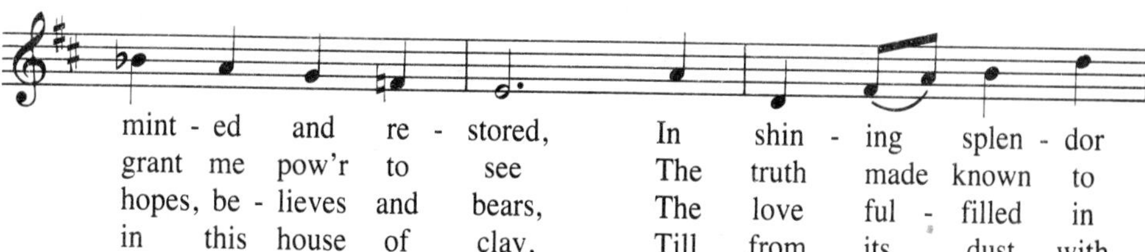
mint - ed and re - stored, In shin - ing splen - dor
grant me pow'r to see The truth made known to
hopes, be - lieves and bears, The love ful - filled in
in this house of clay, Till from its dust with

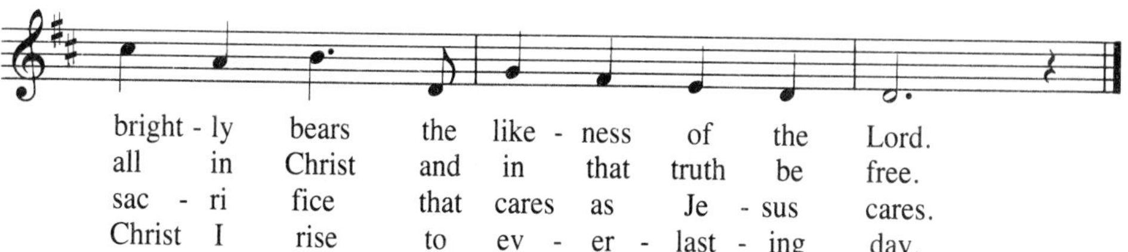
bright - ly bears the like - ness of the Lord.
all in Christ and in that truth be free.
sac - ri fice that cares as Je - sus cares.
Christ I rise to ev - er - last - ing day.

191 Spirit Blowing through Creation

1. Spirit blowing through creation,
Spirit burning in the skies,
Let the hope of your salvation fill our eyes;
God of splendor, God of glory,
You who light the stars above,
All the heavens tell the story of your love.

2. As you moved upon the waters,
As you ride upon the wind,
Move us all, your sons and daughters deep within;
As you shaped the hills and mountains,
Formed the land and filled the deep,
Let your hand renew and waken all who sleep.

3. Love that sends the rivers dancing,
Love that waters all that lives,
Love that heals and holds and rouses and forgives;
You are food for all your creatures,
You are hunger in the soul,
In your hands the broken-hearted are made whole.

4. All the creatures you have fashioned,
All that live and breathe in you,
Find their hope in your compassion, strong and true;
You, O Spirit of salvation,
You alone, beneath, above,
Come, renew your whole creation in your love.

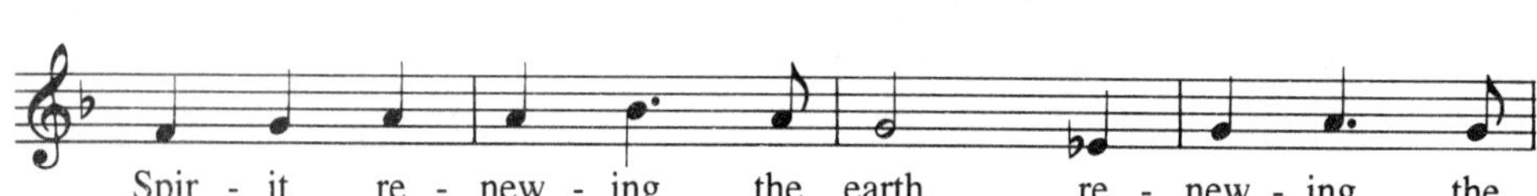
Spir - it re - new - ing the earth, re - new - ing the

hearts of all peo - ple; Burn in the wea-ry souls,

blow through the si - lent lips, come now a - wake us!

Spir - it of God.

Text: Marty Haugen, b.1950
Tune: Marty Haugen, b.1950

Spirit Friend 192

1. God sends us his Spir - it to be - friend and help us.
Re - cre - ate and guide us, Spir - it - Friend.
Spir - it who en - liv - ens, sanc - ti - fies, en - light - ens,
Sets us free, is now our Spir - it - Friend.

2. Dark-ened roads are clear - er, heav - y bur - dens light - er,
When we're walk - ing with our Spir - it - Friend.
Now we need not fear the pow - ers of the dark - ness.
None can o - ver - come our Spir - it - Friend.

3. Now we are God's peo - ple, bond - ed by God's pres - ence,
A - gents of God's pur - pose, Spir - it - Friend.
Lead us for - ward ev - er, slip - ping back-ward nev - er,
To your re - made world, our Spir - it - Friend.

Sung three times after each stanza. *Hand claps*

Spir - it of our Mak - er, Spir - it - Friend.
Spir - it of our Je - su, Spir - it - Friend.
Spir - it of God's peo - ple, Spir - it - Friend.

Text: Tom Colvin, b.1925, © 1969, Hope Publishing Co.
Tune: NATOMAH, 12 9 12 9 with refrain; Gonja Folk Song; Adapt. by Tom Colvin, b.1925, © 1969, Hope Publishing Co.; Acc. Marty Haugen, b.1950, © 1987, GIA Publications, Inc.

193 Veni Sancte Spiritus

Ve - ni San - cte Spi - ri - tus.
pp

To begin this ostinato, the voices enter one at a time in the following order: Bass, Alto, Soprano, Tenor. Sing the ostinato twice before adding the next voice.

Text: *Come Holy Spirit;* Verses drawn from Pentecost Sequence; Taizé Community, 1978
Tune: Jacques Berthier, b.1923

194 What Is Your Name

Cantor:
What is your name? O where can we find you? E - ter - nal

God, we want to see you. Give us to - day a sign of your love,

All:
then. E - ter - nal God, we want to see you. Give us to - day a

Cantor:
sign of your love, then. For what the heav - ens are for the earth,

TRINITY

All:
that is your love for those who be - lieve. Give us to - day a

Cantor:
sign of your love, then. You are for - give - ness for all our

All:
fail - ures, jus - tice and right-eous-ness for all this world. You, the for-

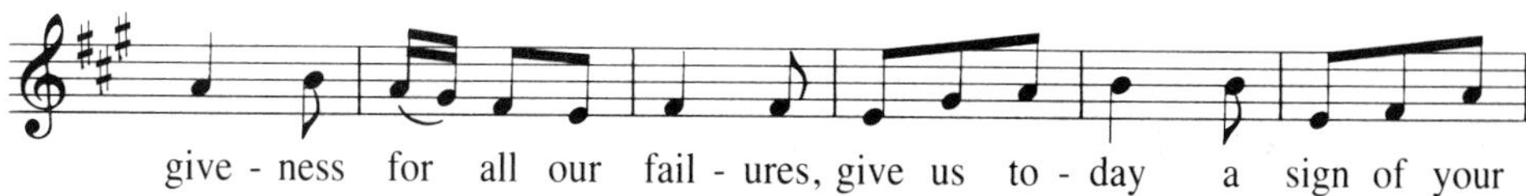
give - ness for all our fail - ures, give us to - day a sign of your

Cantor:
love, then. You know us well, you have not for - got - ten

All:
that we are yours and you are our God. What is your name? O

where can we find you? E - ter - nal God, we want to

see you. Give us to - day a sign of your love, then.

Text: Psalm 103; Huub Oosterhuis, b.1933; Trans. by Franz Jozef van Beeck
Tune: Bernard Huijbers; Harm. by Tom Conry

195 God Is One Unique And Holy

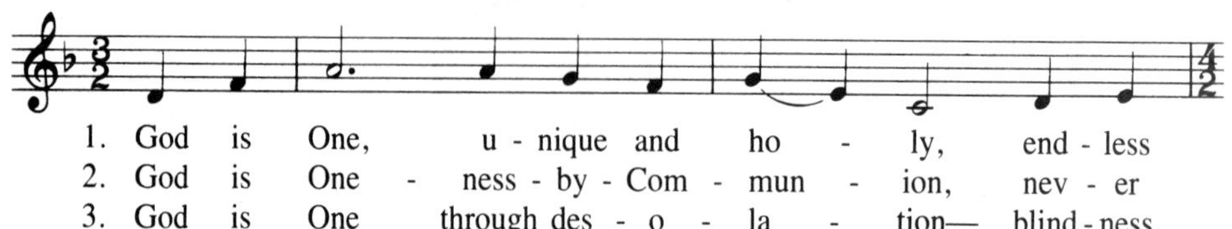
1. God is One, u - nique and ho - ly, end - less
2. God is One - ness - by - Com - mun - ion, nev - er
3. God is One through des - o - la - tion— blind - ness,

dance of love and light; On - ly source of mind and
sin - gle or a - lone; All to - geth - er - ness in-
trea - son, blood and gall; One, though torn by sep - a-

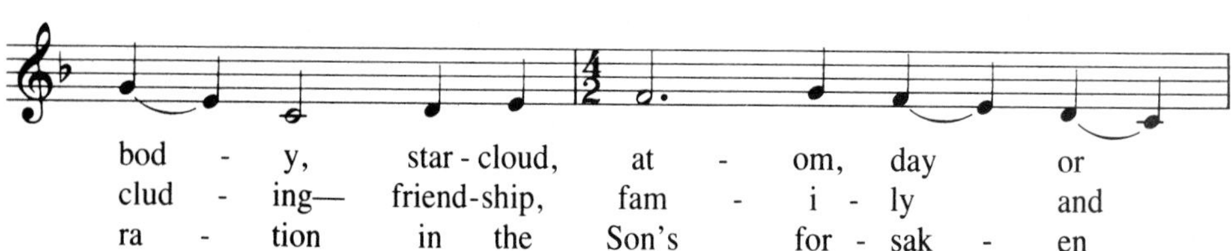
bod - y, star - cloud, at - om, day or
clud - ing— friend-ship, fam - i - ly and
ra - tion in the Son's for - sak - en

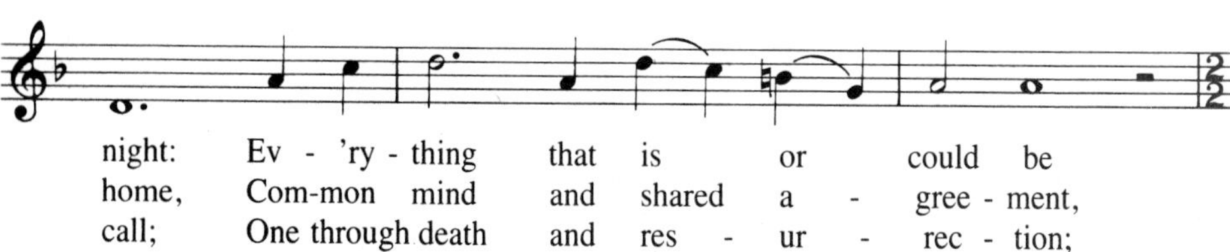
night: Ev - 'ry - thing that is or could be
home, Com-mon mind and shared a - gree - ment,
call; One through death and res - ur - rec - tion;

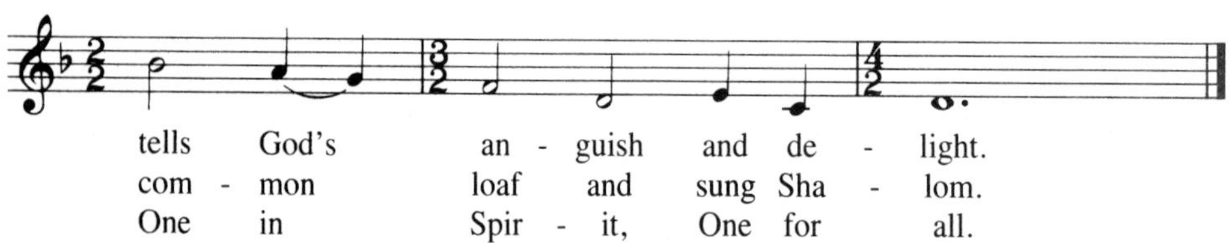
tells God's an - guish and de - light.
com - mon loaf and sung Sha - lom.
One in Spir - it, One for all.

Text: Brian Wren, b.1936, © 1983, Hope Publishing Co.
Tune: GHENT, 87 87 87; M. D. Ridge; Acc. by Patrick Loomis

God of All Creation 196

1. God of the o - cean and sea! Bathe us a - new with
2. God of the wind and the breeze! Breathe in our hearts the
3. God of the for - ests and trees! Col - or our lives with
4. God of the morn-ing and night! Gift all our days with
5. God of the plan - ets and stars! Pow - er our dreams and
wis-dom from heav - en. Riv - ers and life flow - ing
spir - it of Je - sus. Voice and the pres-ence of
love and com - pas - sion. Source of all beau - ty and
signs of your prom - ise. Sun-light and dark-ness are
lift us to glo - ry. Je - sus, the light of the
streams! Call us a - gain to be liv - ing
God! Guide us to hear the call of cre-
truth! Help us to live as shade for the
yours! In death and life may we know your
world! Shine in our lives and be "God a-
wa - ter, Flood-ing and fill - ing the earth with new
a - tion, Sing-ing and danc - ing the cry of de-
wea - ry, Hope for the bro - ken and home for the
ris - ing, Al - pha, O - me - ga: be - gin - ning and
mongus," Build-ing your king-dom, the cit - y of
life!
light!
lost!
end!
peace!

Text: David Haas, b.1957
Tune: CREATION, 7 10 7 10 10; David Haas, b.1957

197 Canticle of the Sun

Refrain
The heav-ens are tell-ing the glo-ry of God, and

all cre-a-tion is shout-ing for joy. Come,

dance in the for-est, come, play in the field, and sing,

sing to the glo-ry of the Lord.

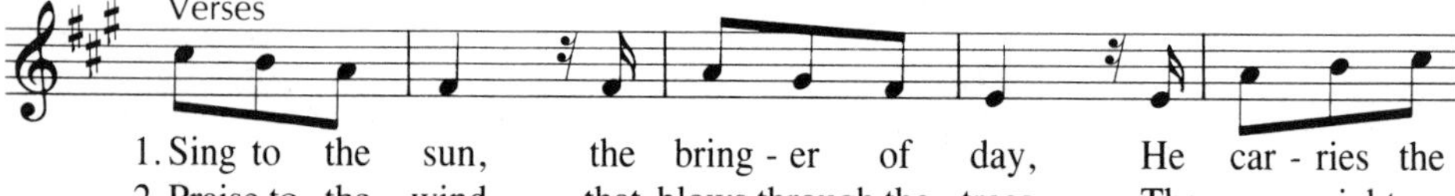
Verses
1. Sing to the sun, the bring-er of day, He car-ries the
2. Praise to the wind that blows through the trees, The seas might-y
3. Praise to the rain that wa-ters our fields, And bless-es our
4. Praise to the fire who gives us his light, The warmth of the

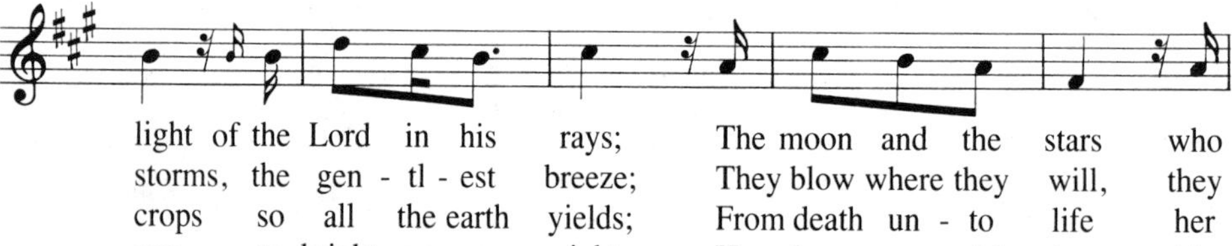
light of the Lord in his rays; The moon and the stars who
storms, the gen-tl-est breeze; They blow where they will, they
crops so all the earth yields; From death un-to life her
sun to bright-en our night; He danc-es with joy, his

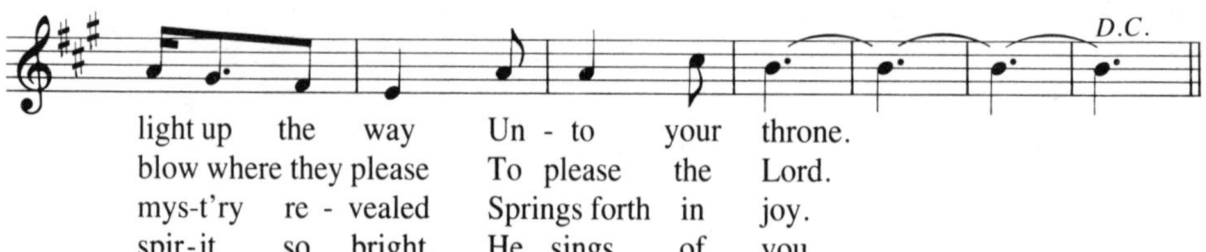
D.C.
light up the way Un-to your throne.
blow where they please To please the Lord.
mys-t'ry re-vealed Springs forth in joy.
spir-it so bright, He sings of you.

5. Sing to the earth who makes life to grow,
The creatures you made to let your life show;
The flowers and trees that help us to know
The heart of love.

6. Praise to our death that makes our life real,
The knowledge of loss that helps us to feel;
The gift of yourself, your presence revealed
To lead us home.

Text: Marty Haugen, b.1950
Tune: Marty Haugen, b.1950

Sing Out Earth and Skies 198

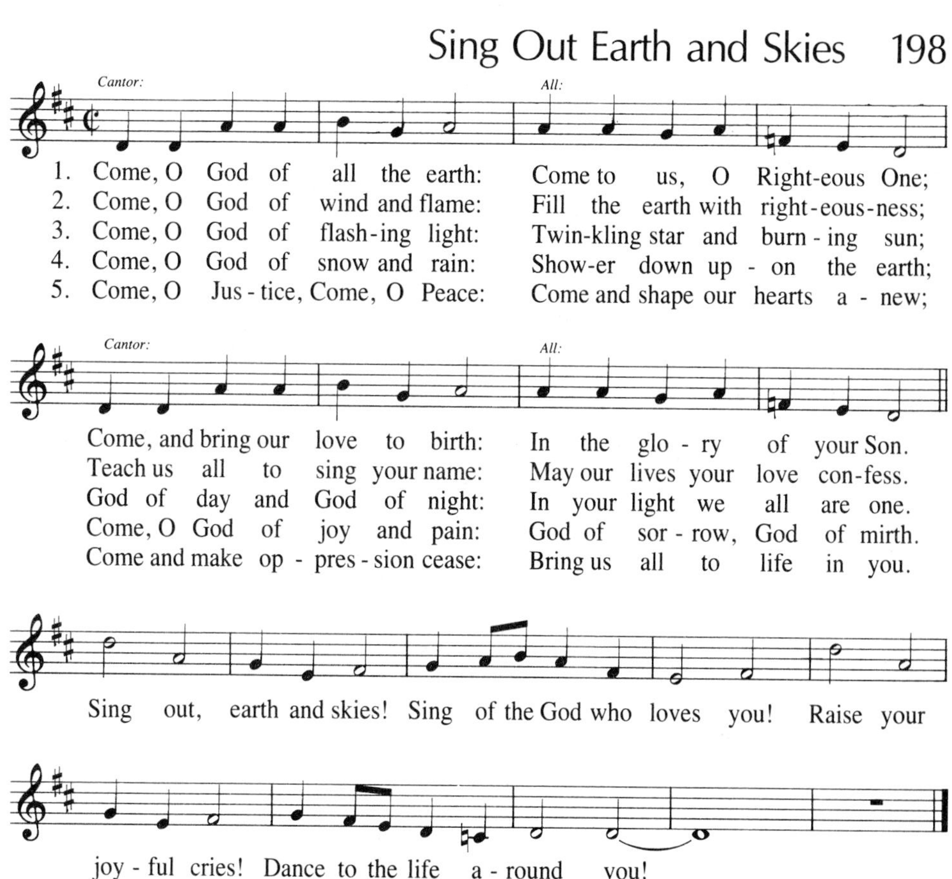
Cantor:
All:
1. Come, O God of all the earth: Come to us, O Right-eous One;
2. Come, O God of wind and flame: Fill the earth with right-eous-ness;
3. Come, O God of flash-ing light: Twin-kling star and burn - ing sun;
4. Come, O God of snow and rain: Show-er down up - on the earth;
5. Come, O Jus - tice, Come, O Peace: Come and shape our hearts a - new;
Cantor:
All:
Come, and bring our love to birth: In the glo - ry of your Son.
Teach us all to sing your name: May our lives your love con-fess.
God of day and God of night: In your light we all are one.
Come, O God of joy and pain: God of sor - row, God of mirth.
Come and make op - pres - sion cease: Bring us all to life in you.
Sing out, earth and skies! Sing of the God who loves you! Raise your
joy - ful cries! Dance to the life a - round you!

Text: Marty Haugen, b.1950
Tune: SING OUT, 77 77 with refrain; Marty Haugen, b.1950

199 Nature's Praise

1. Praise the Lord, *o - cean and riv - er, Surge and de - liv - er
2. Praise the Lord, fal - con and swal-low, Cir - cle and fol - low

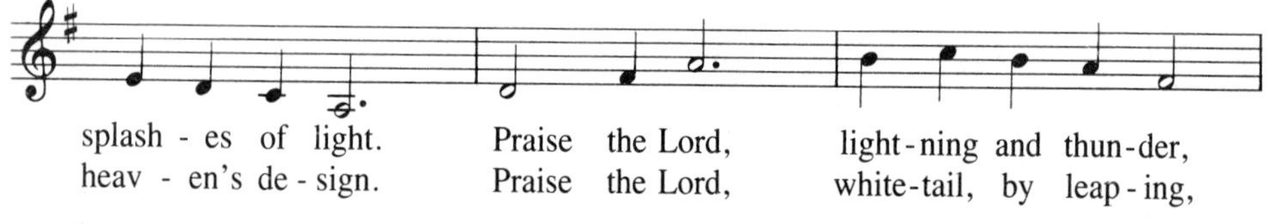

splash - es of light. Praise the Lord, light-ning and thun-der,
heav - en's de - sign. Praise the Lord, white-tail, by leap - ing,

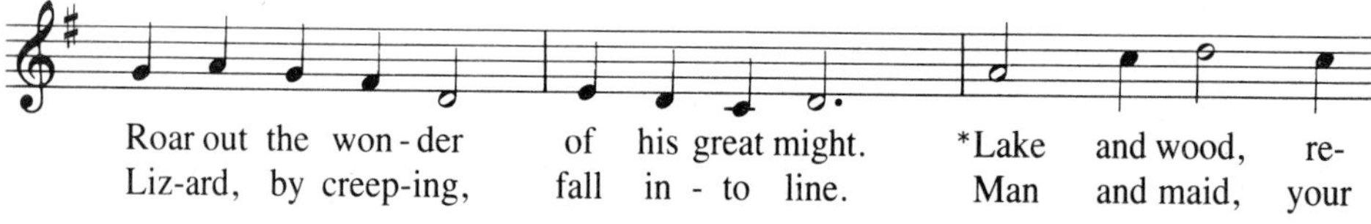

Roar out the won - der of his great might. *Lake and wood, re-
Liz-ard, by creep-ing, fall in - to line. Man and maid, your

sound with his glo - ry, Ech - o the sto - ry of
in - stru - ments ring - ing Fill out the sing - ing of

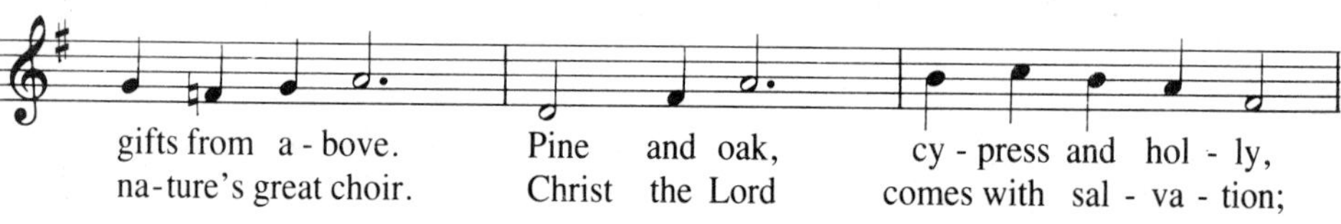

gifts from a - bove. Pine and oak, cy - press and hol - ly,
na-ture's great choir. Christ the Lord comes with sal - va - tion;

Dance at his fol - ly, sway in his love.
All of cre - a - tion glows with his fire.

* Original text: bayou / Swamp

Text: Dominic Braud, OSB
Tune: NATURE'S PRAISE, 89 89 9 10 89; Dominic Braud, OSB; Harm. by Robert LeBlanc, b.1948

Wind upon the Water 200

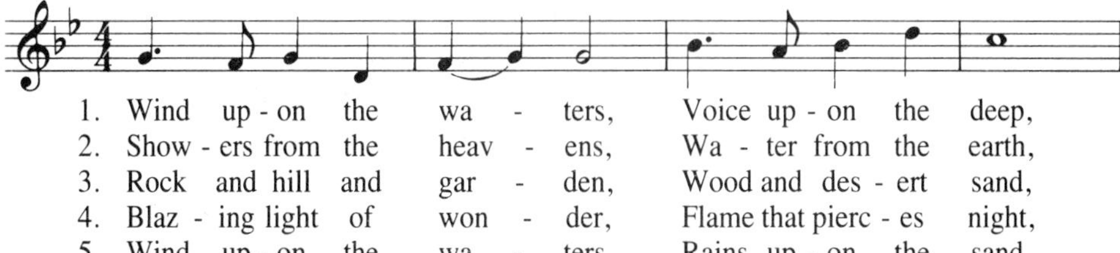
1. Wind up - on the wa - ters, Voice up - on the deep,
2. Show - ers from the heav - ens, Wa - ter from the earth,
3. Rock and hill and gar - den, Wood and des - ert sand,
4. Blaz - ing light of won - der, Flame that pierc - es night,
5. Wind up - on the wa - ters, Rains up - on the sand,

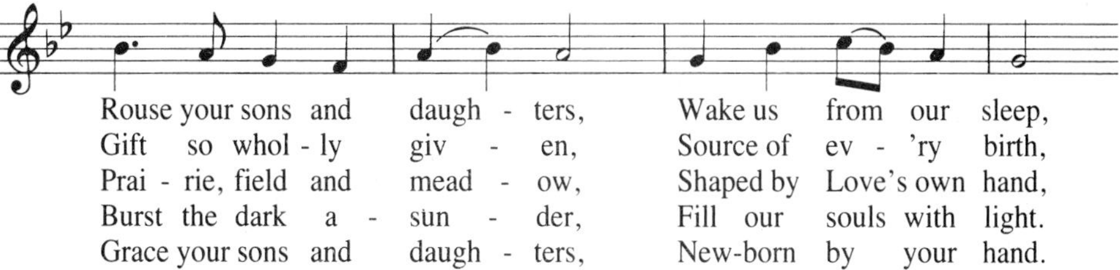
Rouse your sons and daugh - ters, Wake us from our sleep,
Gift so whol - ly giv - en, Source of ev - 'ry birth,
Prai - rie, field and mead - ow, Shaped by Love's own hand,
Burst the dark a - sun - der, Fill our souls with light.
Grace your sons and daugh - ters, New-born by your hand.

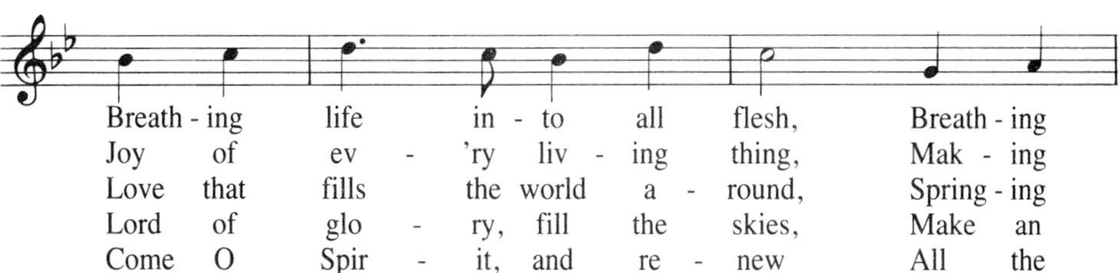
Breath - ing life in - to all flesh, Breath - ing
Joy of ev - 'ry liv - ing thing, Mak - ing
Love that fills the world a - round, Spring - ing
Lord of glo - ry, fill the skies, Make an
Come O Spir - it, and re - new All the

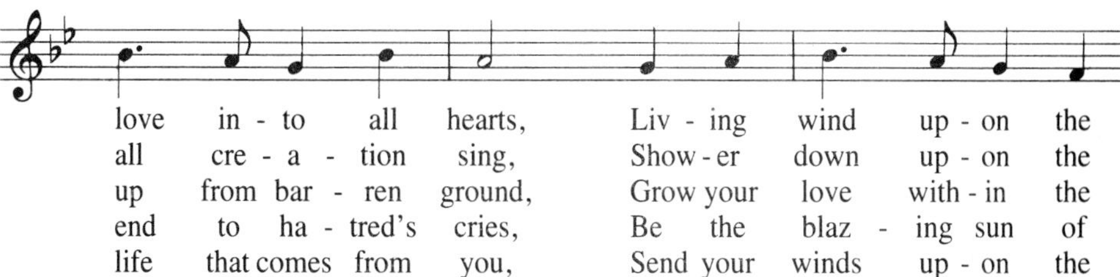
love in - to all hearts, Liv - ing wind up - on the
all cre - a - tion sing, Show - er down up - on the
up from bar - ren ground, Grow your love with - in the
end to ha - tred's cries, Be the blaz - ing sun of
life that comes from you, Send your winds up - on the

wa - ters of my soul.
dry earth of my soul.
gar - den of my soul.
jus - tice in our lives.
wa - ters of my soul.

Text: Marty Haugen, b.1950
Tune: 65 65 77 11, Marty Haugen, b.1950

201 The Stars Declare His Glory

1. The stars declare his glory;
The vault of heaven springs
Mute witness of the Master's hand
In all created things,
And through the silences of space
Their soundless music sings.

2. The dawn returns in splendor,
The heavens burn and blaze,
The rising sun renews the race
That measures all our days,
And writes in fire across the skies
God's majesty and praise.

3. So shine the Lord's commandments
To make the simple wise;
More sweet than honey to the taste,
More rich than any prize,
A law of love within our hearts,
A light before our eyes.

4. So order too this life of mine,
Direct it all my days;
The meditations of my heart
Be innocence and praise,
My rock and my redeeming Lord,
In all my words and ways.

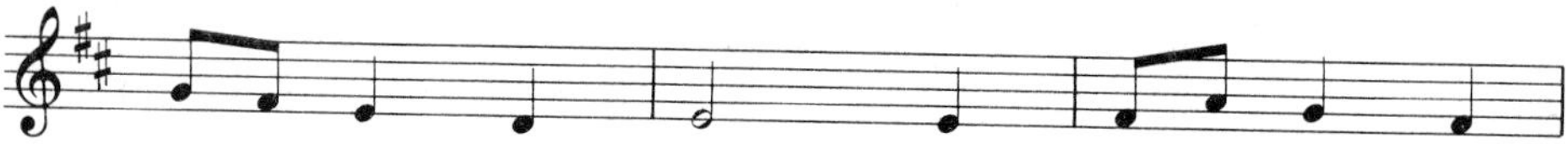

Text: Psalm 19; Timothy Dudley-Smith, b.1926, © 1981, Hope Publishing Co.
Tune: DEERFIELD, 76 86 86; David Haas, b.1957, © 1986, GIA Publications, Inc.

202 Come to the Water

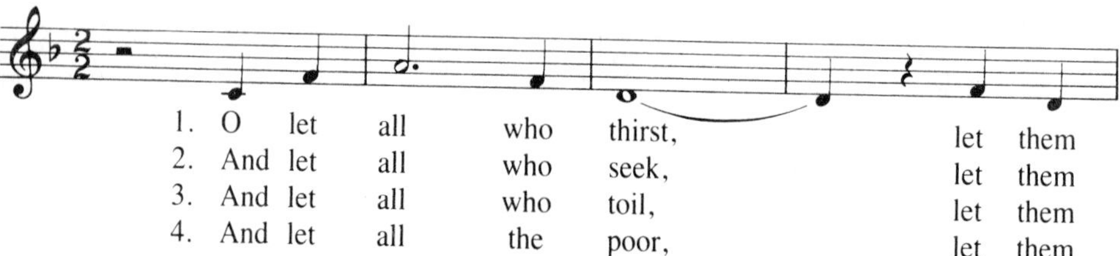
1. O let all who thirst, let them
2. And let all who seek, let them
3. And let all who toil, let them
4. And let all the poor, let them

PROVIDENCE

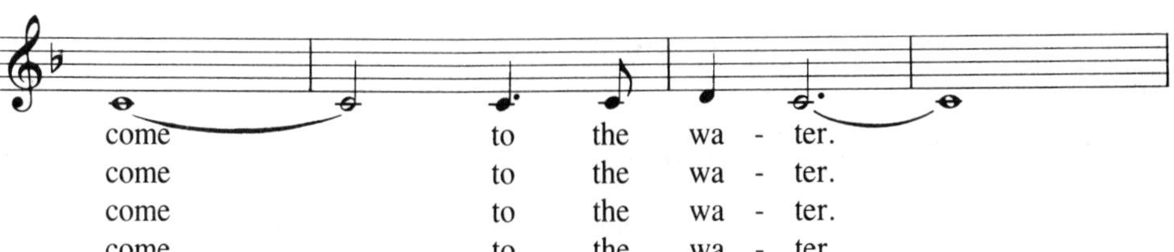
come to the wa - ter.
come to the wa - ter.
come to the wa - ter.
come to the wa - ter.

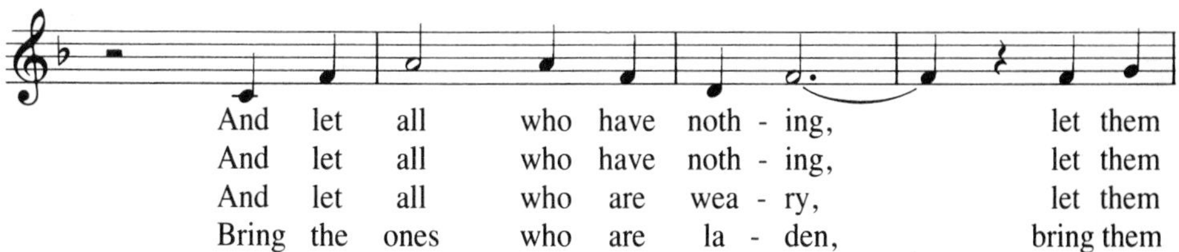
And let all who have noth - ing, let them
And let all who have noth - ing, let them
And let all who are wea - ry, let them
Bring the ones who are la - den, bring them

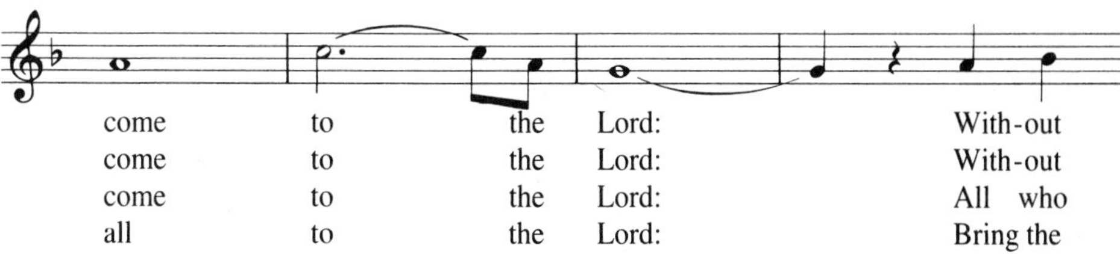
come to the Lord: With-out
come to the Lord: With-out
come to the Lord: All who
all to the Lord: Bring the

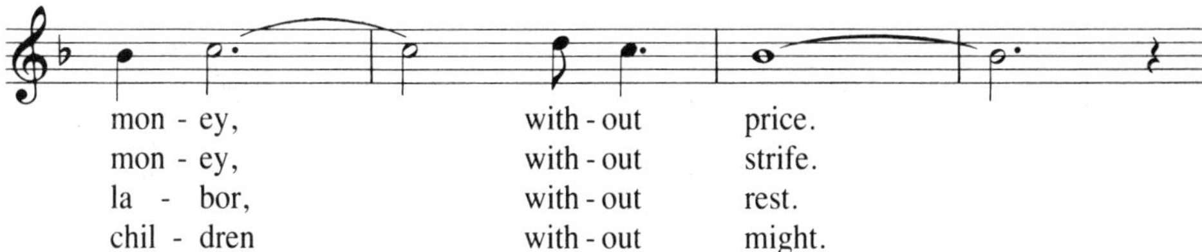
mon - ey, with - out price.
mon - ey, with - out strife.
la - bor, with - out rest.
chil - dren with - out might.

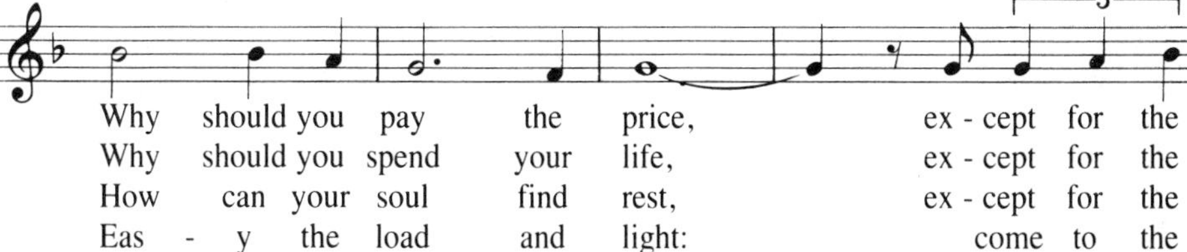
3
Why should you pay the price, ex - cept for the
Why should you spend your life, ex - cept for the
How can your soul find rest, ex - cept for the
Eas - y the load and light: come to the

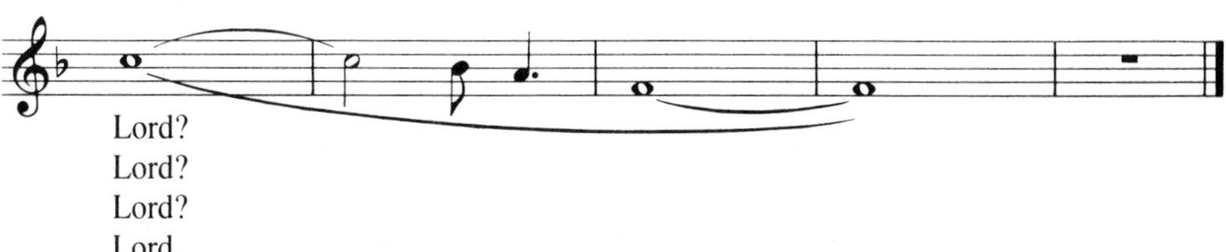
Lord?
Lord?
Lord?
Lord.

Text: Isaiah 55:1,2, Matthew 11:28-30; John B. Foley, SJ
Tune: John B. Foley, SJ

203 I Will Lift Up My Eyes

Refrain
3
I will lift up my eyes at his name to the one who knows me well.

Verses
3
1. You are my God, whom I seek with my life; for you I

3
thirst, as the dry earth for wa - ter. Life - less and parched,

3
D.C.
with-out you I am no - where, no one at all.

3
2. Thus have I seen you in your ho - ly house, with my own
eyes, how faith - ful and sure. More than my life,

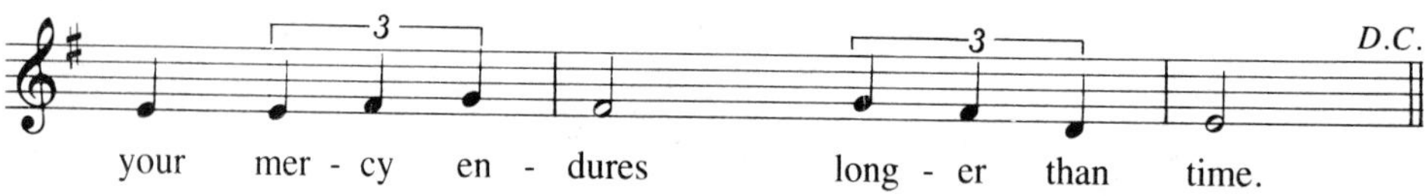
3
D.C.
your mer - cy en - dures long - er than time.

3
3. Thus shall I bless you while I am a - live;

PROVIDENCE
call - ing on you, my breath and my bread. And with a
song through day and the dark - ness cling - ing to you.
D.C.
4. And I shall see that day when his jus - tice and pow'r will
break the chains that bind me. And mine en - e - mies' lies strewn
bro-ken and emp - ty: his might-y hand, that aw-ful grace.
D.C.

Text: Psalm 63; Tom Conry
Tune: Tom Conry

204 All You Who Are Thirsty

Refrain

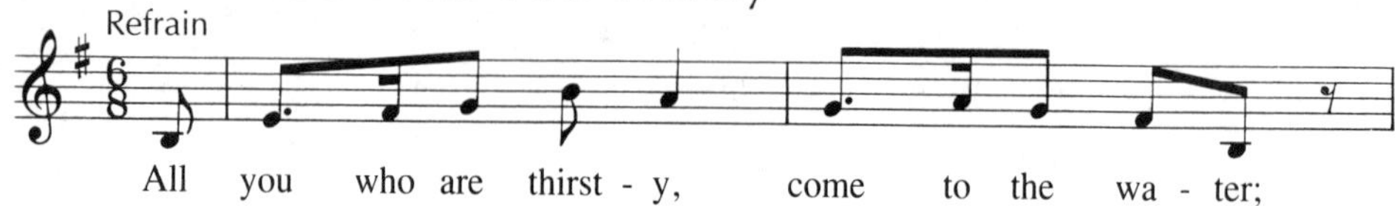
All you who are thirst - y, come to the wa - ter;

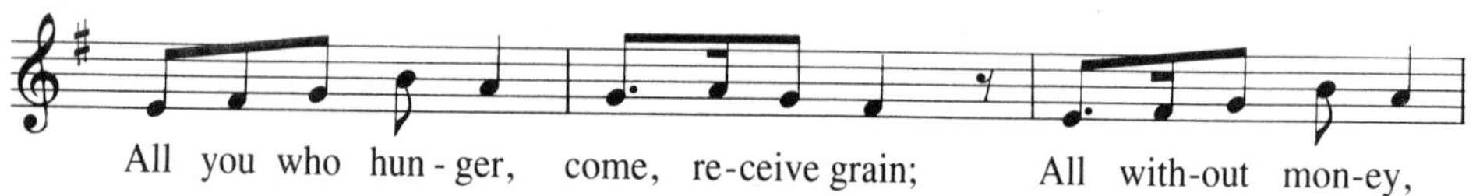
All you who hun - ger, come, re-ceive grain; All with-out mon-ey,

come with-out pay-ing; All you who need me, come for rich fare.

Verses

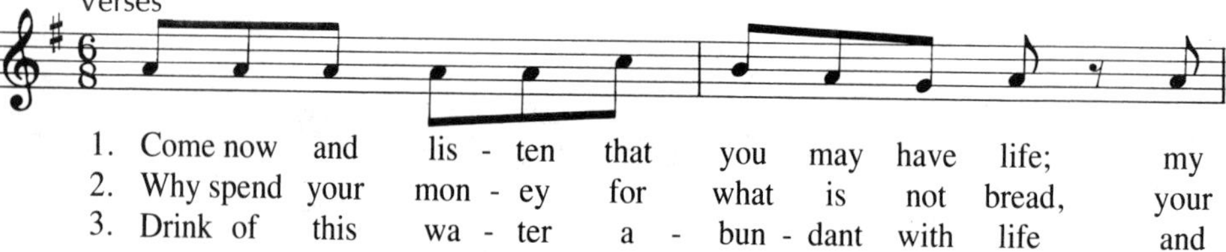
1. Come now and lis - ten that you may have life; my
2. Why spend your mon - ey for what is not bread, your
3. Drink of this wa - ter a - bun - dant with life and

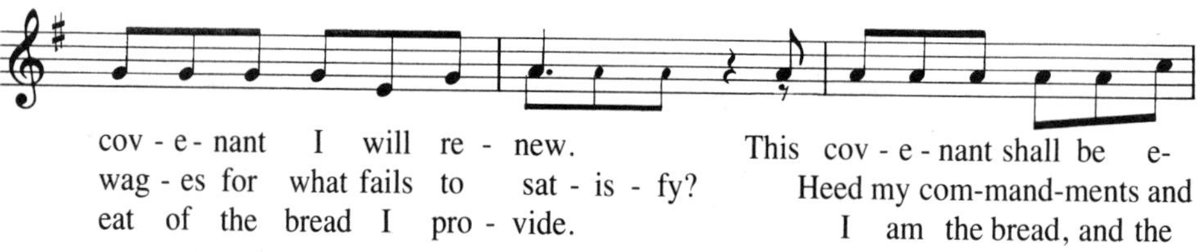
cov - e - nant I will re - new. This cov - e - nant shall be e-
wag - es for what fails to sat - is - fy? Heed my com-mand-ments and
eat of the bread I pro - vide. I am the bread, and the

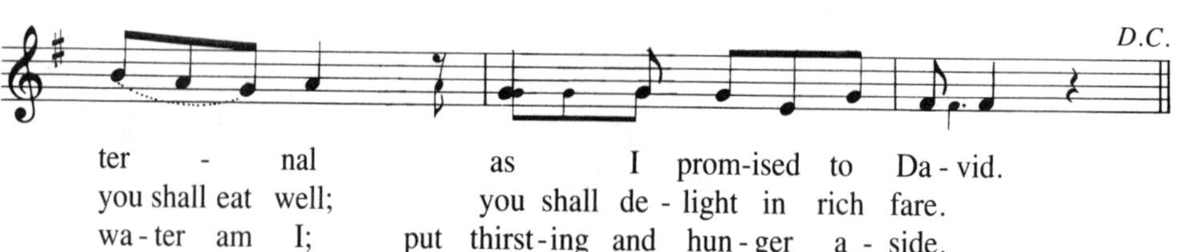
D.C.
ter - nal as I prom-ised to Da - vid.
you shall eat well; you shall de - light in rich fare.
wa - ter am I; put thirst-ing and hun - ger a - side.

Text: Isaiah 55; Adapt. by Michael Connolly
Tune: Michael Connolly

I Am the Light of the World 205

Refrain

"I am the light of the world," says the Lord, "They who fol-low

To verses
Last time
me will have the light of life."
have the light of life."

Verses

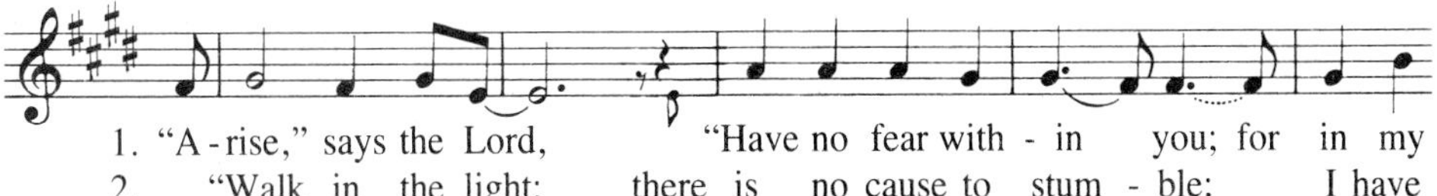
1. "A-rise," says the Lord, "Have no fear with - in you; for in my
2. "Walk in the light; there is no cause to stum - ble; I have

D.C.
pres-ence there will be no dark- ness. I am the light of the world."
come to light the path be - fore you. I am the light of the world."

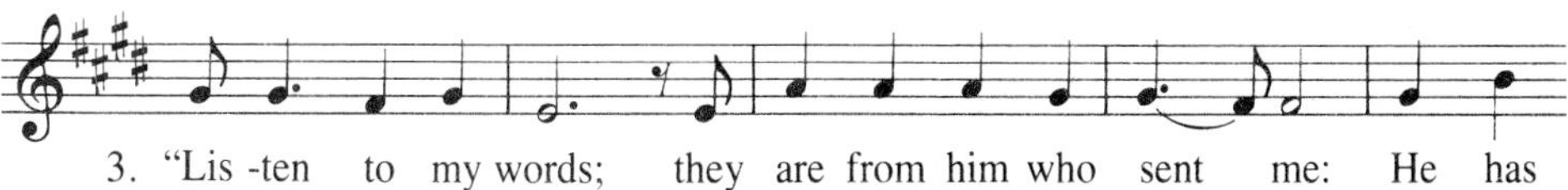
3. "Lis -ten to my words; they are from him who sent me: He has

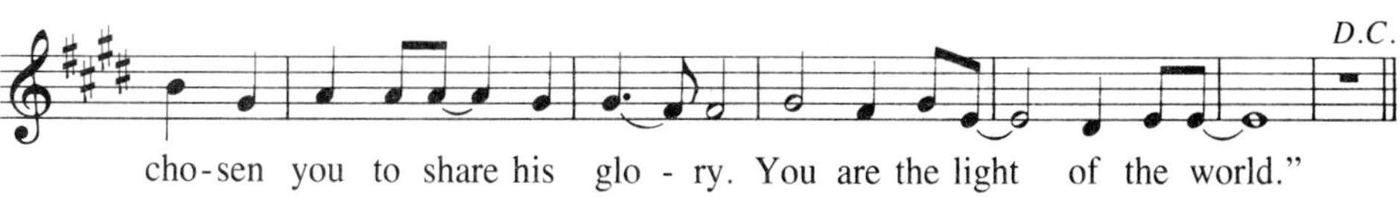
D.C.
cho-sen you to share his glo - ry. You are the light of the world."

Text: John 8:12, Matthew 5:14, Ephesians 5:14, I John 2:10; Greg Hayakawa, © 1978, 1979
Tune: Greg Hayakawa, © 1978, 1979; Acc. by Craig S. Kingsbury, © 1985, Oregon Catholic Press

206 This Little Light of Mine

This lit-tle light of mine, I'm going to let it shine.

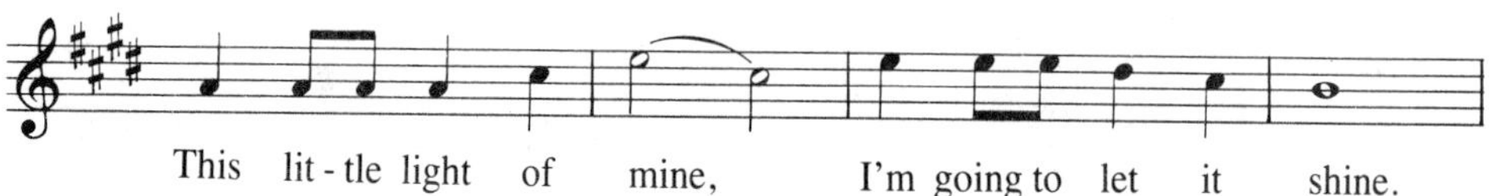
This lit-tle light of mine, I'm going to let it shine.

This lit-tle light of mine, I'm going to let it

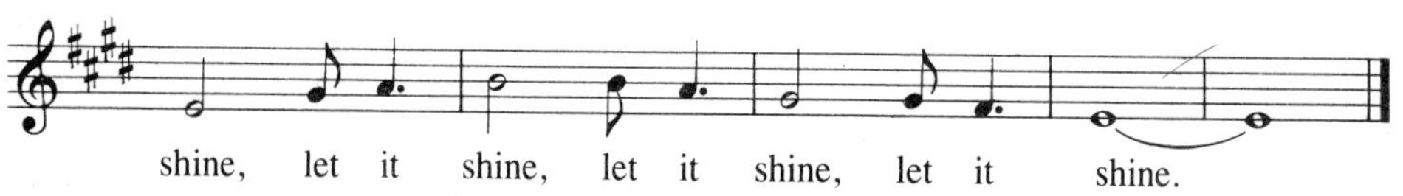
shine, let it shine, let it shine, let it shine.

Text: Afro-American Spiritual
Tune: Afro-American Spiritual; Arr. by James Moore, Jr., © 1987, GIA Publications, Inc.

207 We Are Walking In the Light

We are walk-ing in the light, in the light in the light.

Last time
We are walk-ing in the light, in the light of God.

Text: Traditional
Tune: James Moore, Jr., © 1987, GIA Publications, Inc.

I Want to Walk as a Child of the Light 208

1. I want to walk as a child of the light.
2. I want to see the bright-ness of God.
3. I'm look - ing for the com - ing of Christ.
I want to fol - low Je - sus.
I want to look at Je - sus.
I want to be with Je - sus.
God set the stars to give light to the world. The
Clear sun of right - eous - ness shine on my path, And
When we have run with pa - tience the race, We
star of my life is Je - sus.
show me the way to the Fa - ther.
shall know the joy of Je - sus.
In him there is no dark - ness at all. The
night and the day are both a - like. The
Lamb is the light of the cit - y of God.
Shine in my heart, Lord Je - sus.

Text: Ephesians 5:8-10, Revelation 21:23, John 12:46, I John 1:5, Hebrews 12:1; Kathleen Thomerson, b.1934, © 1970, 1975, Celebration
Tune: HOUSTON, 10 7 10 8 9 9 10 7; Kathleen Thomerson, b.1934, © 1970, 1975, Celebration; Acc. by Robert J. Batastini, b.1942, © 1987, GIA Publications, Inc.

209 The Lord Is My Life

Refrain
The Lord is my life; the Lord is my strength; the Lord is my light and my sal - va - tion. The Lord is my hope; the Lord is my song; the Lord is my light and my sal - va - tion.
Verses
1. The Lord is my light and my sal - va - tion; whom shall I fear? The Lord is the re-fuge of my life; of whom should I be a - fraid?
2. One thing I ask of the Lord, on-ly one thing I seek: to live in the pres-ence of the Lord, to dwell in the house of my God.
D.C.
3. I be - lieve I shall see the Lord's good - ness in the land where the liv - ing dwell. Wait for the Lord and be brave; yes, wait for the liv - ing God!
D.C.

Text: Psalm 27; Michael Joncas, b.1951
Tune: Michael Joncas, b.1951

Praise to You, O Christ, Our Savior 210

Refrain
Praise to you, O Christ, our Sav - ior Word of the Fa - ther,
call - ing us to life; Son of God who leads us to
free - dom: glo - ry to you, Lord Je - sus Christ!
Verses
1. You are the Word who calls us out of dark - ness; You are the
2. You are the one whom proph-ets hoped and longed for; You are the
3. You are the Word who calls us to be ser - vants; You are the
4. You are the Word who binds us and u - nites us; You are the
Word who leads us in - to light; You are the Word who
one who speaks to us to - day; You are the one who
Word whose on - ly law is love; You are the Word - made-
Word who calls us to be one; You are the Word who
D.C.
brings us through the des - ert: Glo - ry to you, Lord Je - sus Christ!
leads us to our fu - ture: Glo - ry to you, Lord Je - sus Christ!
flesh who lives a - mong us: Glo - ry to you, Lord Je - sus Christ!
teach-es us for - give - ness: Glo - ry to you, Lord Je - sus Christ!

Text: Bernadette Farrell
Tune: Bernadette Farrell

211 Sow the Word

1. As the rain and the snow come down from heav-en and
do not re - turn with-out wa - ter - ing the earth, mak-ing it
yield and giv - ing it growth to pro - vide seed for the
sow - er and bread for the world:
Refrain
So the Word came to the world, so the
Word came to stretch his arms and die for the world. As he
loved so we live to sow the Word.
2. This is the Word that we have tast - ed with our eyes, and our

lips speak the love in its pass-ing on to you. God is
light. If we live our love in light, we will reap the grain of the
sow-er and be bread for the world.
D.S.
3. We are God's lov-ers. Give it all a-way
We must be love to the hun-gry at our doors.
O-pen the bread! Bring the robes and rings! Lav-ish the
hun-gry with the plen-ty we have known in the Word.
D.S.

Text: J. Keith Zavelli, Steven R. Janco
Tune: J. Keith Zavelli, Steven R. Janco; Harm. by Steven R. Janco

212 Lord, to Whom Shall We Go

Refrain
Lord, to whom shall we go? Lord, to whom shall we go,
for you a - lone have words of e - ter - nal life.
Verses
1. Your words, O Lord, are my rock and my strength, my
2. Your words, O Lord, are joy for my heart, my
3. Your words, O Lord, are food for my soul, my
light, my for - tress strong.
Lord, my glo - ry, my God.
hope of sal - va - tion.
D.C.

Text: John 6; David Haas, b.1957
Tune: David Haas, b.1957

213 I Will Sing, I Will Sing

Verses
1. I will sing, I will sing a song un - to the Lord.
2. We will come, we will come as one be - fore the Lord.
3. If the Son, if the Son shall make you free,
4. They that sow in tears shall reap in joy.
I will sing, I will sing a song un - to the Lord.
We will come, we will come as one be - fore the Lord.
If the Son, if the Son shall make you free,
They that sow in tears shall reap in joy.

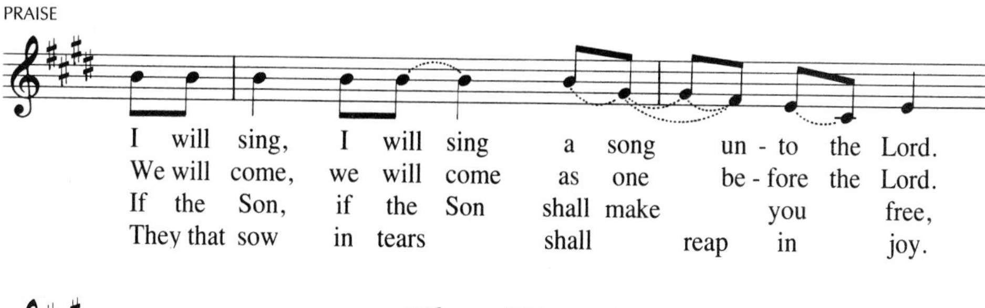
I will sing, I will sing a song un - to the Lord.
We will come, we will come as one be - fore the Lord.
If the Son, if the Son shall make you free,
They that sow in tears shall reap in joy.

Al - le - lu - ia, glo - ry to the Lord.
Al - le - lu - ia, glo - ry to the Lord.
You shall be free in - deed.
Al - le - lu - ia, glo - ry to the Lord.

Refrain
Al - le - lu, al - le - lu - ia, glo - ry to the Lord. Al - le-

lu, al - le - lu - ia, glo - ry to the Lord. Al - le-

lu, al - le - lu - ia, glo - ry to the Lord.

Al - le - lu - ia, glo - ry to the Lord.

5. Ev'ry knee shall bow and ev'ry tongue confess,
Ev'ry knee shall bow and ev'ry tongue confess,
Ev'ry knee shall bow and ev'ry tongue confess
That Jesus Christ is Lord.

6. In his Name, in his name we have the victory.
In his Name, in his Name we have the victory.
In his Name, in his Name we have the victory.
Alleluia, glory to the Lord.

Text: Max Dyer
Tune: PULKINGHAM, Irregular; Max Dyer

214 A New Song

Refrain

I will sing the Lord a new song, a new song. I will sing his prais-es while I live. I will sing his prais-es for ev - er more.

Verses

Sing God a new song, Make it loud and clear.
Sing God a new song, For all he's done.
Sing God a new song, Spread his love a round.

Sing God a new song For all the world to hear.
Sing God a new song Help to make us one.
Sing God a new song Make a joy - ful sound.

D.C.

Text: James E. Moore, Jr.
Tune: James E. Moore, Jr.

215 Alleluia, Sing!

Cantor:
All:
1. Bless - ed be our God! Bless - ed be our God!
2. Gift of love and peace! Gift of love and peace!
3. Come, O Spir - it of truth! Come, O Spir - it of truth!
Cantor:
Joy of our hearts, source of all life and love!
Je - sus the Christ, Je - sus our hope and light!
Prom - ise of hope, kind - ness and mer - cy!

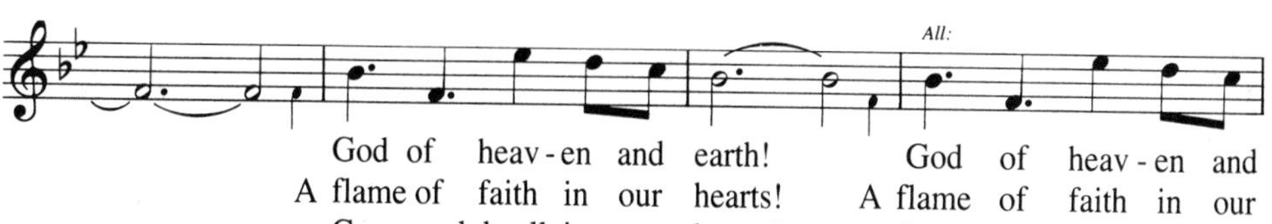
All:
God of heav-en and earth! God of heav-en and
A flame of faith in our hearts! A flame of faith in our
Come and dwell in our hearts! Come and dwell in our

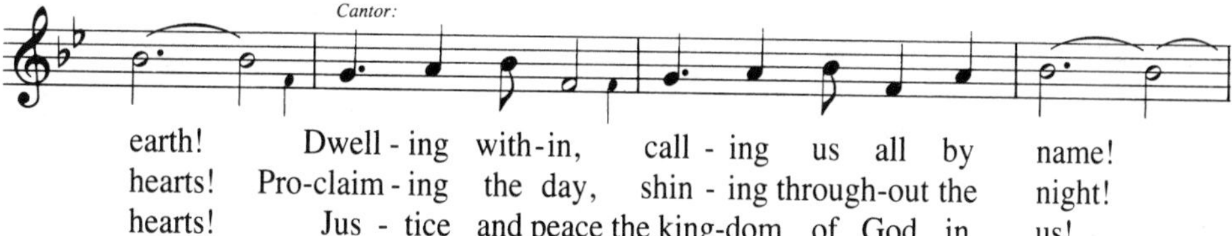
Cantor:
earth! Dwell-ing with-in, call-ing us all by name!
hearts! Pro-claim-ing the day, shin-ing through-out the night!
hearts! Jus-tice and peace the king-dom of God in us!

All:
Al-le-lu-ia, sing! Al-le-lu-ia, sing!
Al-le-lu-ia, sing! Al-le-lu-ia, sing!
Al-le-lu-ia, sing! Al-le-lu-ia, sing!

Text: David Haas, b.1957
Tune: David Haas, b.1957

Laudate Dominum 216

Lau-da-te Do-mi-num, Lau-da-te Do-mi-num
om-nes gen-tes, al-le-lu-ia, al-le-lu-ia.
1.
2.
D.C.

Text: Psalm 117, *Praise the Lord, all you peoples;* Taizé Community, 1980
Tune: Jacques Berthier, b.1923

217 Sing of the Lord's Goodness

1. Sing of the Lord's good - ness, Fa - ther of all wis - dom,
2. Pow-er he has wield - ed, hon - or is his gar - ment,
3. Cour-age in our dark - ness, com-fort in our sor - row,
4. Praise him with your sing - ing, praise him with the trum - pet,

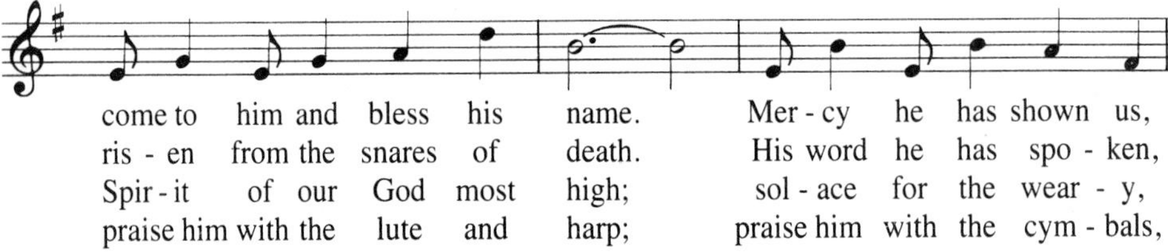
come to him and bless his name. Mer - cy he has shown us,
ris - en from the snares of death. His word he has spo - ken,
Spir - it of our God most high; sol - ace for the wear - y,
praise him with the lute and harp; praise him with the cym - bals,

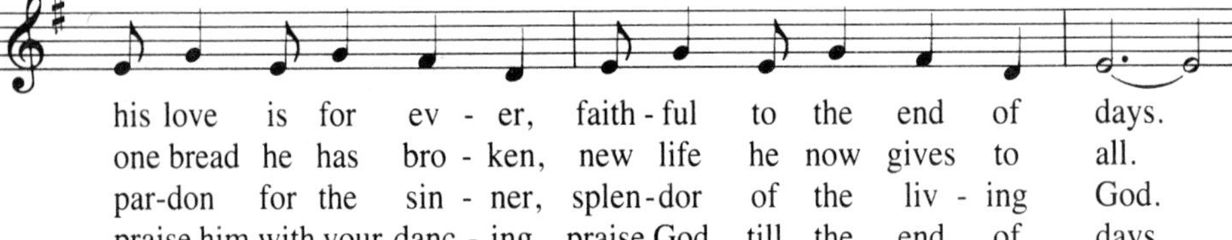
his love is for ev - er, faith - ful to the end of days.
one bread he has bro - ken, new life he now gives to all.
par-don for the sin - ner, splen-dor of the liv - ing God.
praise him with your danc - ing, praise God till the end of days.

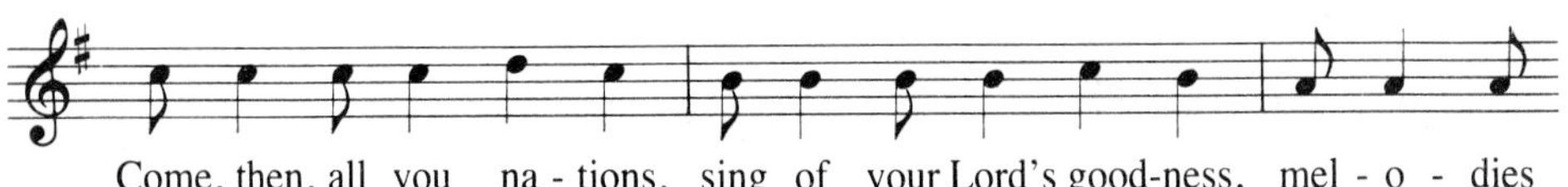
Come, then, all you na - tions, sing of your Lord's good-ness, mel - o - dies

of praise and thanks to God. Ring out the Lord's glo - ry, praise him with

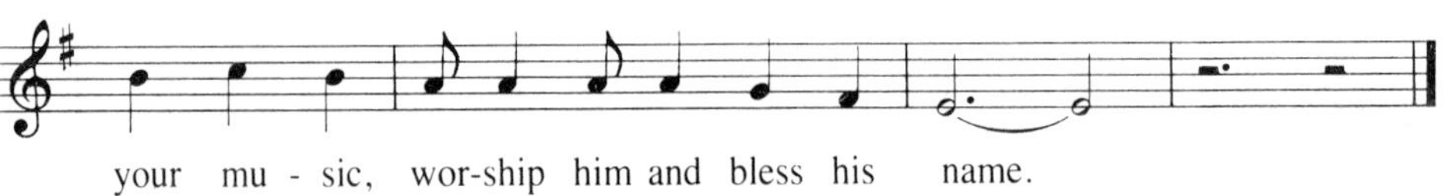
your mu - sic, wor-ship him and bless his name.

Sing a New Song to the Lord 218

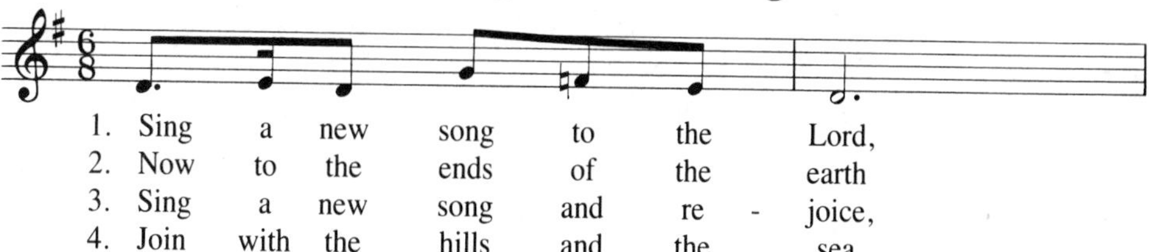
1. Sing a new song to the Lord,
2. Now to the ends of the earth
3. Sing a new song and re - joice,
4. Join with the hills and the sea

He to whom won - ders be - long!
See his sal - va - tion is shown;
Pub - lish his prais - es a - broad!
Thun - ders of praise to pro - long!

Re - joice in his tri - umph and
And still he re - mem - bers his
Let voic - es in cho - rus, with
In judge - ment and jus - tice he

tell of his power,
mer - cy and truth,
trum - pet and horn,
comes to the earth,

O sing to the Lord a new song!
Un - chang - ing in love to his own.
Re - sound for the joy of the Lord!
O sing to the Lord a new song!

Text: Psalm 98; Timothy Dudley-Smith, b.1926
Tune: CANTATE DOMINO, Irregular; David G. Wilson, b.1940

219 The Song of Moses

Refrain
The Lord is my strength and song, and he is be - come
my sal - va - tion. He is my God and I will pre - pare him a
hab - i - ta - tion, my fa-ther's God and I will ex - alt him. (2. The)
Verses
1. He has tri - umphed glo - rious - ly. I will sing
un - to the Lord. He has tri - umphed glo - rious - ly, the
horse and his rid - er has he thrown in the sea.
D.C.
2. The Lord is a man of war, the Lord
is his name. Phar - aoh's char - iots and his host
has he cast, has he cast in - to the sea!
D.C.

3. Your right hand, O Lord, is be-come glo-ri-ous in pow'r.

D.C.

Your right hand, O Lord, has cast in piec-es the en-e-my.

4. Who is like un-to you, O Lord, a-mong the gods?

Who is like you, glo-rious in ho-li-ness,

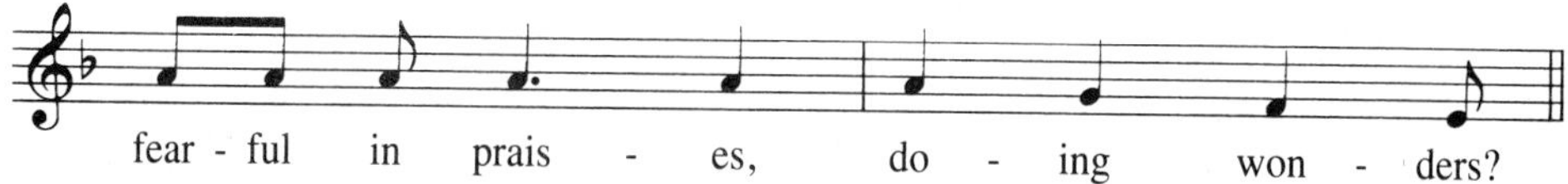
fear-ful in prais-es, do-ing won-ders?

Final refrain

The Lord is my strength and song, and he is be-come my sal-

va-tion. He is my God and I will pre-pare him a

hab-i-ta-tion, my fa-ther's God and I will ex-

alt him, I will ex-alt him!

Text: Exodus 15; Betty Carr Pulkingham, b.1929
Tune: Betty Carr Pulkingham, b.1929

220 Praise the Lord, My Soul

Refrain
Praise the Lord, my soul! Sing al - le - lu - ia, bless his name.

Verses
1. All prais - es to the Fa - ther of our Lord,
3. How great the sign of God's love for us

a God so mer - ci - ful and kind,
in giv - ing us his Son to be our bread:

who gives to us a new birth, who
as prom - ised us so long a - go, re-

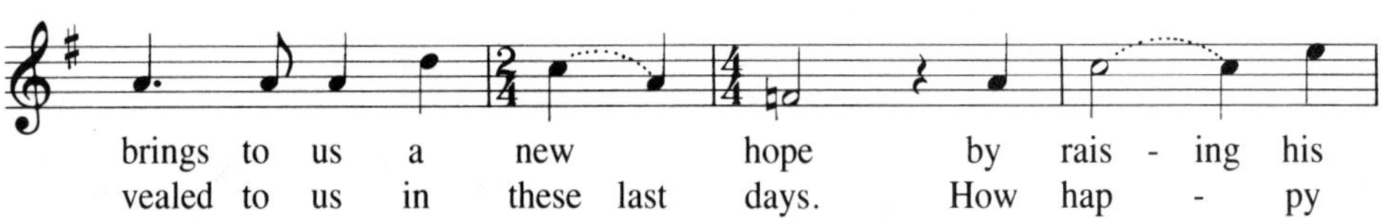
brings to us a new hope by rais - ing his
vealed to us in these last days. How hap - py

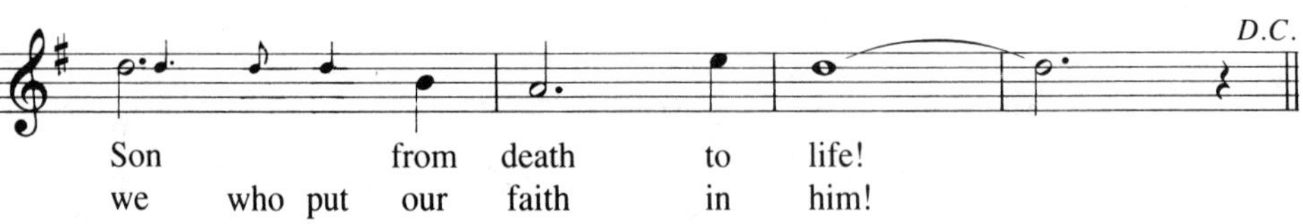
D.C.
Son from death to life!
we who put our faith in him!

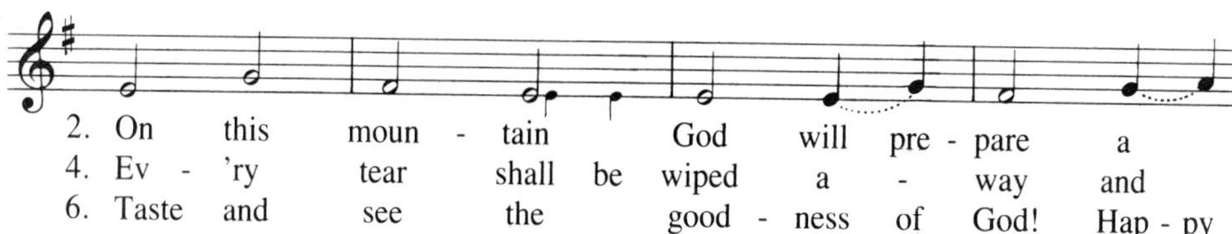
2. On this moun - tain God will pre - pare a
4. Ev - 'ry tear shall be wiped a - way and
6. Taste and see the good - ness of God! Hap - py

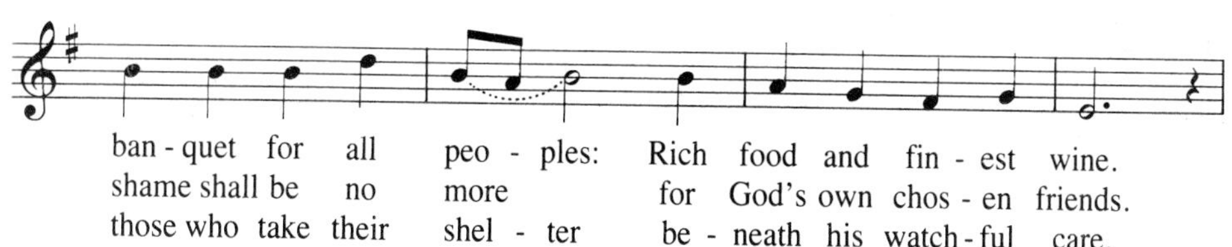
ban - quet for all peo - ples: Rich food and fin - est wine.
shame shall be no more for God's own chos - en friends.
those who take their shel - ter be - neath his watch - ful care.

On this moun - tain he will re - move the
Then they shall say: "This is the one we
Fear the Lord! Proud and rich may

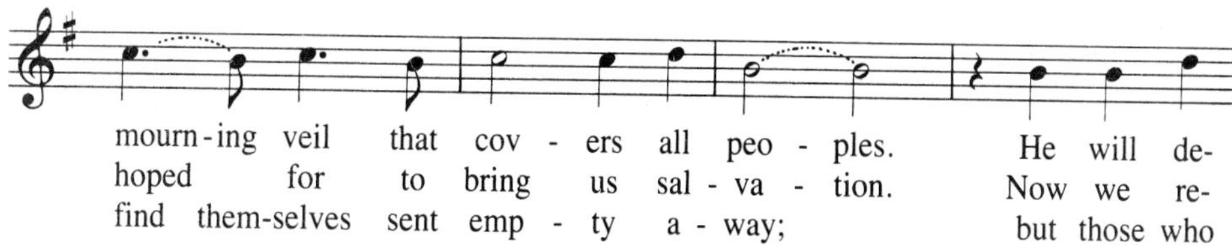
mourn - ing veil that cov - ers all peo - ples. He will de-
hoped for to bring us sal - va - tion. Now we re-
find them-selves sent emp - ty a - way; but those who

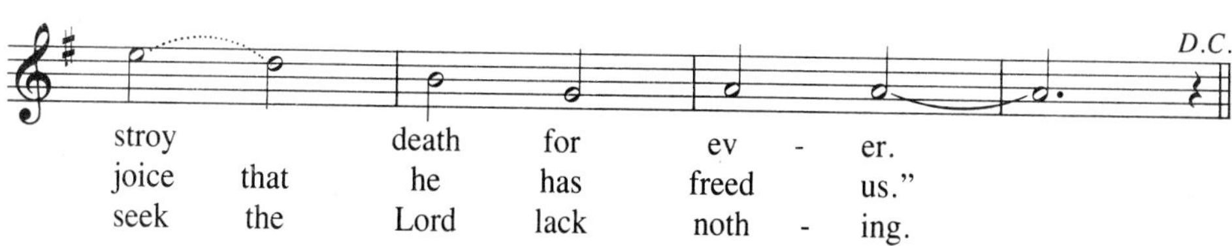
D.C.
stroy death for ev - er.
joice that he has freed us."
seek the Lord lack noth - ing.

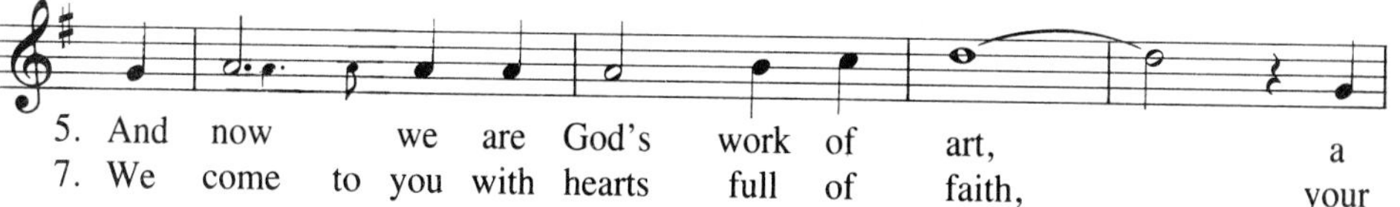
5. And now we are God's work of art, a
7. We come to you with hearts full of faith, your

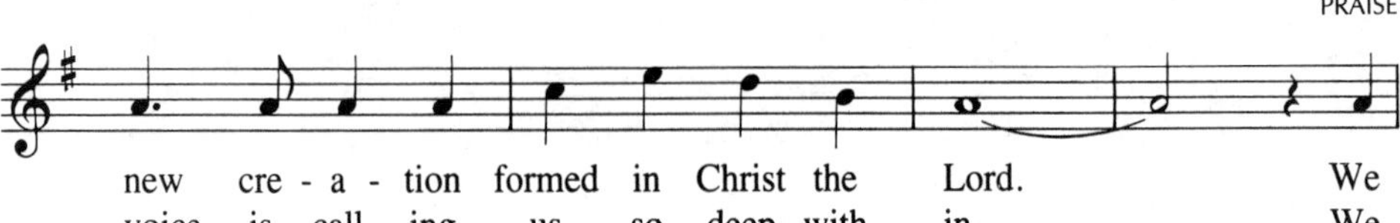
new cre - a - tion formed in Christ the Lord. We
voice is call - ing us so deep with - in. We

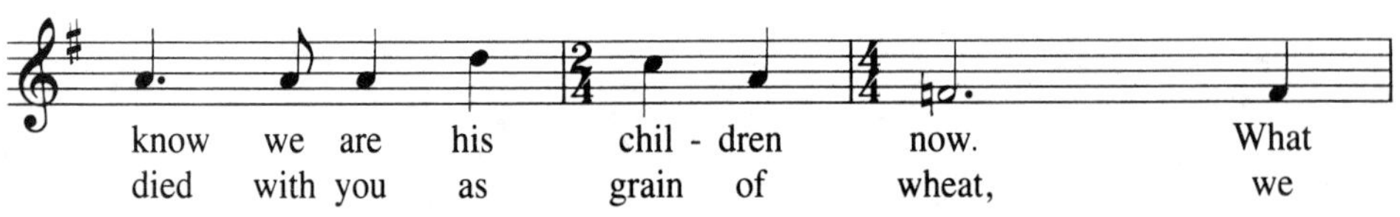
know we are his chil - dren now. What
died with you as grain of wheat, we

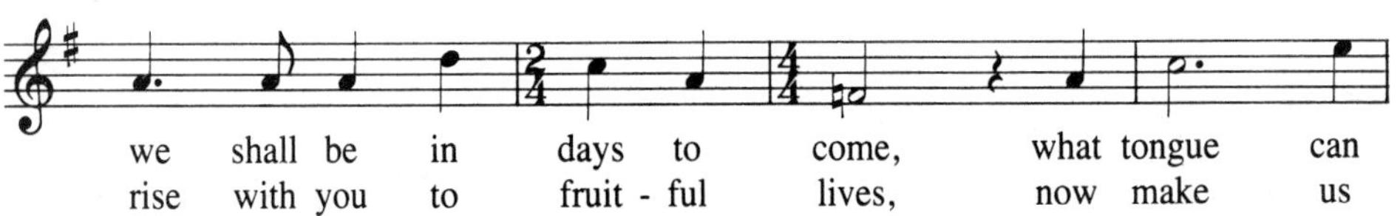
we shall be in days to come, what tongue can
rise with you to fruit - ful lives, now make us

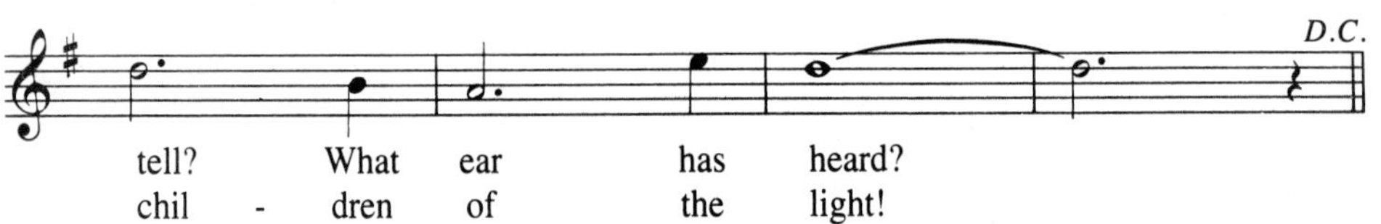
D.C.
tell? What ear has heard?
chil - dren of the light!

Text: Tom Parker
Tune: Tom Parker

221 Adoramus Te Domine II – Gloria

(hum)
A - do - ra - mus te Do - mi - ne.

Text: *We adore you, Lord;* Taizé Community, 1978
Tune: Jacques Berthier, b.1923

You Are the Voice 222

Refrain
You are the voice of the liv - ing God,
call-ing us now to live in your love, to be
chil-dren of God once a - gain!
Verses
1. Praise for the light that shines through the night, from
2. Praise for the wa - ter that springs from the sea, the
3. Praise for the sing - ing and praise for the dance, with
dark-ness to light, from death to new life, and
seed that gives life to all who be - lieve, God's
new heart and voice, all raise the song of
praise to the morn - ing that brings forth the sun, to
love o - ver - flow - ing, our hearts know the joy to be
praise to cre - a - tion; all heav - en and earth, come
o - pen our eyes to the Lord! to
daugh-ters and sons of the Lord! to be
sing of the glo - ry of God! Come
o - pen our eyes to the Lord! For
daugh-ters and sons of the Lord! For
sing of the glo - ry of God! For
D.C.

Text: David Haas, b.1957
Tune: David Haas, b.1957; Acc. by Jeanne Cotter

223 Jubilate, Servite

Canon

1.
2.
Ju - bi - la - te De - o om - nis ter - ra.

Ser - vi - te Do - mi - no in lae - ti - ti - a.

Al - le - lu - ia, al - le - lu - ia, in lae - ti - ti - a.

Al - le - lu - ia, al - le - lu - ia, in lae - ti - ti - a!

Text: Psalm 100, *Rejoice in God, all the earth. Serve the Lord with gladness;* Taizé Community, 1978
Tune: Jacques Berthier, b.1923

224 We Praise You

Refrain

We praise you, O Lord, for all your works are won-der-ful.

We praise you, O Lord, for ev - er is your love.

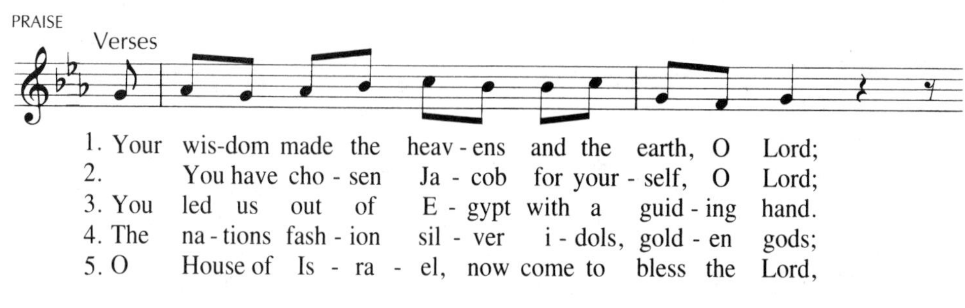
Verses
1. Your wis-dom made the heav - ens and the earth, O Lord;
2. You have cho - sen Ja - cob for your - self, O Lord;
3. You led us out of E - gypt with a guid - ing hand.
4. The na - tions fash - ion sil - ver i - dols, gold - en gods;
5. O House of Is - ra - el, now come to bless the Lord,

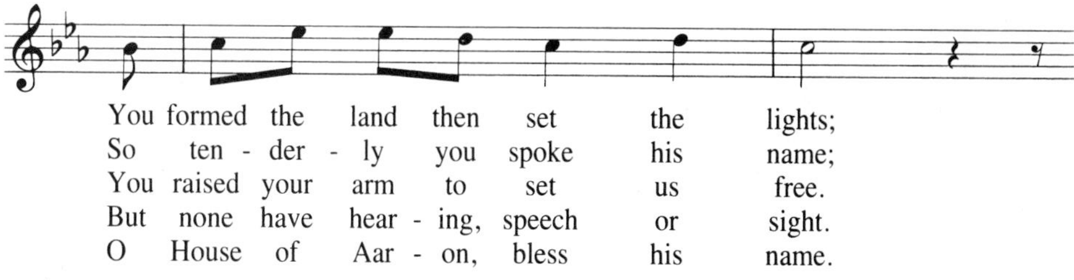
You formed the land then set the lights;
So ten - der - ly you spoke his name;
You raised your arm to set us free.
But none have hear - ing, speech or sight.
O House of Aar - on, bless his name.

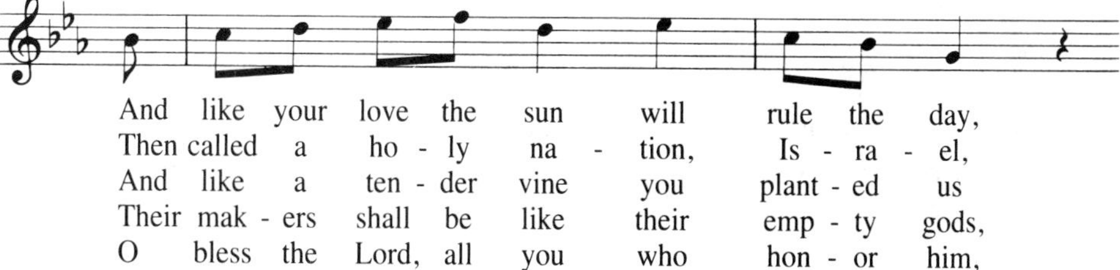
And like your love the sun will rule the day,
Then called a ho - ly na - tion, Is - ra - el,
And like a ten - der vine you plant - ed us
Their mak - ers shall be like their emp - ty gods,
O bless the Lord, all you who hon - or him,

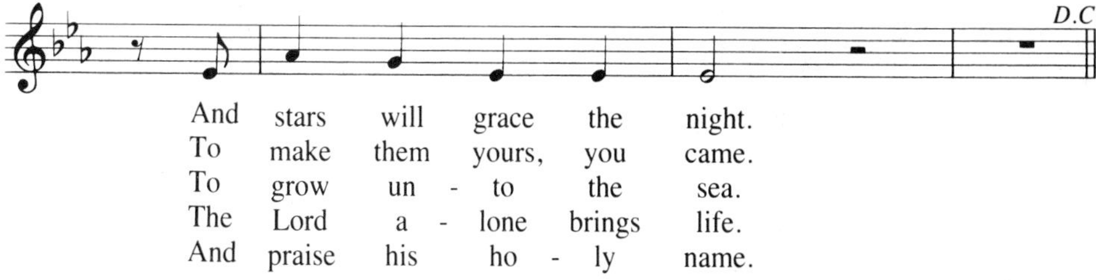
D.C.
And stars will grace the night.
To make them yours, you came.
To grow un - to the sea.
The Lord a - lone brings life.
And praise his ho - ly name.

6. Happy is the home of you that fear the Lord;
So fruitful shall your love become.
Your children flourish like the olive plants,
for ever are you one.

7. May the Lord give you his blessings all your days.
May you see him fill your land
Until your children bring their children home
To show his love again.

Text: Mike Balhoff
Tune: Darryl Ducote, Gary Daigle

225 I Want to Praise Your Name

1. Praise with the trum - pet, Praise with the harp,
2. Moun - tains and val - leys, Riv - ers and seas,
3. Moth - ers and fa - thers, Daugh-ters and sons,

Praise with the tim - brel, the dance and the lyre;
Stars in the heav - ens and fish in the deep;
All of God's peo - ple, the old and the young;

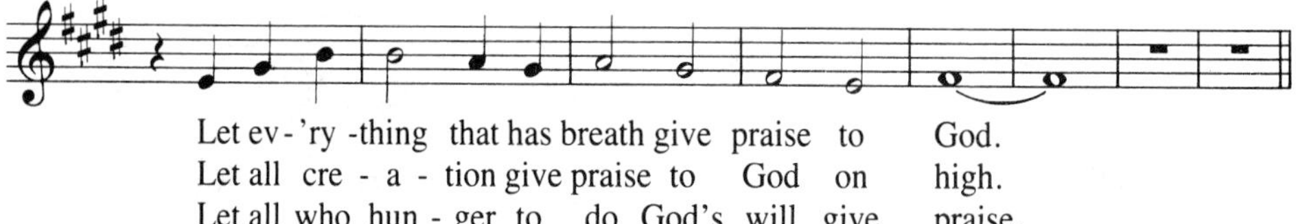

Let ev - 'ry - thing that has breath give praise to God.
Let all cre - a - tion give praise to God on high.
Let all who hun - ger to do God's will give praise.

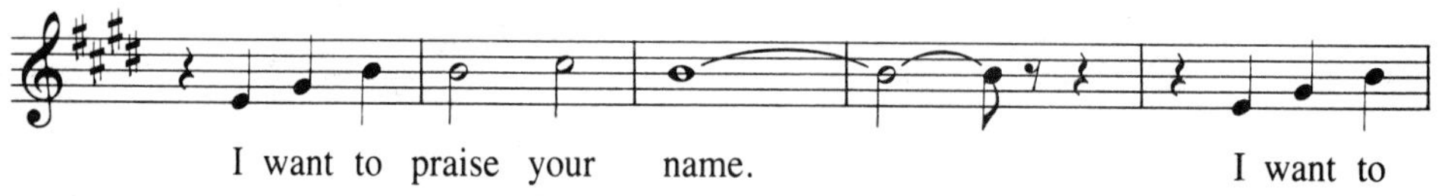

I want to praise your name. I want to

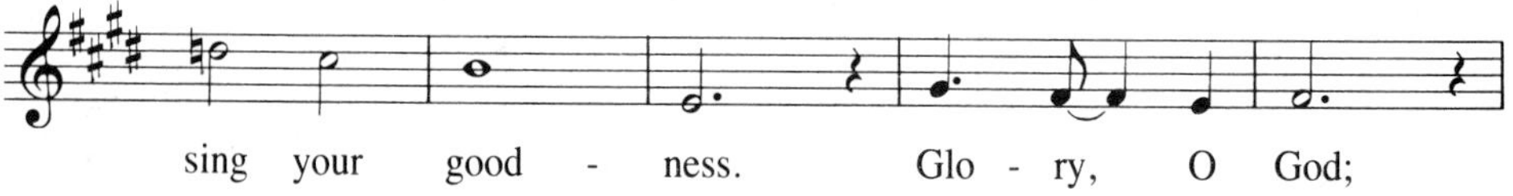

sing your good - ness. Glo - ry, O God;

1.-3. Glo - ry. 4. Glo - ry.

Text: Psalms 148, 149, 150; Adapt. by Bob Hurd, © 1984
Tune: Bob Hurd, © 1984; Acc. by Craig S. Kingsbury, © 1984, Oregon Catholic Press

This is the Day 226

Refrain
This is the day that the Lord has made, Let us re-
joice and be glad, and be glad. This is the day that the
Lord has made, al - le - lu - ia, al - le - lu - ia.
Verses
1. Let us sing un - to the Lord,
2. Let the heav - ens be glad,
3. Bring your gifts be - fore the Lord,
praise his name with our joy - ful shouts,
let the earth now re - joice and sing,
bring your of - f'rings in - to his court;
en - ter in with our joy - ful hearts, to the
let the fields and the trees cry out and the
tell his glo - ry to all the earth and his
God of our sal - va - tion.
o - ceans thun-der his praise.
won - ders for all time.
D.C.

Text: Psalm 95, 96; Marty Haugen, b.1950
Tune: Marty Haugen, b.1950

227 In Praise of His Name

Refrain
Bless the Lord, O my soul; bless the Lord, praise his name!
Bless the Lord, O my soul; let all cre - a - tion praise his name!
Verses
1. Sun and the moon, bless the Lord! Bless him, all of the
earth! Sea and its waves, glo - ry in your power. Let your
thun - der ech - o his name!
D.C.
2. Let all cre - a - tion rise and give praise to our
God, for Yah-weh a - lone is God. He
made us, we be - long to him!
D.C.

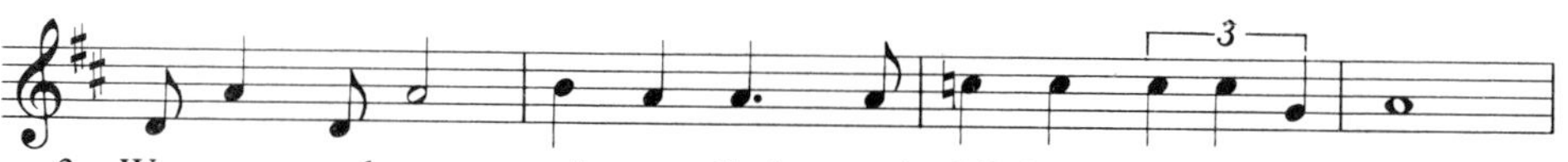

3. Wom-en and men, praise our God, and chil-dren, lift up your hearts.

En-ter his gates with songs of joy; with glad-ness serve you the Lord!

Text: Psalm 100, 148; Roc O'Connor, SJ
Tune: Roc O'Connor, SJ; Acc. by Sr. Theophane Hytrek, OSF

To God with Gladness Sing 228

1. To God with glad - ness sing, Your Rock and Sav - ior bless;
2. He cra - dles in his hand The heights and depths of earth;
3. Your heav'n-ly Fa - ther praise, Ac-claim his on - ly Son,

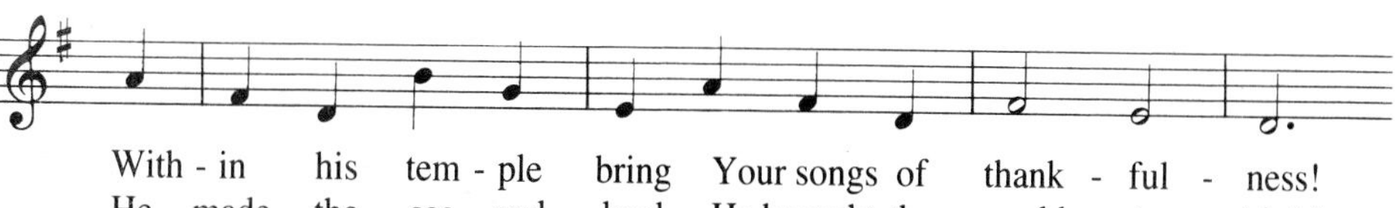

With - in his tem - ple bring Your songs of thank - ful - ness!
He made the sea and land, He brought the world to birth!
Your voice in hom - age raise To him who makes all one!

O God of might, To you we sing,
O God most high, We are your sheep,
O Dove of peace, On us de - scend,

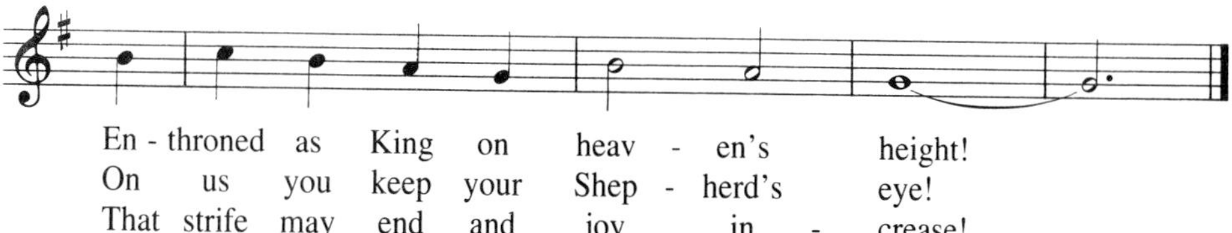

En - throned as King on heav - en's height!
On us you keep your Shep - herd's eye!
That strife may end and joy in - crease!

Text: Psalm 95; Para. by James Quinn, SJ, b.1919, © 1969, Geoffrey Chapman
Tune: CYMBALA, 66 66 4 44 4; Michael Joncas, b.1951, © 1979, GIA Publications, Inc.

229 Praise His Name

Refrain
Al - le - lu - ia! Al - le - lu - ia! Al - le - lu - ia!

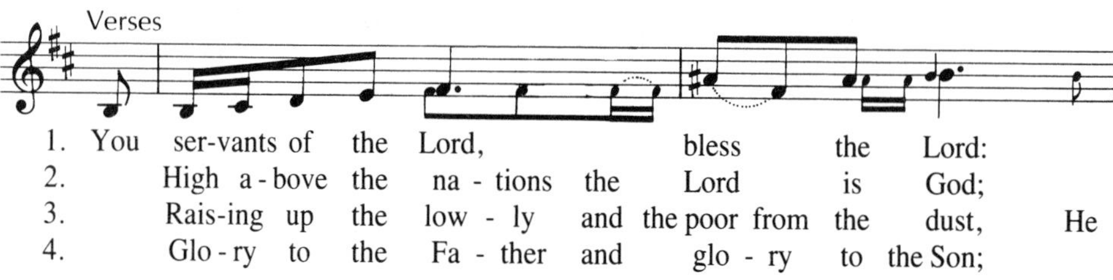
Verses
1. You ser-vants of the Lord, bless the Lord:
2. High a - bove the na - tions the Lord is God;
3. Rais-ing up the low - ly and the poor from the dust, He
4. Glo - ry to the Fa - ther and glo - ry to the Son;

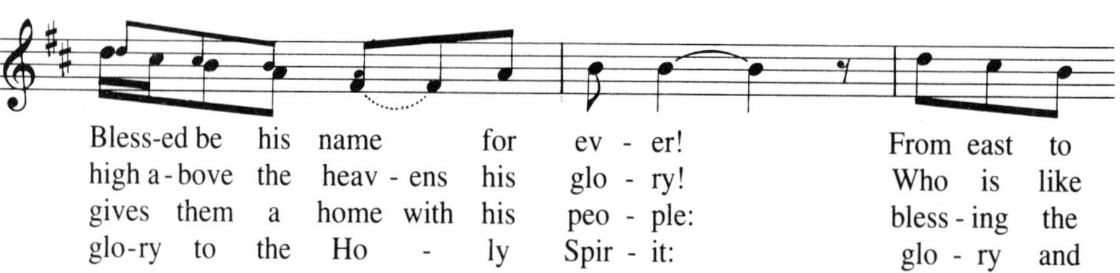
Bless-ed be his name for ev - er! From east to
high a - bove the heav - ens his glo - ry! Who is like
gives them a home with his peo - ple: bless - ing the
glo-ry to the Ho - ly Spir - it: glo - ry and

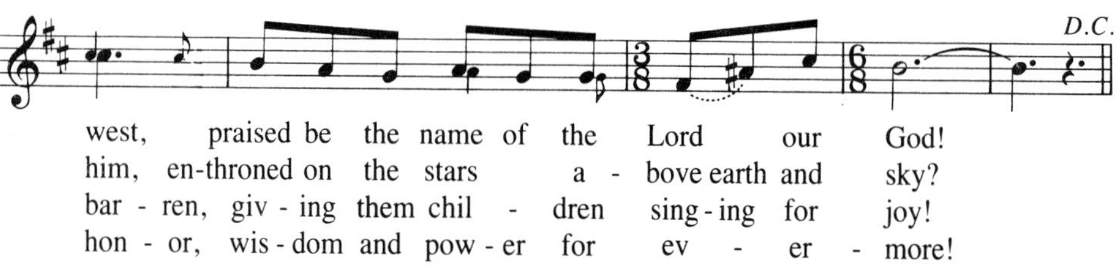
D.C.
west, praised be the name of the Lord our God!
him, en-throned on the stars a - bove earth and sky?
bar - ren, giv - ing them chil - dren sing - ing for joy!
hon - or, wis - dom and pow - er for ev - er - more!

Text: Psalm 113; Michael Joncas, b.1951
Tune: Michael Joncas, b.1951

Sing a New Song 230

Refrain
Sing a new song un - to the Lord; let your song be

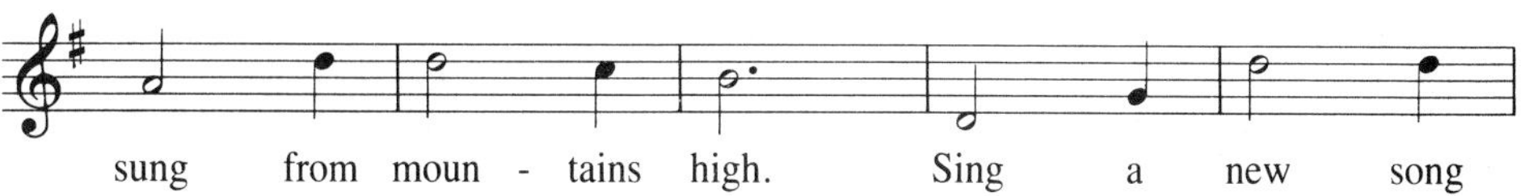
sung from moun - tains high. Sing a new song

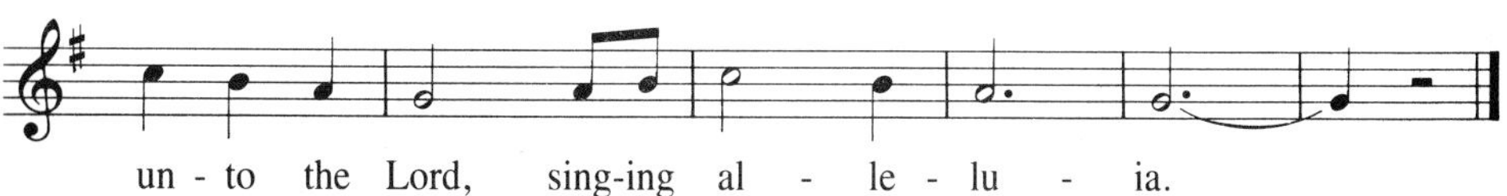
un - to the Lord, sing-ing al - le - lu - ia.

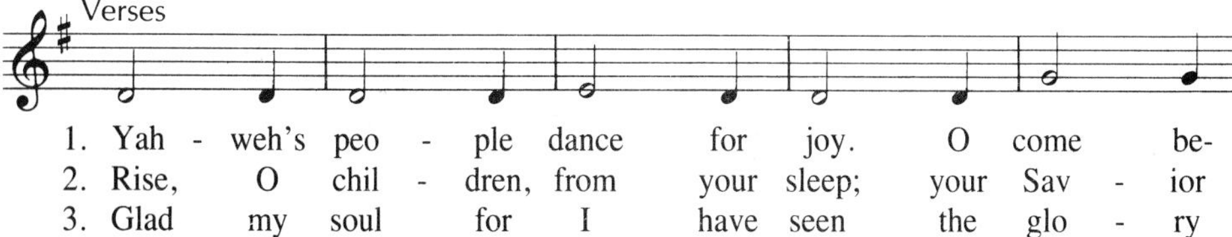
Verses
1. Yah - weh's peo - ple dance for joy. O come be-
2. Rise, O chil - dren, from your sleep; your Sav - ior
3. Glad my soul for I have seen the glo - ry

fore the Lord. And play for him on
now has come. He has turned your
of the Lord. The trum - pet sounds; the

D.C.
glad tam - bou-rines, and let your trum - pet sound.
sor-row to joy, and filled your soul with song.
dead shall be raised. I know my Sav - ior lives.

Text: Psalm 98; Dan Schutte
Tune: Dan Schutte

231 Lift Up Your Hearts

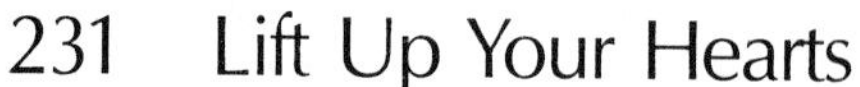

Refrain
Lift up your hearts to the Lord in praise of his mer - cy!

Sing out your joy to the Lord: his love is en - dur - ing.

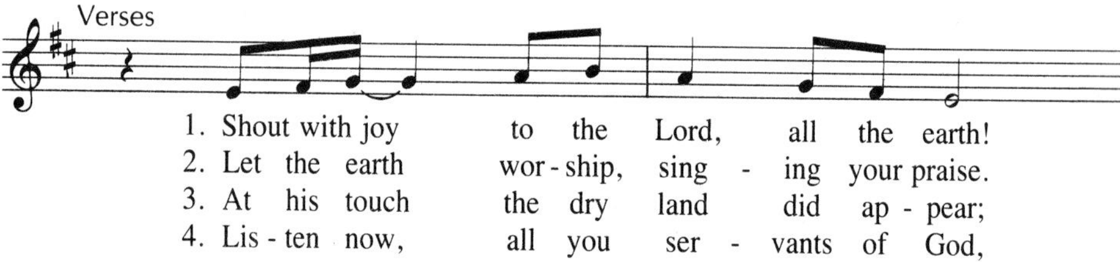
Verses
1. Shout with joy to the Lord, all the earth!
2. Let the earth wor - ship, sing - ing your praise.
3. At his touch the dry land did ap - pear;
4. Lis - ten now, all you ser - vants of God,

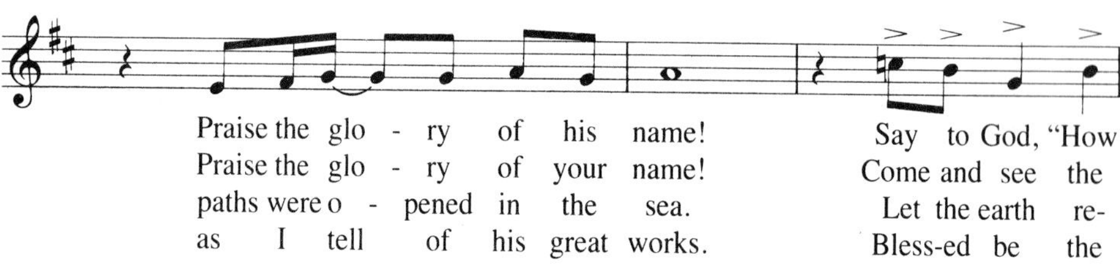
Praise the glo - ry of his name! Say to God, "How
Praise the glo - ry of your name! Come and see the
paths were o - pened in the sea. Let the earth re-
as I tell of his great works. Bless-ed be the

D.C.
won- drous your works, how glo - rious your name!"
deeds of the Lord come, wor - ship his name!"
joice in his might, the might of his love.
Lord of my life! His love shall en - dure!

Text: Psalm 66; Roc O'Connor, SJ
Tune: Roc O'Connor, SJ; Acc. by John Weissrock

With Drums and Dancing 232

Refrain
Praise God with drums and danc-ing. Sing to God a joy - ful song.
Come dance the dawn-ing sto - ry. Tell what God the Lord has done.
Verses
1. Come to the Lord. Count on his kind - ness. Cry out to the Lord with joy. Sing the care of our God.
3. Led through the sea, Test - ed like sil - ver, Brought safe - ly through wind and woe: God has guid - ed our way.
D.C.
2. Lord, you have made us We are marked with your name. Ev - er care for us and lead us Like a shep - herd guards his sheep.
4. Lord, you have heard us When we called out your name. When we cried for one to save us You re- vealed your might - y arm.
D.C.

Text: Dan Schutte
Tune: Dan Schutte

233 Glory and Praise to Our God

Refrain
Glo - ry and praise to our God, who a - lone gives light to our days. Man - y are the bless-ings he bears to those who trust in his ways.
Verses
1. We, the daugh-ters and sons of him who built the val-leys and plains, praise the won-ders our God has done in ev - 'ry heart that sings.
2. In his wis - dom he strength - ens us, like gold that's test-ed in fire. Though the pow - er of sin pre-vails, our God is there to save.
3. Ev - 'ry mom - ent of ev - 'ry day our God is wait-ing to save, al - ways read - y to seek the lost, to an - swer those who pray.
D.C.
4. God has wa - tered our bar - ren land and spent his mer - ci - ful rain. Now the riv - ers of life run full for an - y - one to drink.
D.C.

Text: Psalm 65, 66; Dan Schutte
Tune: Dan Schutte; Acc. by Sr. Theophane Hytrek, OSF

Sing to the Mountains 234

Refrain
Sing to the moun-tains, sing to the sea. Raise your
voic - es, lift your hearts. This is the day the
Lord has made. Let all the earth re - joice.
Verses
1. I will give thanks to you, my Lord.
3. This is the day that the Lord has made.
You have an-swered my plea. You have saved my
Let us be glad and re - joice. He has turned all
D.C.
soul from death. You are my strength and my song.
death to life. Sing of the glo - ry of God.
2. Ho - ly, ho - ly, ho - ly Lord,
D.C.
heav - en and earth are full of your glo - ry.

Text: Psalm 118: Bob Dufford, SJ
Tune: Bob Dufford, SJ; Acc. by Sr. Theophane Hytrek, OSF

235 May We Praise You

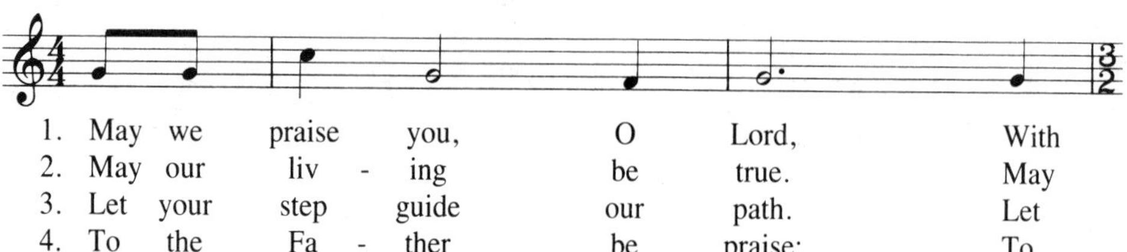
1. May we praise you, O Lord, With
2. May our liv - ing be true. May
3. Let your step guide our path. Let
4. To the Fa - ther be praise; To

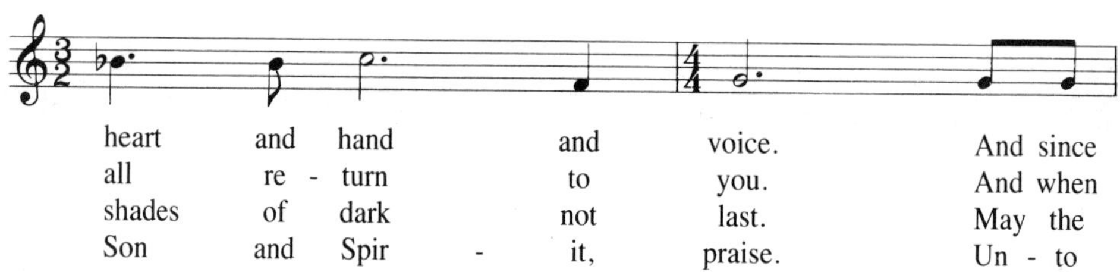
heart and hand and voice. And since
all re - turn to you. And when
shades of dark not last. May the
Son and Spir - it, praise. Un - to

life it - self is your gift to us, Then may
life is done let our pass - ing be Like a
sun of jus - tice re - turn on high, And your
God the one let all praise be done, Till the

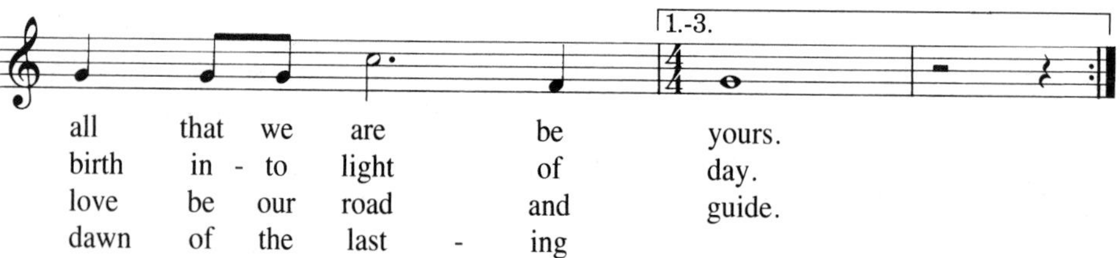
1.-3.
all that we are be yours.
birth in - to light of day.
love be our road and guide.
dawn of the last - ing

4.
day, may we praise.

Text: Vs. 1 from *The Liturgy of the Hours;* John Foley, SJ
Tune: John Foley, SJ

Blessed Be God 236

Refrain
Bless-ed be God. Bless-ed be his ho - ly name. Bless-ed be
Je - sus, the Lord, the Christ. Bless-ed be the Spir - it,
the com-fort - er. Bless-ed be God in his an - gels
and his saints.
To verses
saints.
Last time
saints. Bless-ed be God in his
an - gels and his saints.
Verses
1. You spread out the heav - ens and poured forth the seas, you
2. You pour out the wa - ter in clear run-ning springs which
3. Your moon marks the sea - sons of growth and de - cline and
trav-el on wings of the wind. The winds bring your mes-sage in
trav-el in streams to the sea. The moun-tains re - ply with a
bright-ens the dark - ness of night. Your sun brings the dawn-ing with
whis-per-ing breath and fire bright-ly glows with your word.
blan-ket of green and val - leys bear fruit in due time.
pow-er - ful light, a bea - con of life and of hope.
D.C.

Text: Based on *The Divine Praises* and Psalm 103; Michael Connolly
Tune: Michael Connolly

237 Confitemini Domino

Con-fi - te - mi - ni Do-mi - no quo - ni - am bo - nus.
Con-fi - te - mi - ni Do-mi - no, Al - le - lu - ia!

Text: Psalm 137, *Give thanks to the Lord for he is good;* Taizé Community, 1982
Tune: Jacques Berthier, b.1923

238 Table Prayer

Cantor:
All:
1. The ta - ble which you set has the rich - es of the fields;
2. The peo - ple whom you call come to eat this bless - ed meal; How
3. The sa - cred food you give is the bod - y of your Son;

Cantor:
won-drous are your gifts to us.
You share the fin - est por-tion,
We raise our hearts in thanks to
You nour - ish us with ho - ly

PETITION

Lord, with rev-'rence and with grace;
you a sin - gle prayer of love; How won-drous are your gifts to
wine to sat - is - fy our thirst;

Cantor:
All:

A - bun-dant is your love;
us. You gath-er us as one; How won-drous are your gifts to us.
A ban-quet for all time;

Text: Mike Balhoff, Gary Daigle, Darryl Ducote
Tune: Mike Balhoff, Gary Daigle, Darryl Ducote

Jesu Christe Miserere 239

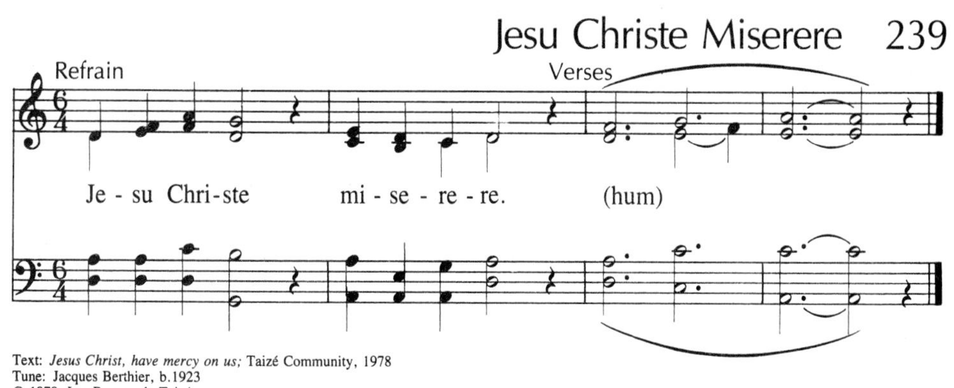

Refrain
Verses
Je - su Chri-ste mi - se - re - re.
(hum)

Text: *Jesus Christ, have mercy on us;* Taizé Community, 1978
Tune: Jacques Berthier, b.1923

240 O Lord, Hear My Prayer

O Lord, hear my prayer, O Lord, hear my prayer: when I call an - swer me. O Lord, hear my prayer, O Lord, hear my prayer. Come and lis - ten to me.

Text: Psalm 102; Taizé Community, 1982
Tune: Jacques Berthier, b. 1923

241 Hold Me in Life

Refrain
Hold me in life for you are my safe - ty,
al - ways my eyes are look - ing for you.

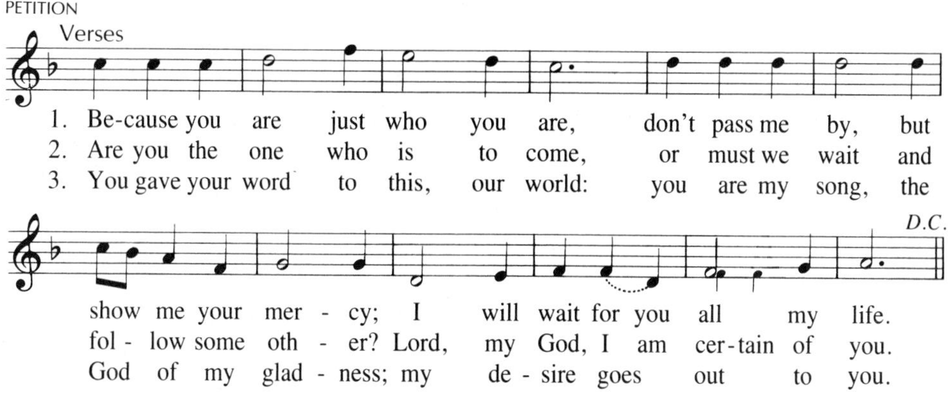
Verses
1. Be-cause you are just who you are, don't pass me by, but show me your mer - cy; I will wait for you all my life.
2. Are you the one who is to come, or must we wait and fol - low some oth - er? Lord, my God, I am cer-tain of you.
3. You gave your word to this, our world: you are my song, the God of my glad - ness; my de - sire goes out to you.
D.C.

Text: Psalm 25; Huub Oosterhuis, b.1933; Trans. by David Smith
Tune: Bernard Huijbers

O Healing River 242

1. O heal - ing riv - er, send down your wa - ters, Send down your wa - ters up - on this land. O heal - ing riv - er, send down your wa-ters, And wash the blood from off the sand.

2. This land is parch - ing, this land is burn-ing, No seed is grow-ing in the bar - ren ground. O heal - ing riv - er, send down your wa-ters, O heal-ing riv-er, send your wa - ters down.

3. Let the seed of free - dom, a - wake and flour-ish, Let the deep roots nour - ish, let the tall stalks rise. O heal - ing riv - er, send down your wa-ters, O heal-ing riv-er, from out of the skies.

May be sung with the assembly echoing each phrase after the cantor.

Text: Traditional Baptist Hymn
Tune: Traditional Baptist Hymn; Arr. by Michael Joncas, b.1951,

243 Take Our Bread

Refrain

Take our bread, we ask you; take our hearts, we love you. Take our lives, O Fa - ther; we are yours, we are yours.

Verses

1. Yours as we stand at the ta - ble you set; Yours as we eat the bread our hearts can't for - get. We are the sign of your life with us yet, We are yours, we are yours.

D.C.

2. Your ho - ly peo-ple stand-ing washed in your blood, Spir - it filled yet hun-gry we a - wait your food. We are poor, but we've brought our-selves

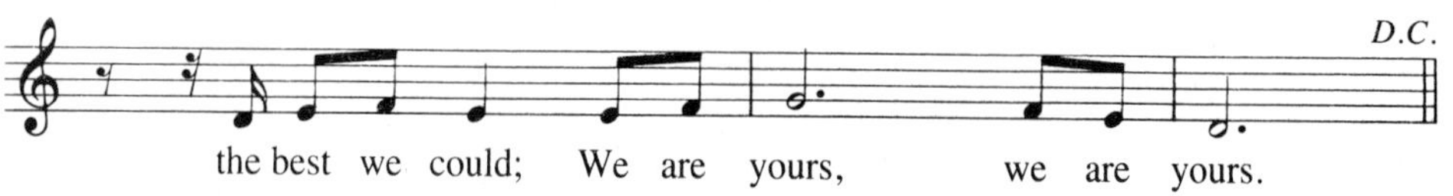
D.C.
the best we could; We are yours, we are yours.

Text: Joe Wise, © 1966
Tune: Joe Wise, © 1966; Acc. by Robert J. Batastini, b.1942, © 1987, GIA Publications, Inc.

Be Light For Our Eyes 244
Refrain
Come and be light for our eyes; be the air we breathe, be the voice we speak! Come, be the song we sing, be the path we seek!
Verses
1. Your life was giv - en; food for all peo - ple, bod - y and blood, new life in our midst! Death is no long - er, life is our fu - ture, Je - sus, Mes - si - ah; name of all names!
2. We hold your pres - ence; ris - en for ev - er! Your name now names us peo - ple of God! Filled with your vi - sion, peo - ple of mis - sion, heal - ing, for - giv - ing; light for the world!
3. Lead us to jus - tice, light in the dark - ness; sing - ing, pro - claim - ing Je - sus is Lord! Teach us to speak, and help us to lis - ten for when your truth and our dreams em - brace!
D.C.

Text: David Haas, b.1957
Tune: David Hass, b.1957; Keyboard arr. by David Haas, b.1957, and Marty Haugen, b.1950

245 Come to Us, Creative Spirit

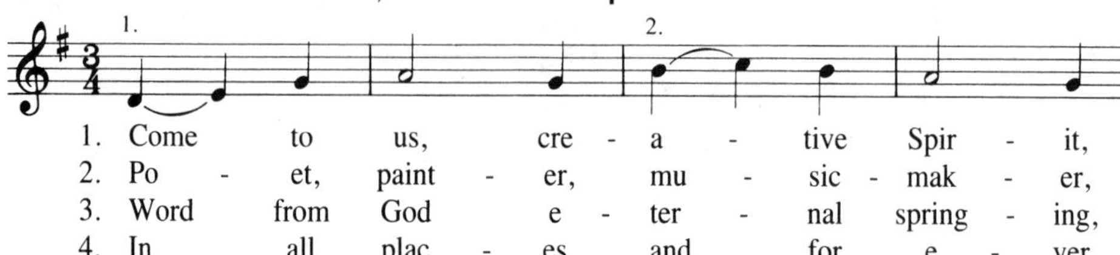
1.
2.
1. Come to us, cre - a - tive Spir - it,
2. Po - et, paint - er, mu - sic - mak - er,
3. Word from God e - ter - nal spring - ing,
4. In all plac - es and for e - ver

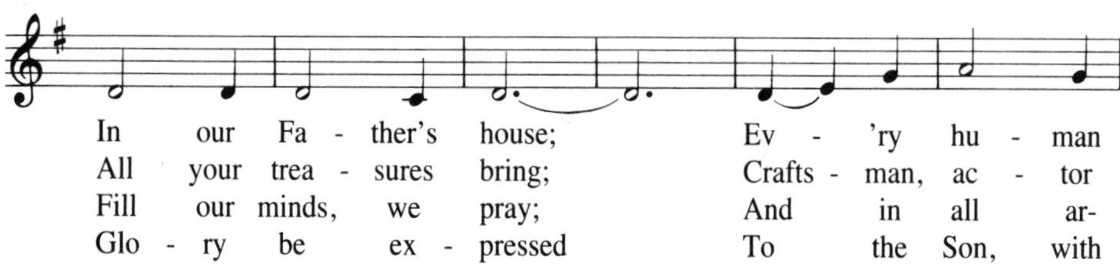
In our Fa - ther's house; Ev - 'ry hu - man
All your trea - sures bring; Crafts - man, ac - tor
Fill our minds, we pray; And in all ar-
Glo - ry be ex - pressed To the Son, with

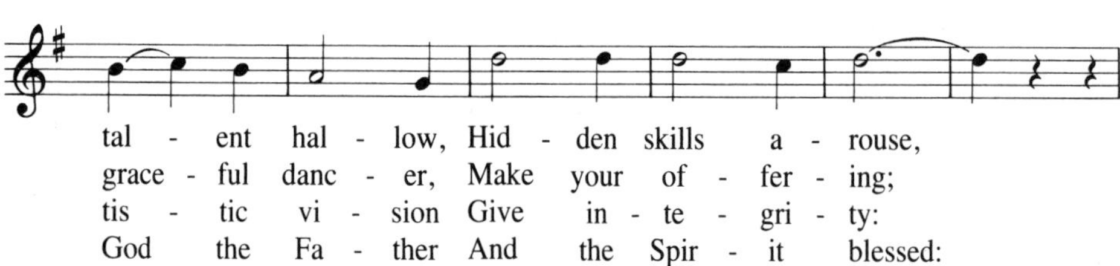
tal - ent hal - low, Hid - den skills a - rouse,
grace - ful danc - er, Make your of - fer - ing;
tis - tic vi - sion Give in - te - gri - ty:
God the Fa - ther And the Spir - it blessed:

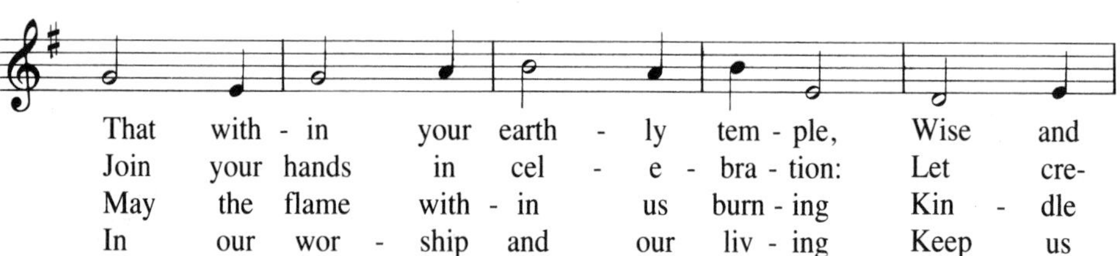
That with - in your earth - ly tem - ple, Wise and
Join your hands in cel - e - bra - tion: Let cre-
May the flame with - in us burn - ing Kin - dle
In our wor - ship and our liv - ing Keep us

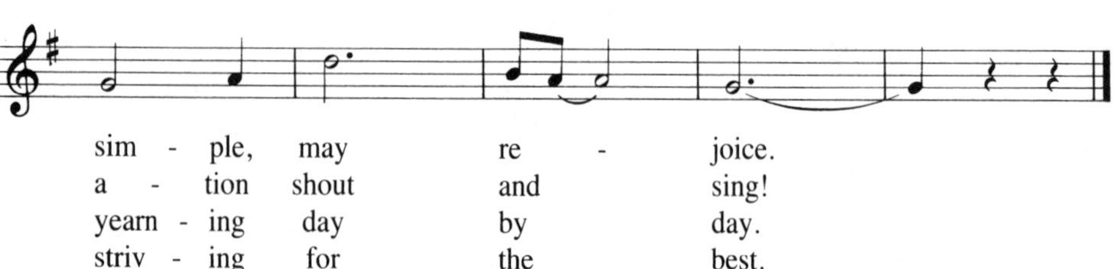
sim - ple, may re - joice.
a - tion shout and sing!
yearn - ing day by day.
striv - ing for the best.

Text: David Mawbray, b.1938, © 1979, Stainer and Bell Publications
Tune: CREATOR SPIRITUS, 8 5 8 5 84 3; Thomas F. Savoy, b.1955, © 1987, GIA Publications, Inc.

Bless the Lord 246

Refrain
Bless the Lord, O my soul, let all that

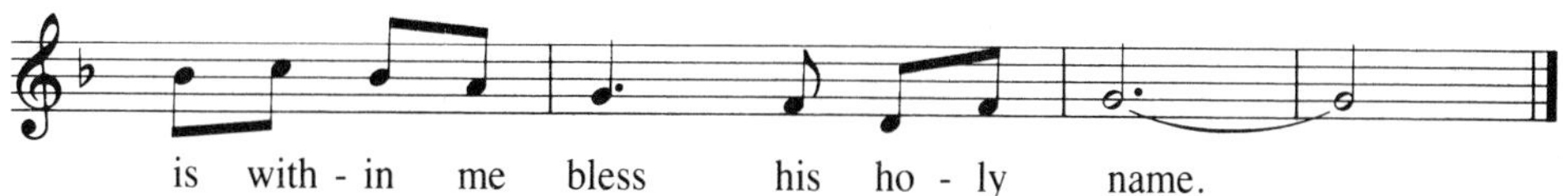
is with - in me bless his ho - ly name.

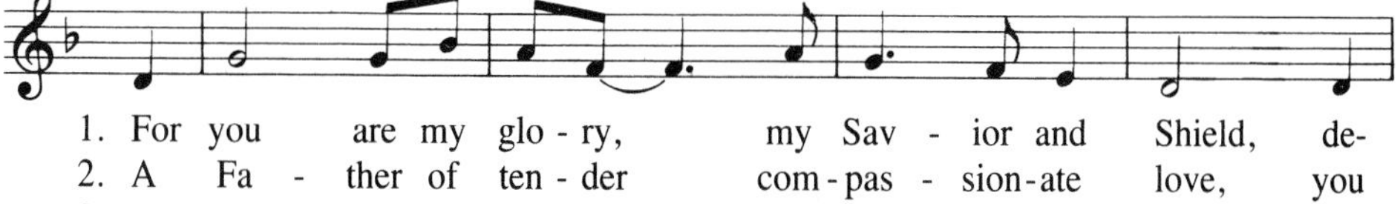
Verses
1. For you are my glo - ry, my Sav - ior and Shield, de-
2. A Fa - ther of ten - der com - pas - sion - ate love, you
3. For you are my Shep-herd who keeps me from need, Sus-

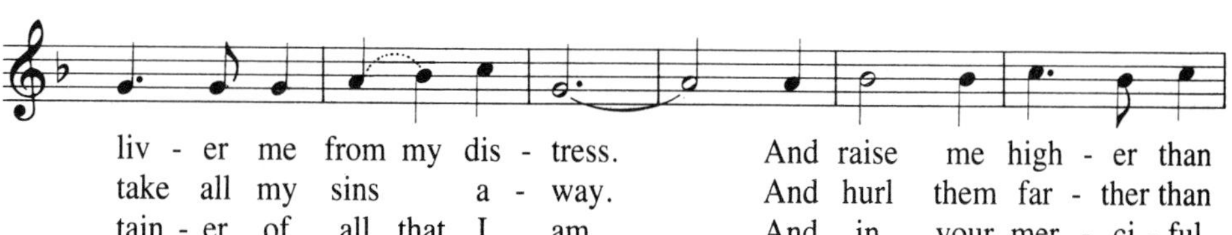
liv - er me from my dis - tress. And raise me high - er than
take all my sins a - way. And hurl them far - ther than
tain - er of all that I am. And in your mer - ci - ful

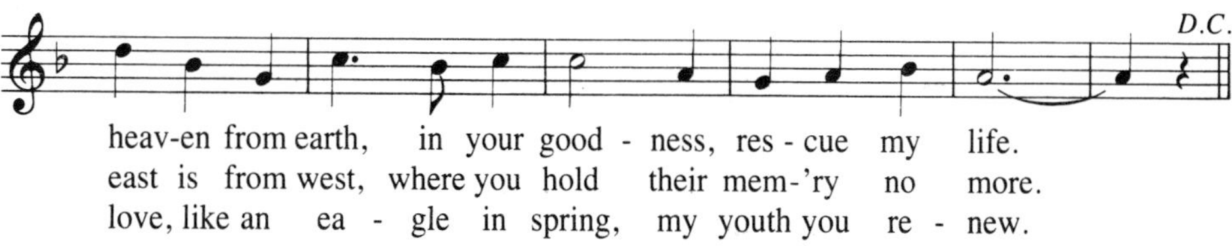
D.C.
heav-en from earth, in your good - ness, res - cue my life.
east is from west, where you hold their mem-'ry no more.
love, like an ea - gle in spring, my youth you re - new.

Text: Psalm 104; Edward Walker
Tune: Edward Walker; Acc. by Patrick Loomis, © 1985, Oregon Catholic Press

247 Song of St. Patrick

Refrain

May the Spir - it of Christ be our hope through the day,

be our guard through the night, our com-pan-ion on the way.

Verses

1. Christ be ev - er be - fore us, Christ be ev - er be-

hind us, Christ be ev - er with - in.

D.C.

2. Christ up - on our left hand watch - ing, At our right hand
3. Christ be in each ho - ly si - lence, Christ be in our
4. Let us be God's light in the dark - ness, Let us be God's
5. God Cre - a - tor, bless and keep us, Christ, be ev - er

guid - ing, Christ a - bove, be - neath us guard - ing,
speak - ing, Christ in ev - 'ry work we of - fer,
kind - ness; Let us be God's jus - tice and mer - cy,
near us; Spir - it be the light be - fore us,

Near to us a - bid - ing.
Ev - er in our seek - ing.
Hands and feet of Christ.
Gen - tle be our path - way.

D.C.

Text: Based on *St. Patrick's Breastplate*; Marty Haugen, b.1950
Tune: Marty Haugen, b.1950

Your Love is Finer Than Life 248

Refrain
O God, I seek you, my soul thirsts for

you, your love is fin - er than life.

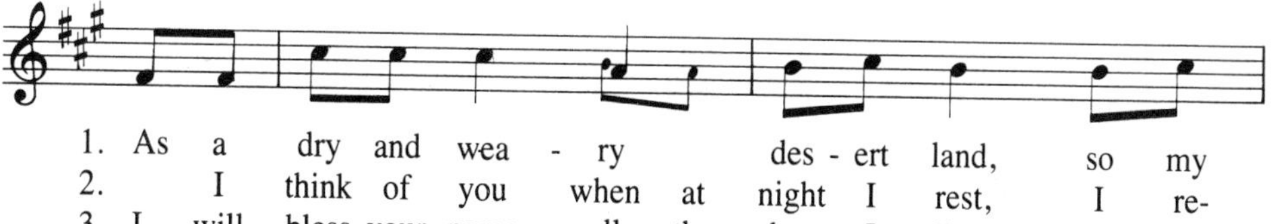
Verses
1. As a dry and wea - ry des - ert land, so my
2. I think of you when at night I rest, I re-
3. I will bless your name all the days I live, I will

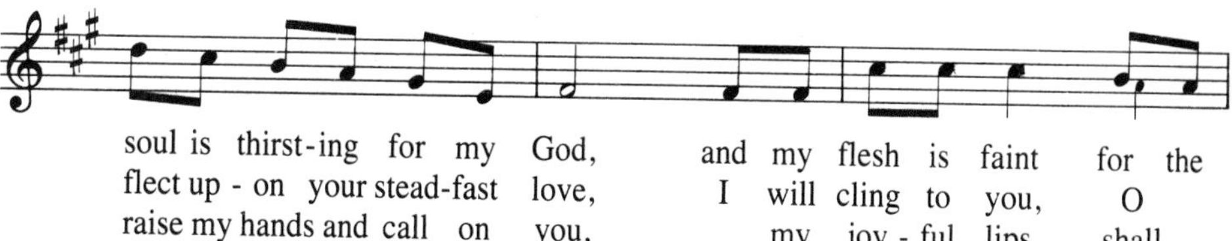
soul is thirst-ing for my God, and my flesh is faint for the
flect up - on your stead-fast love, I will cling to you, O
raise my hands and call on you, my joy - ful lips shall

D.C.
God I seek, for your love is more to me than life.
Lord my God, in the shad-ow of your wings I sing.
sing your praise, you a - lone have filled my hun-gry soul.

Text: Psalm 63; Marty Haugen, b.1950
Tune: Marty Haugen, b.1950

249 We Remember

Refrain
We re-mem-ber how you loved us to your death,
and still we cel-e-brate, for you are with us here;
and we be-lieve that we will see you when you
come, in your glo-ry, Lord. We re-mem-ber,
we cel-e-brate, we be-lieve.
2
Verses
1. Here, a mil-lion woun-ded souls are yearn-ing just to touch you and be healed.
2. Now we re-cre-ate your love, we bring the bread and wine to share a meal.
3. Christ, the Fa-ther's great "A-men" to all the hopes and dreams of ev-'ry heart,
4. See the face of Christ re-vealed in ev-'ry per-son stand-ing by your side,
D.C.
Gath-er all your peo-ple, and hold them to your heart.
Sign of grace and mer-cy, the pres-ence of the Lord.
Peace be-yond all tell-ing, and free-dom from all fear.
Gift to one an-oth-er, and tem-ples of your love.

Text: Marty Haugen, b.1950
Tune: Marty Haugen, b.1950

We Live a Mystery 250

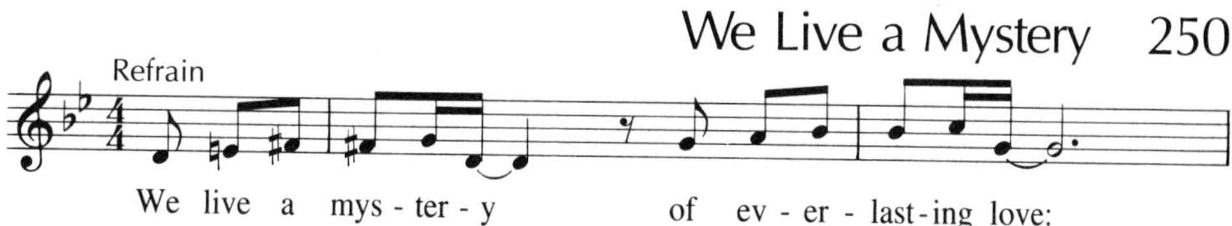
Refrain
We live a mys - ter - y of ev - er - last - ing love:

Je - sus, the liv - ing Lord, the God who came to earth

to die and rise a-gain; We live your mys - t'ry Lord.

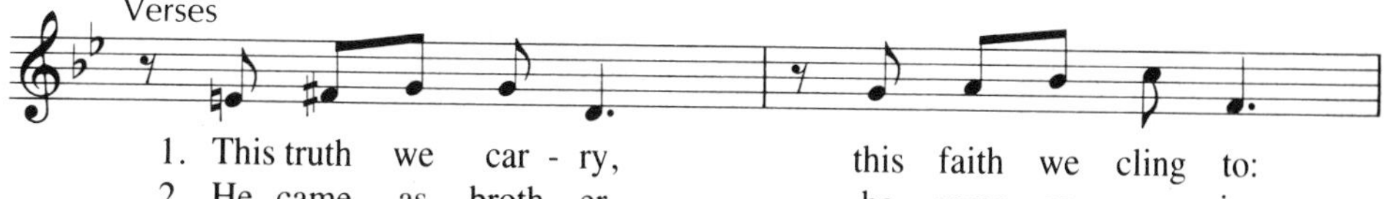
Verses
1. This truth we car - ry, this faith we cling to:
2. He came as broth - er, he came as sav - ior.
3. No eye has seen it, no ear has heard it:

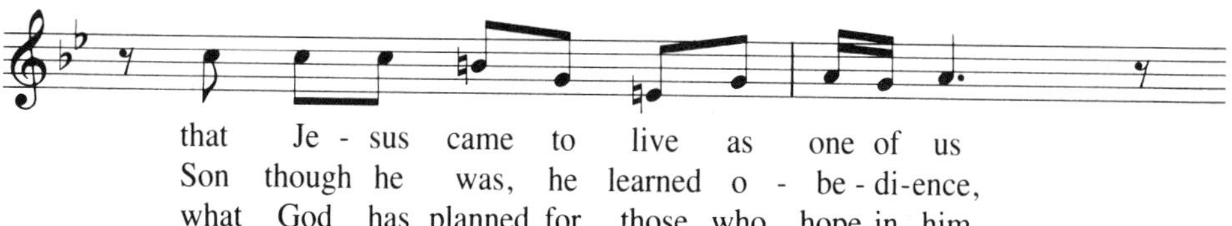
that Je - sus came to live as one of us
Son though he was, he learned o - be - di - ence,
what God has planned for those who hope in him,

D.C.
and die for all of us. We wait for your re - turn.
a harsh in - her - i - tance. We wait for your re - turn.
who put their trust in him. We wait for your re - turn.

Text: Michael Connolly
Tune: Michael Connolly

251 Center of My Life

Refrain

O Lord, you are the cen - ter of my life:

I will al - ways praise you, I will al - ways serve you,

To verses *Last time*

I will al - ways keep you in my sight. sight.

3. And

Verses

1. Keep me safe, O God I take ref - uge in you. I
2. I will bless the Lord who gives me coun - sel, who
so my heart re - joic - es, my soul is glad;

say to the Lord, "You are my God. My
e - ven at night di - rects my heart. I
e - ven in safe - ty shall my bod - y rest. For

hap - pi - ness lies in you a - lone; my
keep the Lord ev - er in my sight: since
you will not leave my soul a - mong the dead, nor

D.C.

hap - pi - ness lies in you a - lone."
he is at my right hand, I shall stand firm.
let your be - lov - ed know de - cay.

FAITH

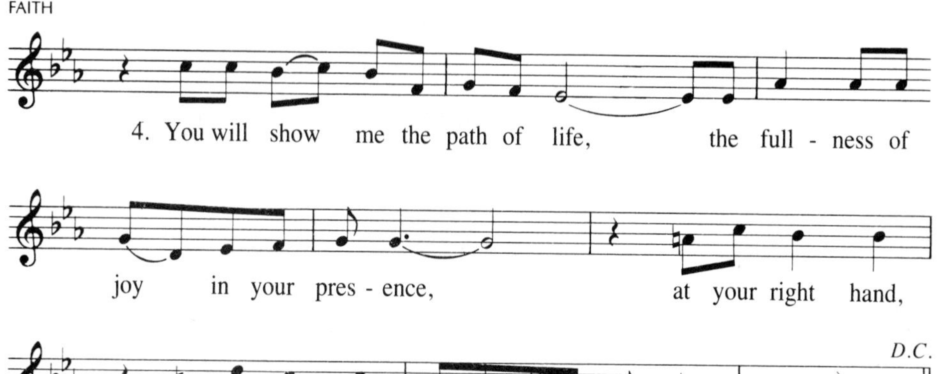
4. You will show me the path of life, the full - ness of
joy in your pres - ence, at your right hand,
D.C.

at your right hand hap - pi - ness for ev - er.

Text: Psalm 16; Verses trans. © 1963, 1986, The Grail; Refrain © 1985, Paul Inwood
Tune: Paul Inwood, © 1985

We Walk by Faith 252

1., 5. We walk by faith, and not by sight: No gracious words we hear Of him who spoke as none e'er spoke, But we believe him near.

2. We may not touch his hands and side, Nor follow where he trod; Yet in his promise we rejoice, And cry "My Lord and God!"

3. Help then, O Lord, our unbelief, And may our faith abound; To call on you when you are near, And seek where you are found:

4. That when our life of faith is done In realms of clearer light We may behold you as you are In full and endless sight.

Text: Henry Alford, 1810-1871, alt.
Tune: SHANTI, CM; Marty Haugen, b.1950, © 1984, GIA Publications, Inc.

253 Jesus the Lord

Refrain

We have no name that can save us but the

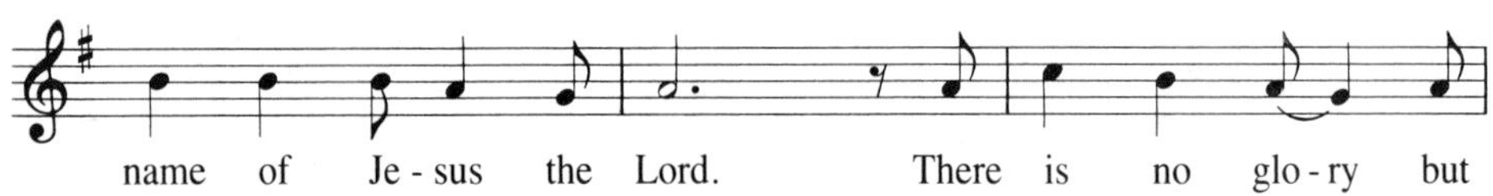
name of Je - sus the Lord. There is no glo - ry but

in his cross. Je - sus the Lord, Je - sus the Lord.

Verses

1. The Lord is mer - cy; his pow-er is his love.

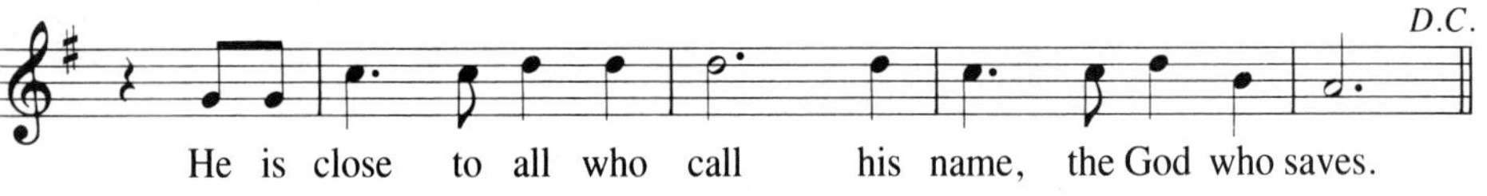
D.C.
He is close to all who call his name, the God who saves.

2. For ev - er faith - ful, he is jus - tice for the

poor and for all who seek his ways; his

FAITH

D.C.
love em - bra - ces all, his love em - brac - es all.

3. It is good to sing. I will praise him all my

life. The poor shall see his face and bro - ken

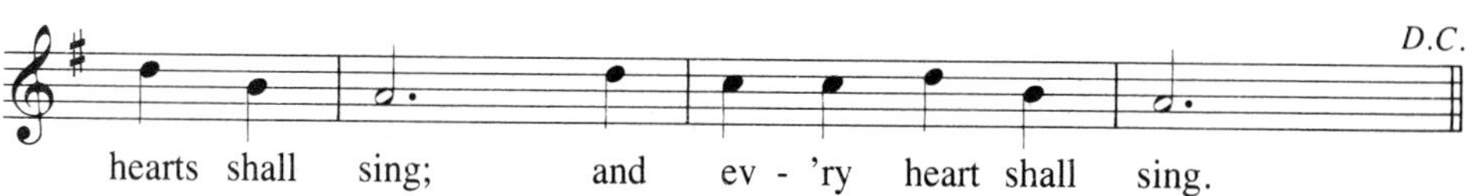
D.C.
hearts shall sing; and ev - 'ry heart shall sing.

Text: Jeffrey Keyes, *A Gentle Strength*
Tune: Jeffrey Keyes, *A Gentle Strength*

254 Our Help is the Name of the Lord

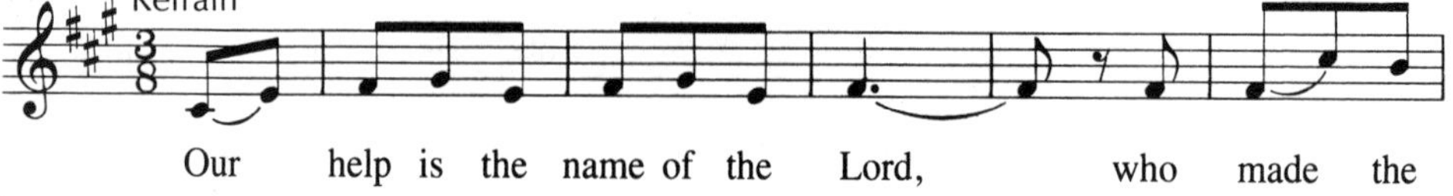
Refrain
Our help is the name of the Lord, who made the

earth and the heav - ens. Toward us he is a most mer - ci - ful

fa - ther, and his fi - del - i - ty knows no end. Our help is the

name of the Lord, and his fi - del - i - ty knows no end.

Verses
1. He calls to me: "Come forth from your grave."
2. He does not haunt us with our sins;
3. Just as a man is mer - ci-ful to his sons,

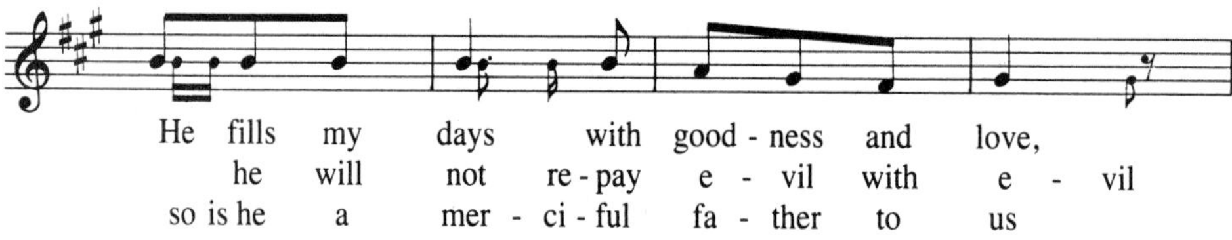
He fills my days with good - ness and love,
he will not re - pay e - vil with e - vil
so is he a mer - ci - ful fa - ther to us

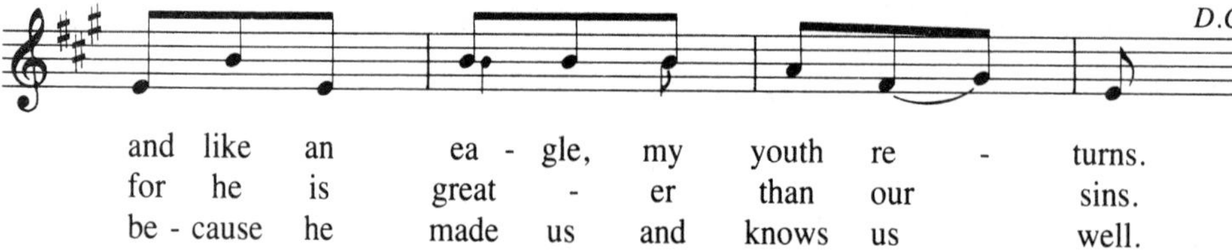
D.C.
and like an ea - gle, my youth re - turns.
for he is great - er than our sins.
be - cause he made us and knows us well.

Text: Psalm 103; Huub Oosterhuis, b.1933; Trans. by Redmond McGoldrick
Tune: Bernard Huijbers

My Refuge 255

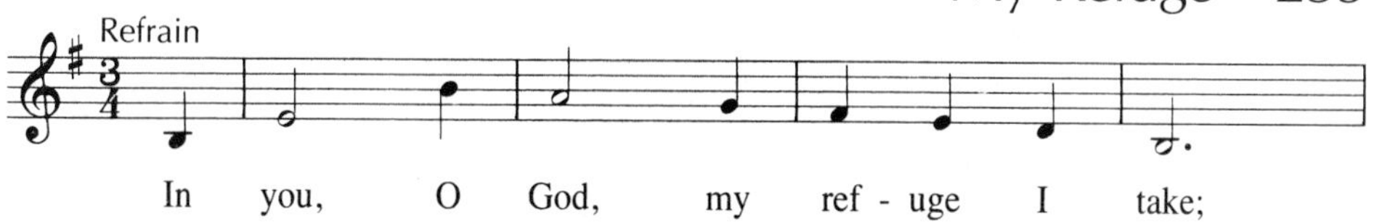
Refrain
In you, O God, my ref - uge I take;

I will not be a - fraid.

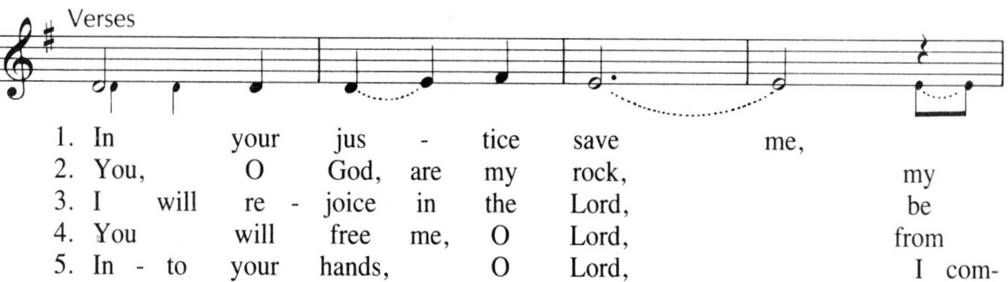
Verses
1. In your jus - tice save me,
2. You, O God, are my rock, my
3. I will re - joice in the Lord, be
4. You will free me, O Lord, from
5. In - to your hands, O Lord, I com-

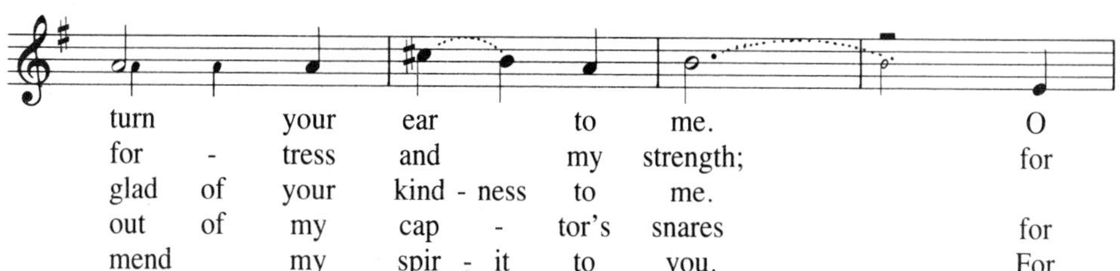
turn your ear to me. O
for - tress and my strength; for
glad of your kind - ness to me.
out of my cap - tor's snares for
mend my spir - it to you. For

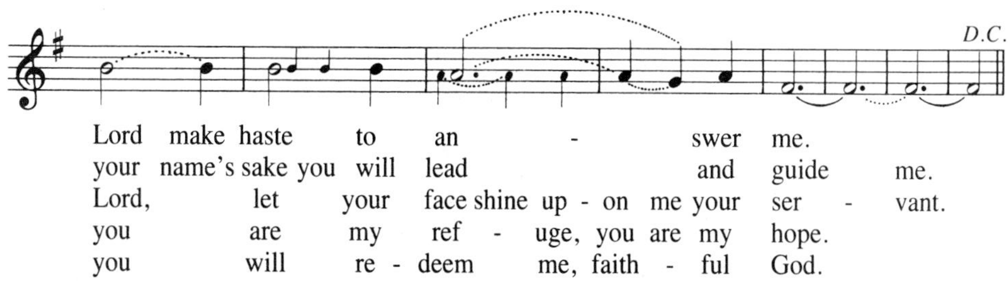
D.C.
Lord make haste to an - swer me.
your name's sake you will lead and guide me.
Lord, let your face shine up - on me your ser - vant.
you are my ref - uge, you are my hope.
you will re - deem me, faith - ful God.

Text: Psalm 31; Adapt. by Dennis Vessels
Tune: Dennis Vessels; Keyboard arr. by Sheryl Soderberg

256 When From Our Exile

Refrain

When from our ex - ile God leads us home a - gain,
we'll think we're dream - ing. When from our ex - ile
God leads us home a - gain, we'll think we're dream - ing.

Verses

1. We shall be sing - ing, laugh - ing for hap - pi - ness.
The world will say: "Their God does won - ders." Yes, you do
won - ders, God here a - mong us, you, our glad - ness.

D.C.

2. Then lead us home, bring us to life a - gain.
e - ven in riv - ers which, in the des - ert,

when the first rain falls, start flow - ing a - gain.
3. Sow seed in sad - ness, har - vest in glad - ness. A
man goes his way and sows seed with tears.
Back he comes, sing - ing, sheaves on his shoul - der.
Final refrain
When from our ex - ile God leads us home a - gain,
we'll think we're dream - ing. When from our ex - ile
God leads us home a - gain, we'll think we're dream - ing.

Text: Psalm 126; Huub Oosterhuis, b.1933; Trans. by Redmond McGoldrick
Tune: Bernard Huijbers

257 All That We Have

Refrain

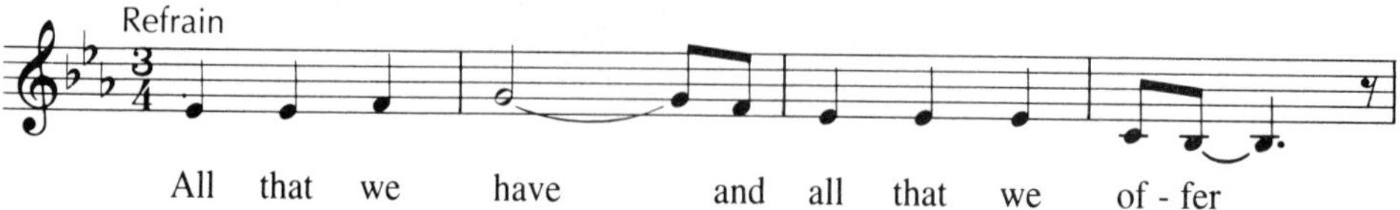
All that we have and all that we of - fer

Comes from a heart both fright-ened and free. Take what we

bring now and give what we need,

All done in his name.

Verses

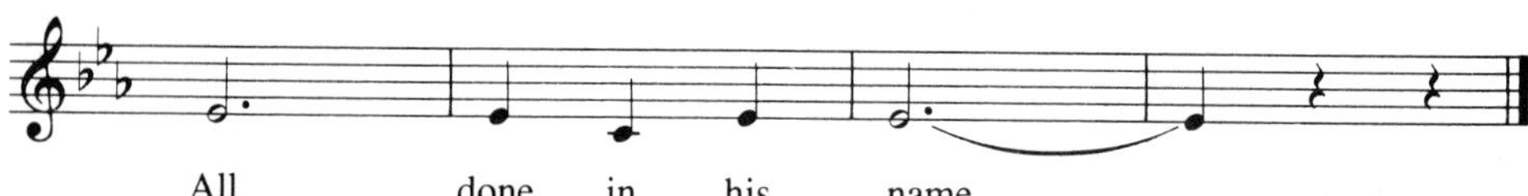
1. Some would re - ly on their pow - er, Oth - ers put
2. Some-times the road may be lone - some, Of - ten we
3. Some-times when trou - bles are man - y, Life can seem

trust in their gold. Some have on - ly their
may lose our way; Take cour - age and al - ways re-
emp - ty, it's true, But look at the life of the

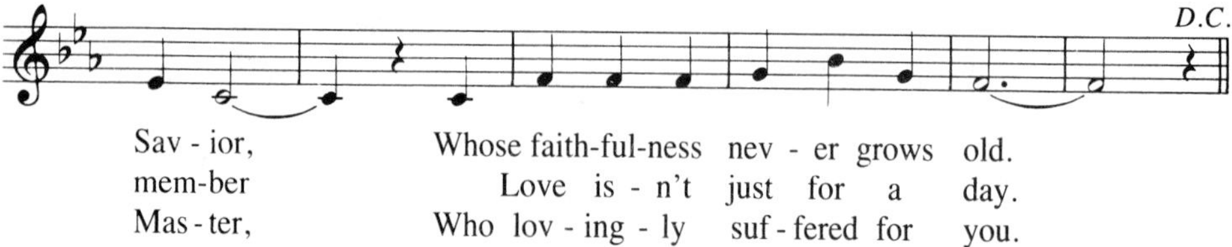
D.C.
Sav - ior, Whose faith-ful-ness nev - er grows old.
mem-ber Love is - n't just for a day.
Mas - ter, Who lov - ing - ly suf - fered for you.

Text: Gary Ault
Tune: Gary Ault; Acc. by Gary Daigle

From My Mother's Womb 258

Refrain

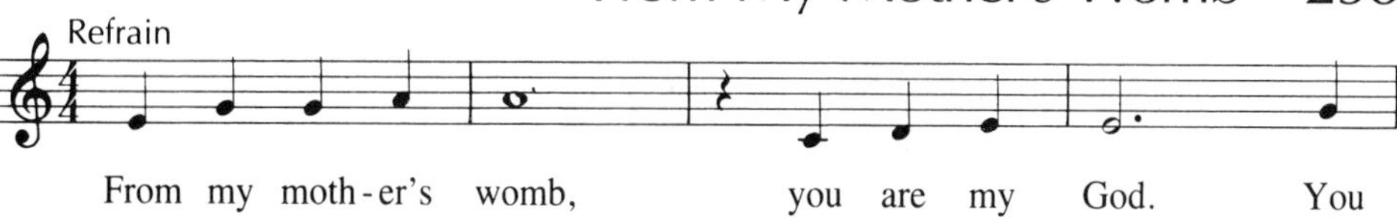
From my moth-er's womb, you are my God. You

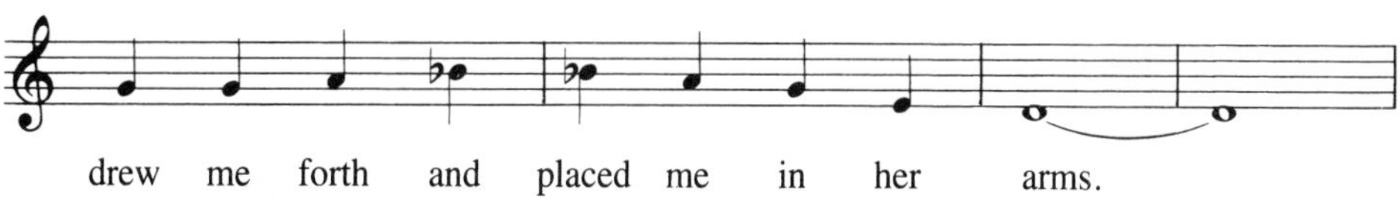
drew me forth and placed me in her arms.

From my moth-er's womb, you are my God.

Verses

1. All the day and night my cries go un-
2. My en-cir-cling foes close in up-
3. I have not re-belled, not once have I

D.C.
an-swered. Why have you a-ban-doned me?
on me. They have pierced my hands and feet.
turned back; know-ing I would not be shamed.

Text: Based on Psalm 22, Isaiah 50; Bob Hurd, © 1986
Tune: Bob Hurd, © 1986; Acc. by Dominic MacAller, © 1986, Oregon Catholic Press

259 The Lord Is Near

Refrain
The Lord is near to all who call on him,
rest in him a - lone,
rest in him a - lone.
Verses
1. He will guard your com - ing and your go - ing;
2. He has seen a thou - sand years go past him
3. Lord, in you I come to take my ref - uge;
4. Trust in him for ev - er, O my peo - ple;
He will be the one to guard your life.
Swift-ly as a morn - ing fades to night.
Through the night you ev - er coun - sel me.
Pour out all your hearts be - fore the Lord.
The sun will not harm you in the day - light,
So come, let him fill you with his wis - dom,
O Lord, you have formed me to be ho - ly
Your God is a rock of strength, your glo - ry;
And the Lord will watch you through the night.
To num - ber all your days a - right.
And to rest with - in you peace - ful - ly.
In the Lord is all your hope re - stored.
D.C.

Text: Mike Balhoff
Tune: Darryl Ducote, Gary Daigle

How Can I Keep from Singing 260

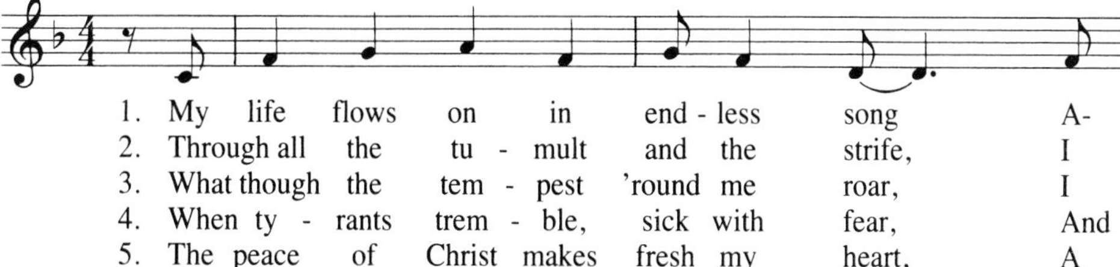
1. My life flows on in end - less song A-
2. Through all the tu - mult and the strife, I
3. What though the tem - pest 'round me roar, I
4. When ty - rants trem - ble, sick with fear, And
5. The peace of Christ makes fresh my heart, A

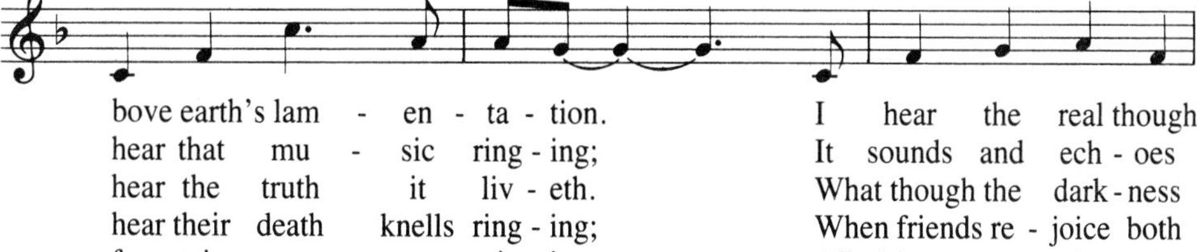
bove earth's lam - en - ta - tion. I hear the real though
hear that mu - sic ring - ing; It sounds and ech - oes
hear the truth it liv - eth. What though the dark - ness
hear their death knells ring - ing; When friends re - joice both
foun-tain ev - er spring-ing. All things are mine since

far off hymn That hails a new cre - a - tion.
in my soul; How can I keep from sing - ing?
'round me close, Songs in the night it giv - eth.
far and near, How can I keep from sing - ing?
I am his; How can I keep from sing - ing?

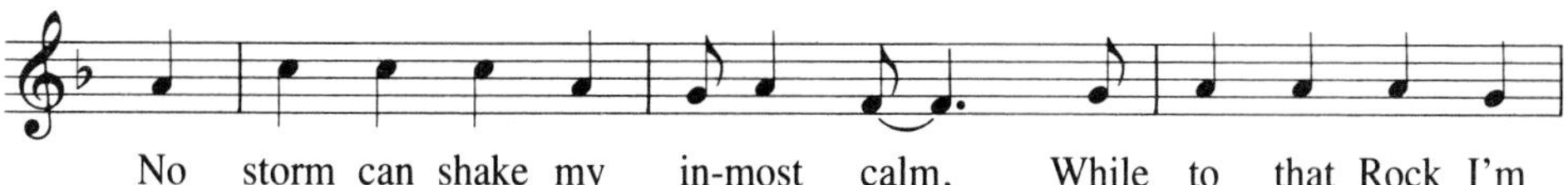
No storm can shake my in-most calm, While to that Rock I'm

cling - ing. Since Love is Lord of heav-en and earth,

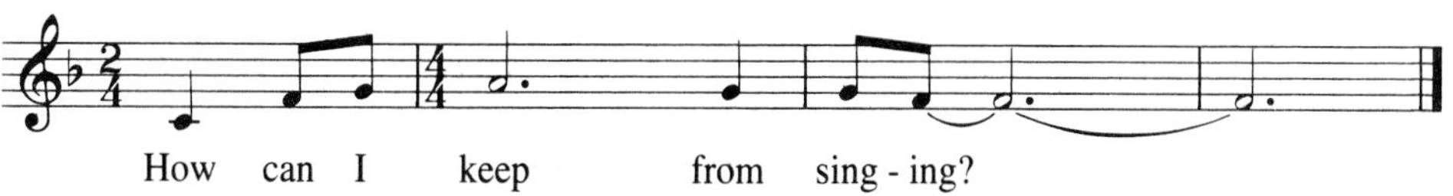
How can I keep from sing - ing?

Text: Quaker Hymn
Tune: Quaker Hymn; Harm. by Robert J. Batastini, b.1942, © 1987, GIA Publications, Inc.

261 On Eagle's Wings

1. You who dwell in the shel - ter of the Lord, who a- bide in his shad - ow for life, say to the Lord: "My ref - uge, my rock in whom I trust!"

Refrain

And he will raise you up on ea - gle's wings, bear you on the breath of dawn, make you to shine like the sun, and hold you in the palm of his hand.

After last refrain

And hold you, hold you in the palm of his hand.

2. The snare of the fowl - er will nev - er cap-ture you, and

TRUST

3
fam-ine will bring you no fear: un - der his wings your
D.S.
ref - uge, his faith-ful - ness your shield.
3
3. You need not fear the ter-ror of the night, nor the
ar-row that flies by day; though thou - sands fall a-
D.S.
bout you, near you it shall not come.
3
4. For to his an-gels he's giv - en a com-mand to
guard you in all of your ways; up - on their hands they will
D.S.
bear you up, lest you dash your foot a-gainst a stone.

Text: Psalm 91; Michael Joncas, b.1951
Tune: Michael Joncas, b.1951

262 Though the Mountains May Fall

Refrain

Though the moun - tains may fall and the hills turn to dust,
yet the love of the Lord will stand
as a shel - ter for all who will call on his name.
Sing the praise and the glo - ry of God.

Verses

1. Could the Lord ev - er leave you? Could the Lord for - get his love?
2. Should you turn and for - sake him, he will gent - ly call your name.

Though a moth - er for - sake her child, he will not a - ban - don you.
Should you wan - der a - way from him, he will al - ways take you back.

D.C.

TRUST
3. Go to him when you're wea - ry; he will
4. As he swore to your fa - thers, when the
give you ea - gle's wings.
flood de - stroyed the land:
You will run, nev - er tire, for your
he will nev - er for - sake you; he will
D.C.
God will be your strength.
swear to you a - gain.

Text: Isaiah 54:6-10, 49:15, 40:31-32; Dan Schutte
Tune: Dan Schutte; Acc. by Michael Pope, SJ

263 Be Not Afraid

1. You shall cross the bar-ren des - ert, but you
shall not die of thirst. You shall wan-der far in
safe - ty though you do not know the way. You shall
speak your words in for - eign lands and all will un - der-
stand. You shall see the face of God and live.
Refrain
Be not a - fraid. I go be - fore you al-ways.
Come, fol-low me, and I will give you rest.
2. If you pass through rag-ing wa-ters in the sea, you shall not

drown. If you walk a - mid the burn-ing flames,

you shall not be harmed. If you stand be - fore the

pow'r of hell and death is at your

side, know that I am with you through it all. *D.S.*

3. Bless - ed are your poor, for the king - dom shall be

theirs. Blest are you that weep and mourn, for

one day you shall laugh. And if wick-ed men in-

sult and hate you all be - cause of me,

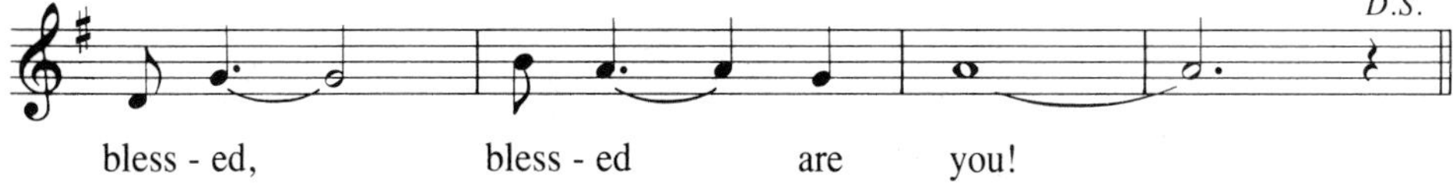
D.S.
bless - ed, bless - ed are you!

Text: Isaiah 43:2-3, Luke 6:20ff; Bob Dufford, SJ
Tune: Bob Dufford, SJ

264 Blessed Be the Lord

Refrain
Blest be the Lord; blest be the Lord, the God of mer - cy, the God who saves. I shall not fear the dark of night, nor the ar - row that flies by day.
Verses
1. He will re - lease me from the nets of all my foes. He will pro - tect me from their wick-ed hands. Be-neath the shad-ow of his wings I will re - joice to find a dwell-ing place se - cure.
D.C.
2. I need not shrink be - fore the ter - rors of the night

nor stand a - lone be - fore the light of day.

No harm shall come to me no ar - row strike me down,

no e - vil set - tle in my soul.

D.C.

3. Al - though a thou - sand strong have fall - en at my side

I'll not be shak - en with the Lord at hand.

His faith - ful love is all the ar - mor that I

need to wage my bat - tle with the foe.

D.C.

Text: Psalm 91; Dan Schutte
Tune: Dan Schutte; Arr. by Sr. Theophane Hytrek, OSF

265 The Lord Is Near

Refrain
O the Lord is near to all who call on him; he is
(For the)
close to all who seek his face, slow to an-ger and full of com-
To verses
Last time
pas-sion and a-bound-ing in mer-ci-ful love. love. A - men.
Verses
1. The Lord is my light and my sal - va - tion, there is
3
noth-ing at all I fear; the Lord is the ref-uge of my
D.S.
life; of whom should I be a - fraid? For the
2. One thing I ask of the Lord; there is on - ly one thing I
D.C.
seek: to dwell in the house of the Lord all the days of my life.

3. For God will hide me in his house and con - ceal me in the
shel - ter of his tent. E - ven now my head is held
high o - ver those who would see me fall. For the
D.S.
Alternate Refrain for Funerals
May the an - gels lead you in - to par - a - dise; may the
mar - tyrs come to wel-come you, and take you to the ho - ly
cit - y, the new and e - ter - nal Je - ru - sa - lem.

Text: Psalm 27; Michael Joncas, b.1951
Tune: Michael Joncas, b.1951

266 You Will Draw Water

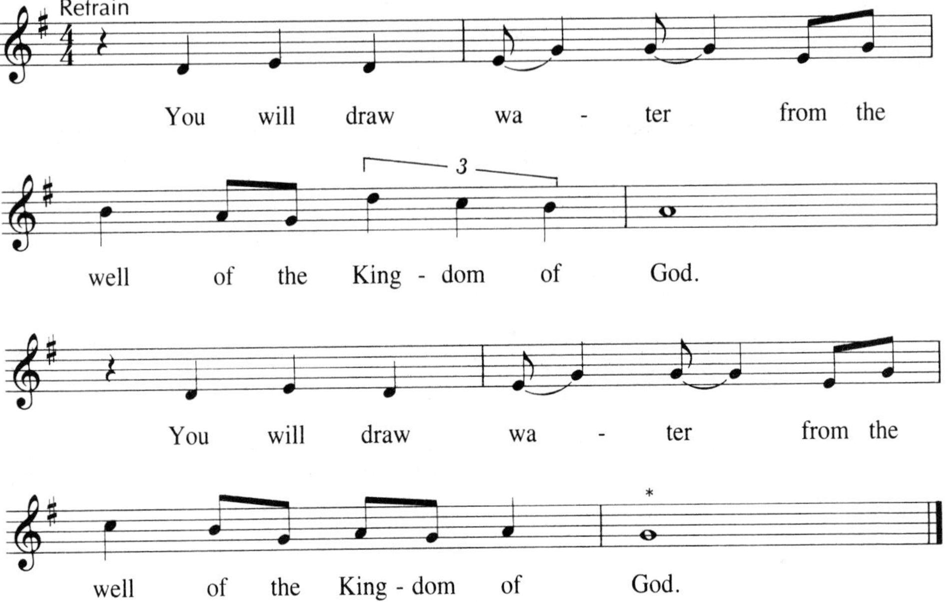
Refrain
You will draw wa - ter from the
well of the King - dom of God.
You will draw wa - ter from the
well of the King - dom of God.

Verses

1. God alone is my rock;
   how then should I be afraid?

2. God alone is my strength;
   who then can stand before me?

3. God alone is my rest;
   the Lord God is my safety.

4. God alone is my peace;
   he shatters steel and nations.

5. God alone is my day;
   his name will shine before me.

6. God alone is my prize;
   though mountains fall to pieces.

*Verses to overlap refrain begin here.

Text: Tom Conry
Tune: Tom Conry; Acc. by T.C. Harvey

Where Charity and Love Prevail 267

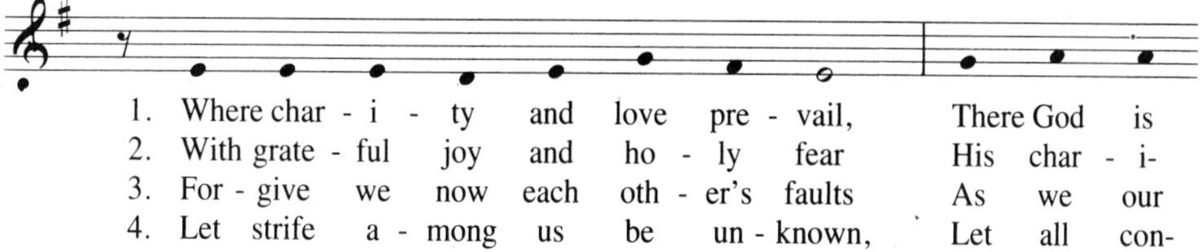
1. Where char - i - ty and love pre - vail, There God is
2. With grate - ful joy and ho - ly fear His char - i-
3. For - give we now each oth - er's faults As we our
4. Let strife a - mong us be un - known, Let all con-

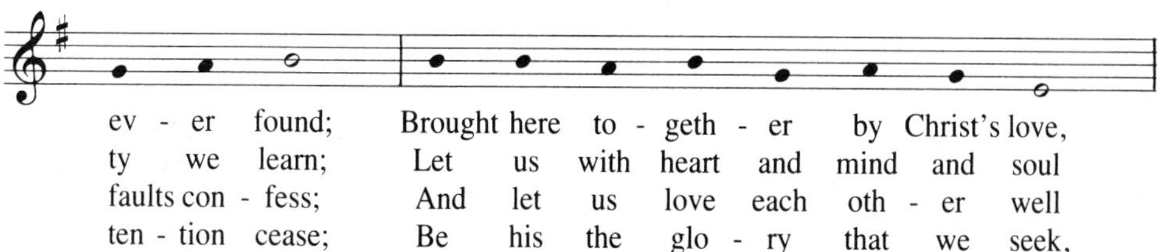
ev - er found; Brought here to - geth - er by Christ's love,
ty we learn; Let us with heart and mind and soul
faults con - fess; And let us love each oth - er well
ten - tion cease; Be his the glo - ry that we seek,

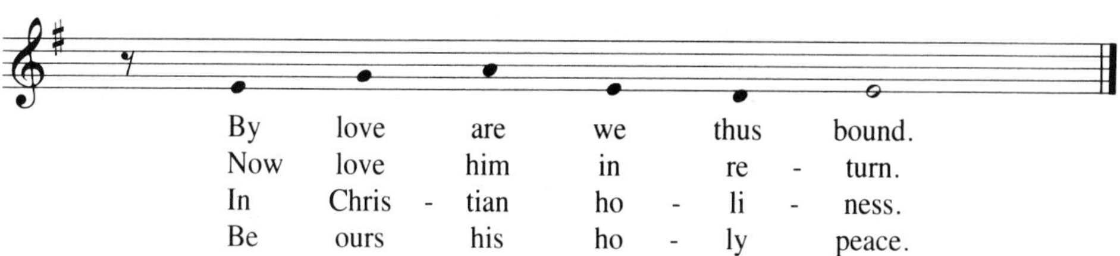
By love are we thus bound.
Now love him in re - turn.
In Chris - tian ho - li - ness.
Be ours his ho - ly peace.

5. Let us recall that in our midst
Dwells God's begotten Son;
As members of his Body joined,
We are in him made one.

6. No race nor creed can love exclude,
If honored be God's name;
Our family embraces all
Whose Father is the same.

Text: *Ubi caritas;* Trans. by Omer Westendorf, b.1916
Tune: CHRISTIAN LOVE, CM; Paul Benoit, OSB, 1893-1979

268 Love One Another

Refrain

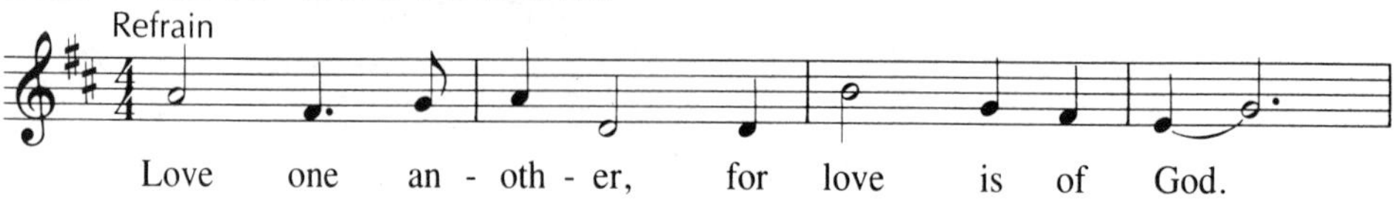
Love one an - oth - er, for love is of God.

Love one an - oth - er, for God is love.

Verses

1. God loved the world so much he sent us his on - ly

D.C.
son, that all who be-lieve in him might have e - ter - nal life.

2. Since God has giv-en his love to us, there-fore let us

love one an - oth - er. If we love one an - oth - er,

D.C.
God will love us, and live in us in per - fect love.

3. Ev - 'ry -one who loves is be - got - ten of God and

LOVE

knows him as the Fa - ther. But they who do not

D.C.

love do not know God, for God is love.

4. Let not your hearts be trou-bled, for love has no room for

D.C.

fear. In love all fear is for - got-ten, for God is here with us.

5. God is love, and they who a - bide in

D.C.
love, a - bide in God, and God in them.

Text: 1 John 4; James J. Chepponis, b.1956
Tune: James J. Chepponis, b.1956

269 No Greater Love

Refrain

There is no great - er love, says the Lord, than to

lay down your life for a friend; there is no great-er love,

no great-er love, than to lay down your life for a friend.

Verses

1. As the Fa-ther has loved me, so I have loved you.

Live on in my love. You will live in my love if you

D.C.
keep my com-mands, ev - en as I have kept my Fa - ther's.

2. All this I tell you that my joy may be yours and

your joy may be com - plete. Love one an - oth - er as

I have loved you: This is my com - mand. *D.C.*

3. You are my friends if you keep my com-mands; no long - er

slaves but friends to me. All I heard from my Fa - ther,

I have made known to you: Now I call you friends. *D.C.*

4. It was not you who chose me, it was I who chose you, chose

you to go forth and bear fruit. Your fruit must en-dure, so

D.C.
you will re - ceive all you ask the Fa-ther in my name.

Text: John 15:9-17; Michael Joncas, b.1951
Tune: Michael Joncas, b.1951

270 God Is Love

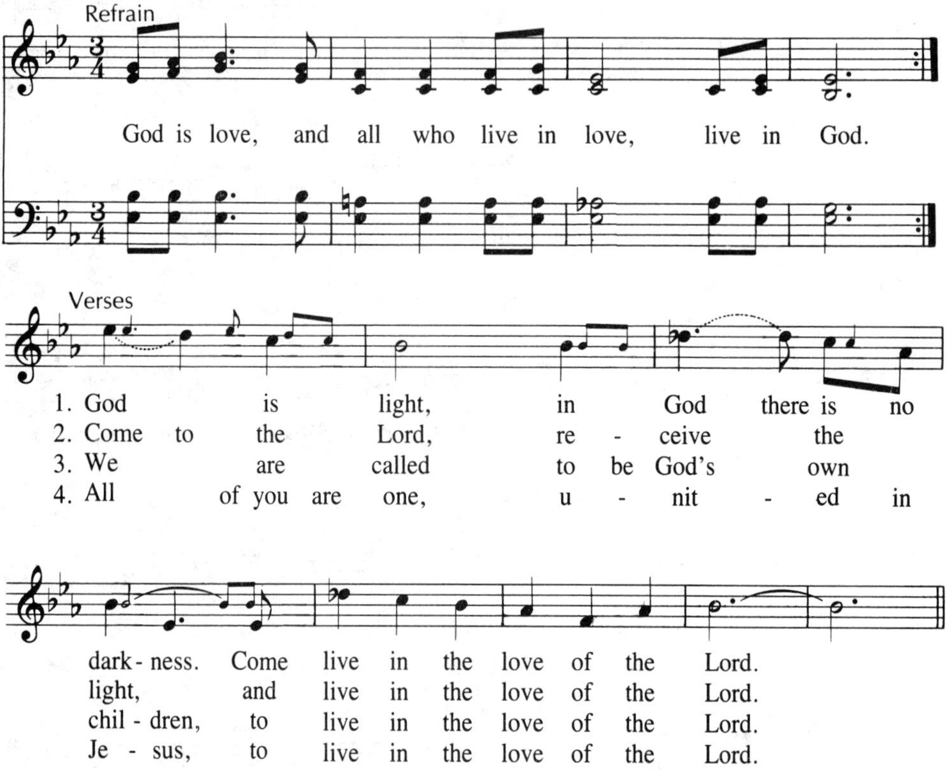

Refrain

God is love, and all who live in love, live in God.

Verses

1. God is light, in God there is no dark-ness. Come live in the love of the Lord.
2. Come to the Lord, re - ceive the light, and live in the love of the Lord.
3. We are called to be God's own chil - dren, to live in the love of the Lord.
4. All of you are one, u - nit - ed in Je - sus, to live in the love of the Lord.

Text: 1 John 1:5, 3:2, 4:15, Psalm 33:6, Galatians 3:28; David Haas, b.1957
Tune: David Haas, b.1957

271 Ubi Caritas

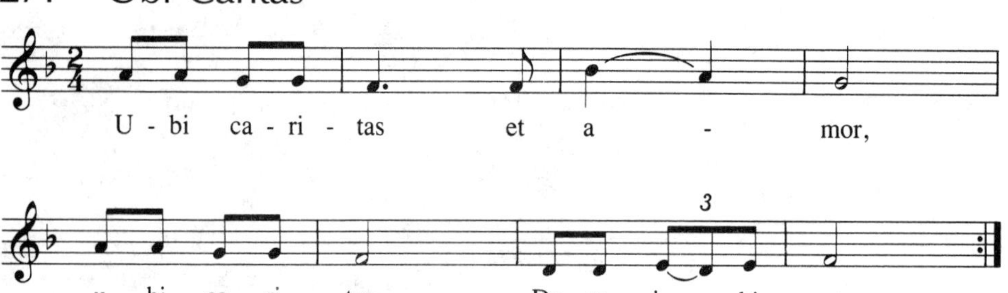
U - bi ca - ri - tas et a - mor,
u - bi ca - ri - tas De - us i - bi est.
3

Text: 1 Corinthians 13:2-8; *Where charity and love are found, God is there;* Taizé Community, 1978
Tune: Jacques Berthier, b.1923

Gift of Love 272

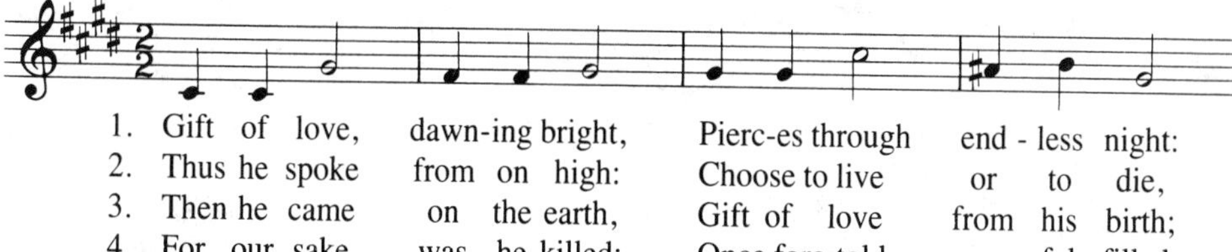
1. Gift of love, dawn-ing bright, Pierc-es through end - less night:
2. Thus he spoke from on high: Choose to live or to die,
3. Then he came on the earth, Gift of love from his birth;
4. For our sake was he killed; Once fore-told, now ful - filled;

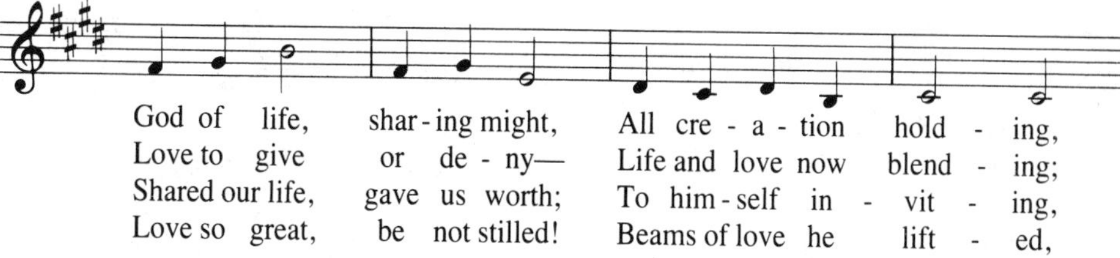
God of life, shar - ing might, All cre - a - tion hold - ing,
Love to give or de - ny— Life and love now blend - ing;
Shared our life, gave us worth; To him - self in - vit - ing,
Love so great, be not stilled! Beams of love he lift - ed,

Earth and sky en - fold - ing.
Love is life un - end - ing.
God with us u - nit - ing.
And with life was gift - ed.
Gift of love, love, love. Gift of

love, love, love. Glo-ry be, Lord, to thee, God of our sal - va - tion.

Text: Robert C. Trupia, © 1980
Tune: PERSONET HODIE, 666 66 with refrain; *Piae cantiones*, Griefswald, 1582; Harm. by Bob Hurd, Paul Ford, Craig Kingsbury, © 1980

273 Not for Tongues of Heaven's Angels

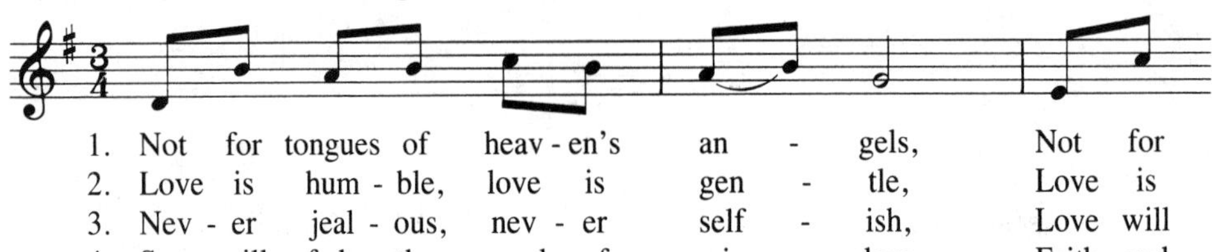
1. Not for tongues of heav - en's an - gels, Not for
2. Love is hum - ble, love is gen - tle, Love is
3. Nev - er jeal - ous, nev - er self - ish, Love will
4. Soon will fade the word of wis - dom, Faith and

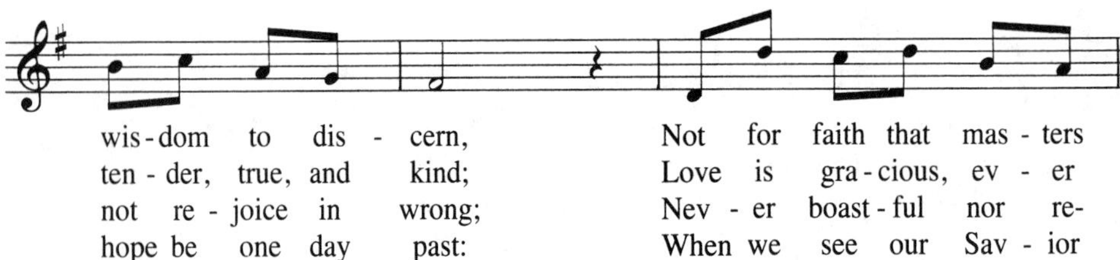
wis - dom to dis - cern, Not for faith that mas - ters
ten - der, true, and kind; Love is gra - cious, ev - er
not re - joice in wrong; Nev - er boast - ful nor re-
hope be one day past: When we see our Sav - ior

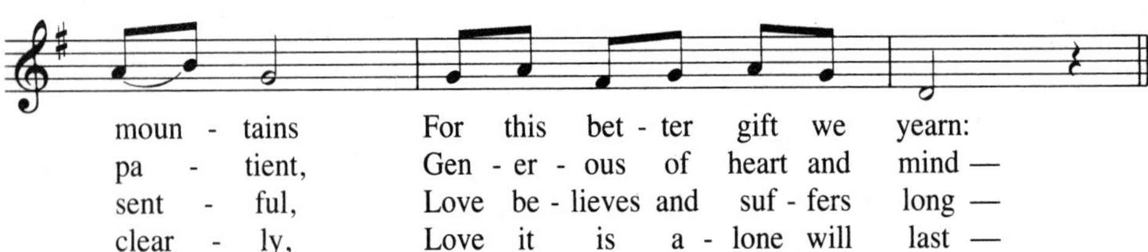
moun - tains For this bet - ter gift we yearn:
pa - tient, Gen - er - ous of heart and mind —
sent - ful, Love be - lieves and suf - fers long —
clear - ly, Love it is a - lone will last —

May love be ours, Lord; may love be

ours. May love be ours, O Lord.

Text: Timothy Dudley-Smith, b.1926, © 1985, Hope Publishing Co.
Tune: COMFORT, 8 7 8 7 6; Michael Joncas, b.1951, © 1988, GIA Publications, Inc.

The Lord Is My Shepherd 274

1. The Lord is my shep - herd, my shield and my
2. If I walk in the val - ley of dark - ness, the
3. Sure - ly good - ness and kind - ness will al - ways pur-
4. The Lord is my shep - herd, green pas - tures, cool
strong-hold, de - fend - ing me sound - ly, re - deem - ing my shame.
shad-ow of death, then no fear will I have, you are there
sue me. My ta - ble is full now; my cup o - ver - flows.
wa - ter: he ten - ders me al - ways, love ev - er the same.
He will an - swer my call 'til the fall of the moun-tains and
with your staff and your rod, O my God, give me com - fort, me
While my head is a - noint - ed the time is ap - point - ed; for-
He will an - swer my call 'til the fall of the moun-tains and
3rd verse only
[ ] cit - ies; he's true to his name.
[ ] com - fort, as al - ways you have.
ev - er I live in the house of the Lord.
[ ] cit - ies; he's true to his name.
Al - le - lu - ia, al - le - lu - ia, the
Lord is my shep-herd and ev - er the same.
Al - le - lu - ia, al - le - lu - ia, the
Lord is my shep-herd; he's true to his name.

Text: Psalm 23; Joe Wise, © 1979
Tune: Joe Wise, © 1979; Acc. by Marty Haugen, b.1950, © 1987, GIA Publications, Inc.

275 Eye Has Not Seen

Refrain
Eye has not seen, ear has not heard what God has
read-y for those who love him; Spir-it of love, come, give us the
To verses
mind of Je-sus, teach us the wis-dom of God.
Coda - after last refrain
Eye has not seen, ear has not heard what God has
read-y for those who love him.
Verses
1. When pain and sor-row weigh us down, be near to us, O
2. Our lives are but a sin-gle breath, we flow-er and we
3. To those who see with eyes of faith, the Lord is ev-er
Lord, for-give the weak-ness of our faith, and
fade, yet all our days are in your hands, so
near, re-flect-ed in the fac-es, of
bear us up with-in your peace-ful word.
we re-turn in love what love has made.
all the poor and low-ly of the world.
D.C.

COMFORT

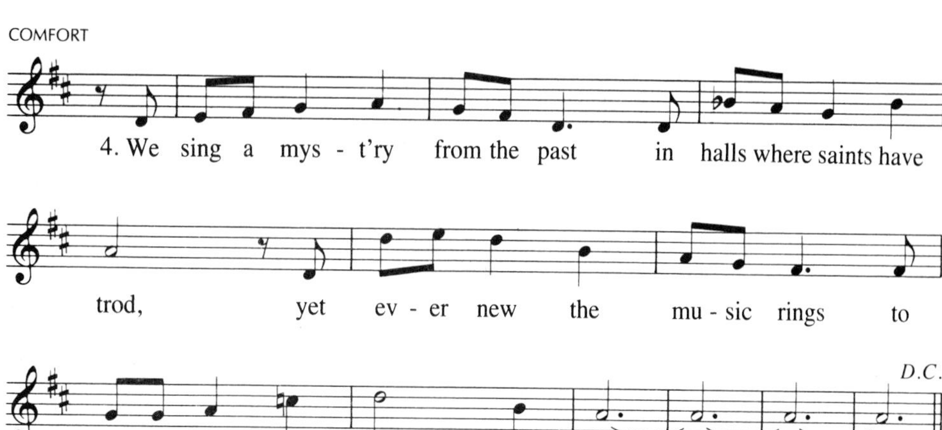

4. We sing a mys - t'ry from the past in halls where saints have
trod, yet ev - er new the mu - sic rings to

Je - sus, Liv - ing Song of God. *D.C.*

Text: 1 Corinthians 2:9-10; Marty Haugen, b.1950
Tune: Marty Haugen, b.1950

Shelter Me, O God 276

Refrain

Shel - ter me, O God; hide me in the shad - ow of your wings. You a - lone are my hope.

Verses

1. When my foes sur - round me, set me high a - bove their reach. Hear me when I call your name.
2. As a moth - er gath - ers her young be - neath her care, gath - er me in - to your arms.
3. Though I walk in dark - ness, through the nee - dle's eye of death, you will nev - er leave my side.

D.C.

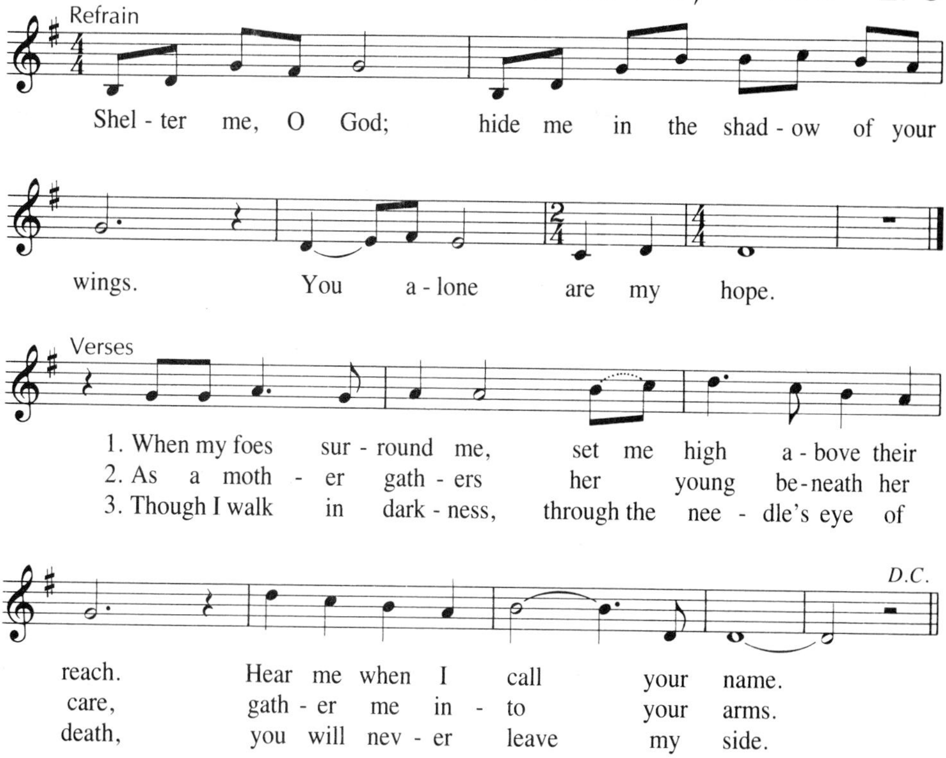

Text: Psalm 16, 61, Luke 13:34; Adapt. by Bob Hurd, © 1984
Tune: Bob Hurd, © 1984; Harm. by Craig S. Kinsbury, © 1984, Oregon Catholic Press

277 You Will Show Me the Path of Life

Refrain
Lord, come show us the path of life, we will

walk ev - er joy - ful, near to your side.

Verses
1. Keep me safe, O Lord, with - out you I am noth-ing,

D.C.
run-ning af - ter shad-ows, fol-low-ing an emp-ty dream.

2. Let us tell the sto - ry of how our God has loved us,

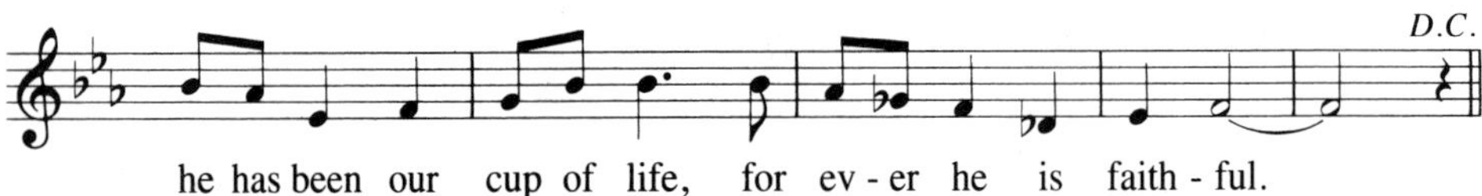
D.C.
he has been our cup of life, for ev - er he is faith - ful.

3. Glo-ry in his coun - sel, the wis-dom of e - ter - ni - ty,

D.C.
lead-ing us through dark - ness, sing-ing in each si - lent heart.

COMFORT

4. I re-joice in you, Lord, your love and light sur - round me;

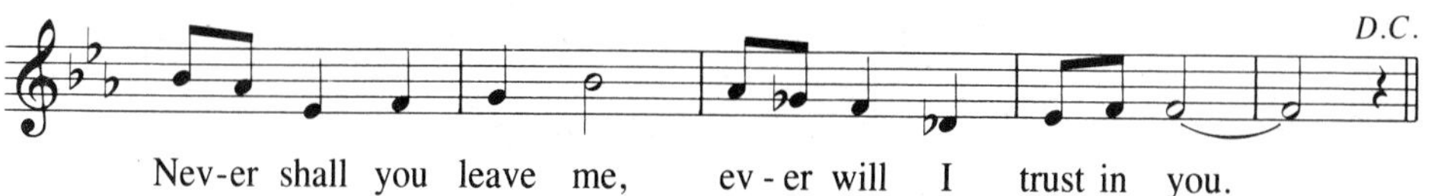
D.C.
Nev-er shall you leave me, ev - er will I trust in you.

Text: Psalm 16; Marty Haugen, b.1950
Tune: Marty Haugen, b.1950

O Christe Domine Jesu 278

3
3
O Chri-ste Do-mi-ne Je - su, O Chri-ste Do-mi-ne Je - su!
3
3

Text: *O Christ, Lord Jesus;* Psalm 23; Taizé Community, 1984
Tune: Jacques Berthier, b.1923

279 Because the Lord is My Shepherd

1. Be - cause the Lord is my shep - herd, I have ev' - ry - thing I need. He lets me rest in the mead - ow and leads me to the qui - et streams. He re - stores my soul and he leads me in the paths that are right:
2. And when the road leads to dark - ness, I shall walk there un - a - fraid. E - ven when death is close I have cour - age for your help is there. You are close be - side me with com - fort, you are guid - ing my way:
3. In love you make me a ban - quet for my en - e - mies to see. You make me wel - come, pour - ing down hon - or from your might-y hand; and this joy fills me with glad - ness, it is too much to bear:
4. Your good-ness al - ways is with me and your mer - cy I know. Your lov - ing kind - ness strength - ens me al - ways as I go through life. I shall dwell in your pres - ence for - ev - er, giv - ing praise to your name:
Lord, you are my shep - herd, you are my friend.
I want to fol - low you al - ways, just to fol - low my friend.

Text: Psalm 23; Christopher Walker
Tune: Christopher Walker

Bring Forth the Kingdom 280

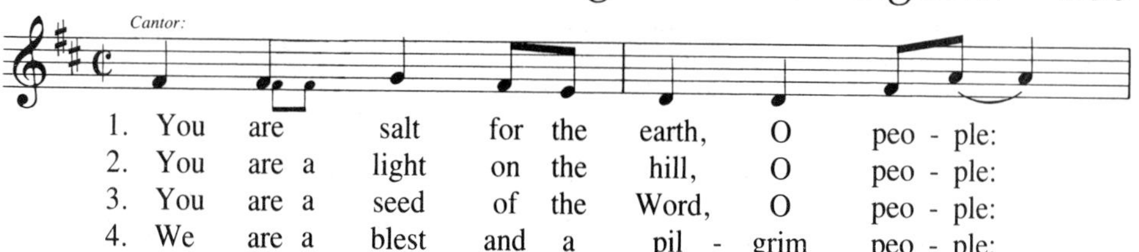
Cantor:
1. You are salt for the earth, O peo - ple:
2. You are a light on the hill, O peo - ple:
3. You are a seed of the Word, O peo - ple:
4. We are a blest and a pil - grim peo - ple:

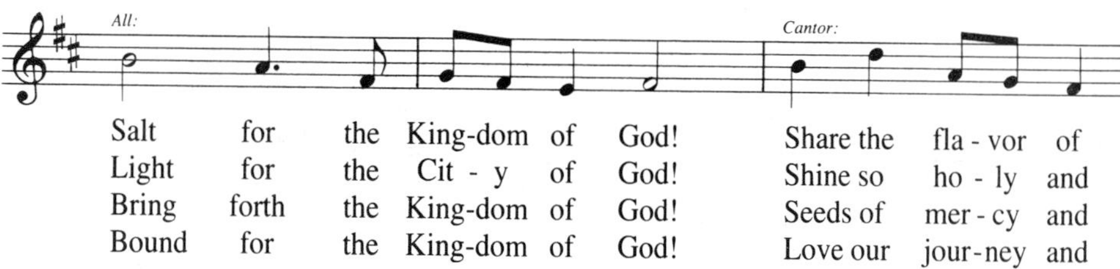
All:
Cantor:
Salt for the King-dom of God! Share the fla - vor of
Light for the Cit - y of God! Shine so ho - ly and
Bring forth the King-dom of God! Seeds of mer - cy and
Bound for the King-dom of God! Love our jour-ney and

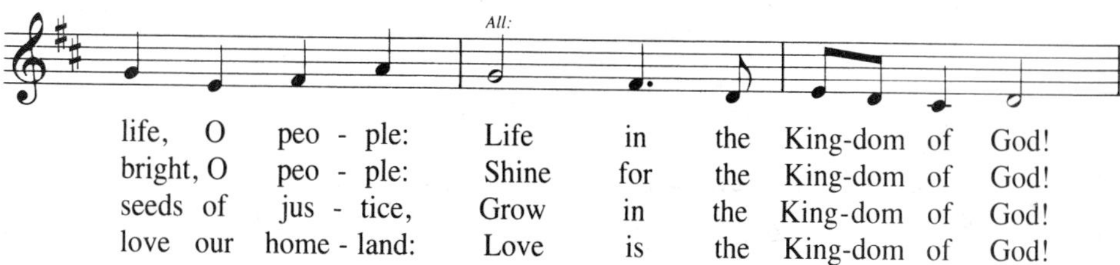
All:
life, O peo - ple: Life in the King-dom of God!
bright, O peo - ple: Shine for the King-dom of God!
seeds of jus - tice, Grow in the King-dom of God!
love our home - land: Love is the King-dom of God!

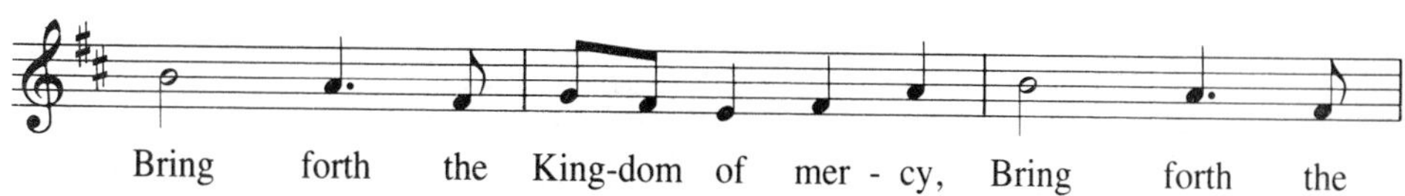
Bring forth the King-dom of mer - cy, Bring forth the

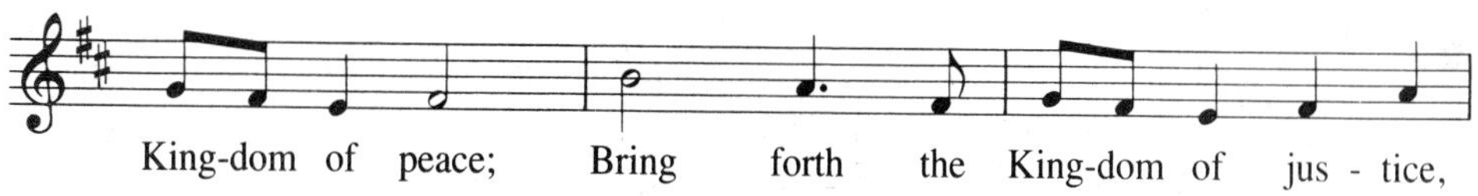
King-dom of peace; Bring forth the King-dom of jus - tice,

Bring forth the Ci - ty of God!

Text: Matthew 5:13-15; Marty Haugen, b.1950
Tune: Marty Haugen, b.1950

281 I Will Not Die

1., 5. I will not die be-fore I've lived to see that land;
3. And I will breathe in that might - y wind of jus - tice;

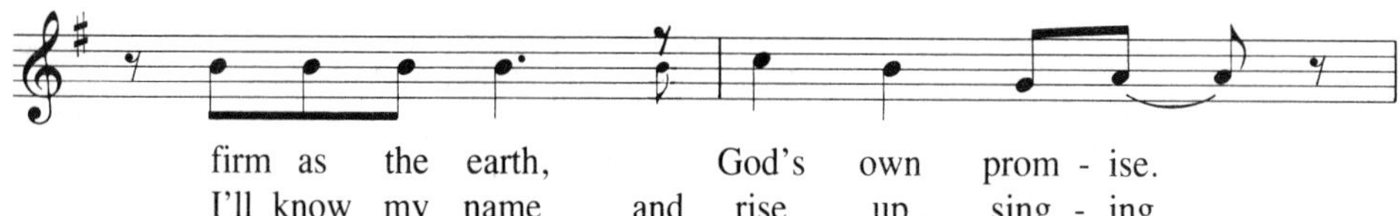

firm as the earth, God's own prom - ise.
I'll know my name and rise up sing - ing.

I'll not let go un - til I've held it in my hand;
And I will call un - til my words bring on the thun - der;

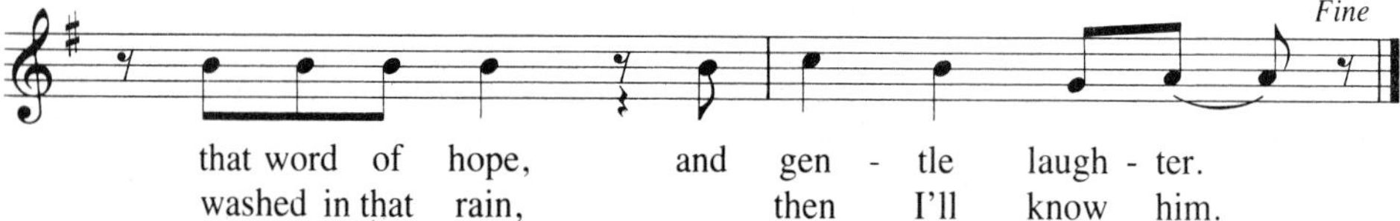

that word of hope, and gen - tle laugh - ter.
washed in that rain, then I'll know him.

2. I will not rest un - til his dawn is in my eyes;
4. He will stand up for the poor and the need - y;

that frag - ile light, new like morn - ing.
he'll break the chains that bind his peo - ple.

I will not sleep be-fore I've wak - ened to that sun - rise;
For he is home for the lost and the des-p'rate;

and all the world knows his glo - ry.
his strong right hand goes be - fore us.

For his right hand has de-

KINGDOM

liv-ered us from death; He has re-gard -ed our tears,
he who is good - ness and grace. grace.
1. D.C.
2. D.C. al fine

Text: Tom Conry
Tune: Tom Conry

282 Singing Songs of Expectation

1. Sing - ing songs of ex - pec - ta - tion, On - ward goes the
2. One the light of God's own pres - ence, O'er his ran - somed
3. One the strain the lips of thou - sands Lift as from the

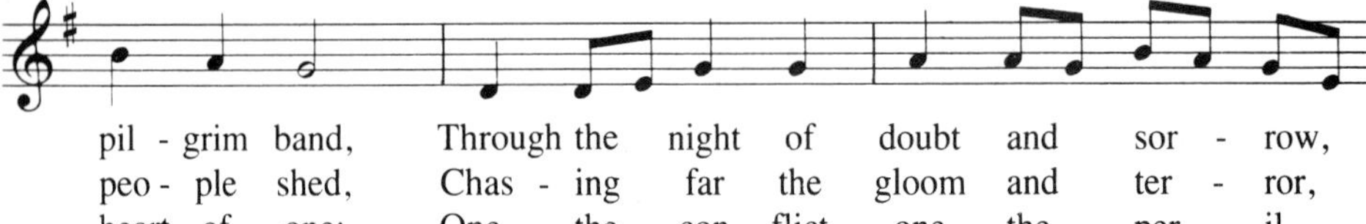

pil - grim band, Through the night of doubt and sor - row,
peo - ple shed, Chas - ing far the gloom and ter - ror,
heart of one; One the con - flict, one the per - il,

March-ing to the prom - ised land. Clear be - fore us
Bright-'ning all the path we tread: One the ob - ject
One the march in God be - gun: One the glad - ness

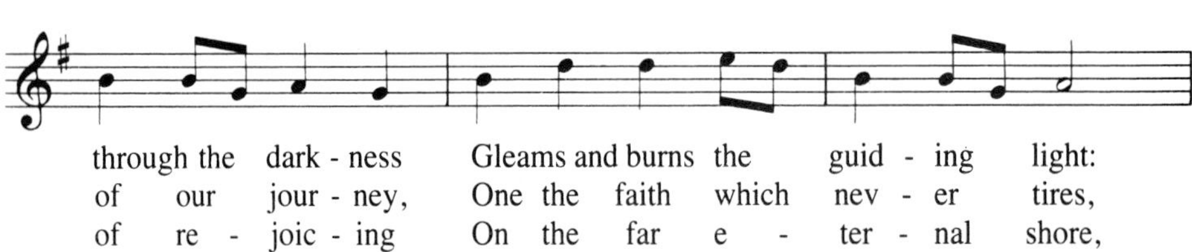

through the dark - ness Gleams and burns the guid - ing light:
of our jour - ney, One the faith which nev - er tires,
of re - joic - ing On the far e - ter - nal shore,

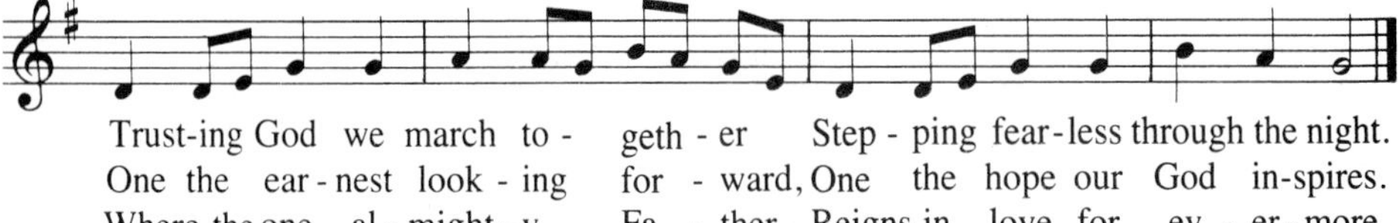

Trust-ing God we march to - geth - er Step - ping fear-less through the night.
One the ear - nest look - ing for - ward, One the hope our God in-spires.
Where the one al - might - y Fa - ther Reigns in love for ev - er - more.

Text: Bernard Severin Ingeman, 1798-1862; Trans. by Sabin Baring-Gould, 1834-1924, alt.
Tune: HOLY MANNA, 87 87 D; William Moore, fl. 1830; Acc. by Marty Haugen, b.1950,

Renew Your People 283

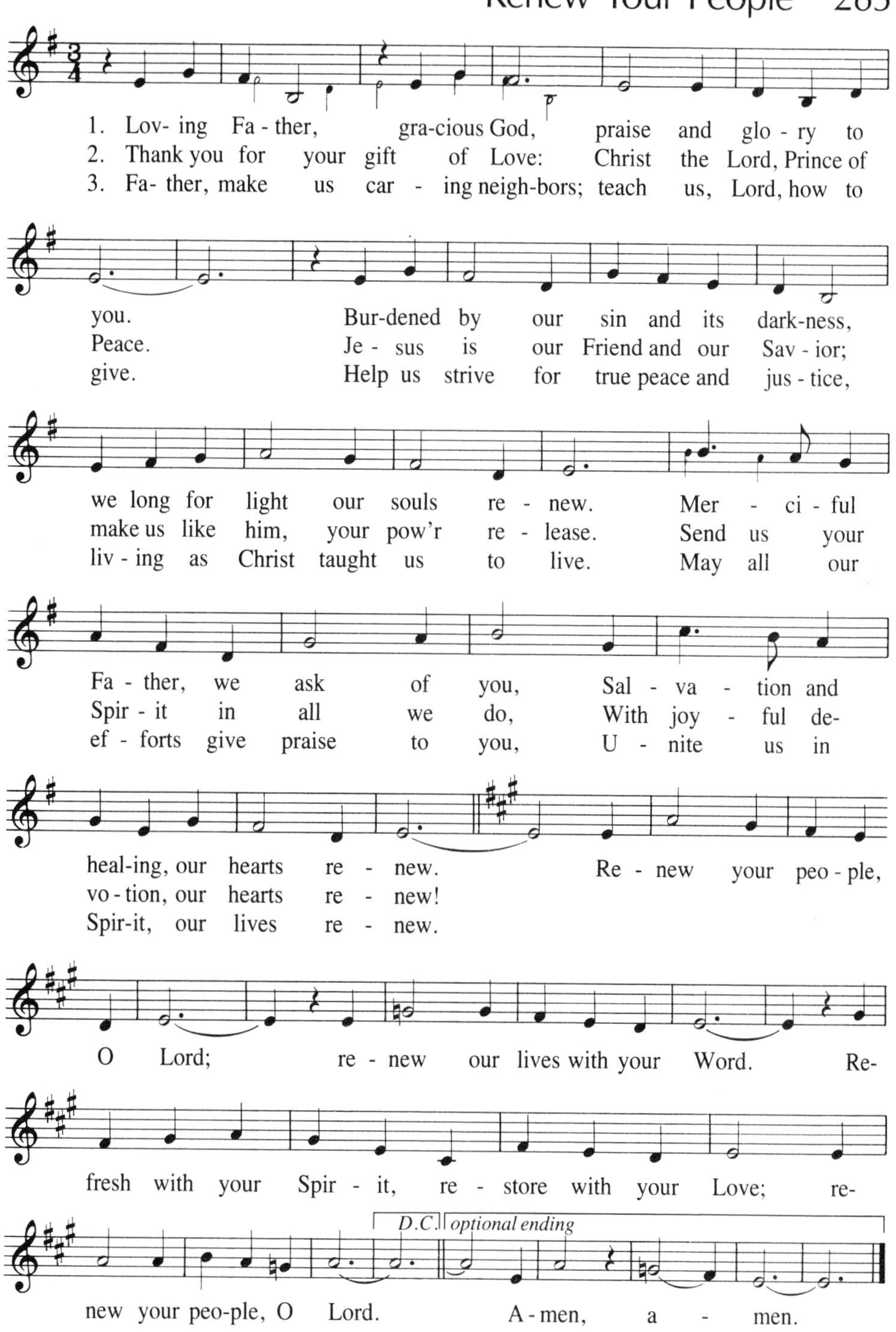
1. Lov- ing Fa - ther, gra-cious God, praise and glo - ry to
2. Thank you for your gift of Love: Christ the Lord, Prince of
3. Fa- ther, make us car - ing neigh-bors; teach us, Lord, how to
you. Bur-dened by our sin and its dark-ness,
Peace. Je - sus is our Friend and our Sav - ior;
give. Help us strive for true peace and jus - tice,
we long for light our souls re - new. Mer - ci - ful
make us like him, your pow'r re - lease. Send us your
liv - ing as Christ taught us to live. May all our
Fa - ther, we ask of you, Sal - va - tion and
Spir - it in all we do, With joy - ful de-
ef - forts give praise to you, U - nite us in
heal-ing, our hearts re - new. Re - new your peo - ple,
vo - tion, our hearts re - new!
Spir-it, our lives re - new.
O Lord; re - new our lives with your Word. Re-
fresh with your Spir - it, re - store with your Love; re-
new your peo-ple, O Lord. A - men, a - men.
D.C.
optional ending

Text: Lucia Welch
Tune: Randolph N. Currie, b.1943

284 Blest Are They

1. Blest are they, the poor in spir - it, theirs is the
king - dom of God. Blest are they,
full of sor - row, they shall be con - soled.
Refrain
Re - joice and be glad! Bless - ed are
you, ho - ly are you! Re - joice and be
glad! Yours is the king-dom of God!
2. Blest are they, the low - ly ones, they shall in-
3. Blest are they who show mer - cy, mer - cy
her - it the earth. Blest are they who
shall be theirs. Blest are they, the

D.S.

hun-ger and thirst, they shall have their fill.
pure of heart, they shall see God!

4. Blest are they who seek peace; they are the
5. Blest are you who suf - fer hate, all be-

chil-dren of God. Blest are they who
cause of me. Re-joice and be glad,

D.S.

suf-fer in faith, the glo-ry of God is theirs.
yours is the king-dom; shine for all to see.

Text: Matthew 5:3-12; David Haas, b.1957
Tune: David Haas, b.1957; Vocal arr. by David Haas, b.1957, Michael Joncas, b.1951

The Servant Song 285

1., 6. Will you let me be your ser-vant, Let me be as Christ to you;
2. We are pil-grims on a jour-ney, We are trav-'lers on the road;
3. I will hold the Christ-light for you In the night-time of your fear;
4. I will weep when you are weep-ing; When you laugh I'll laugh with you.
5. When we sing to God in heav-en We shall find such har-mo-ny,
Pray that I may have the grace to Let you be my ser - vant, too.
We are here to help each oth-er Walk the mile and bear the load.
I will hold my hand out to you, Speak the peace you long to hear.
I will share your joy and sor-row 'Til we've seen this jour - ney through.
Born of all we've known to-geth-er Of Christ's love and ag - o - ny.

Text: Richard Gillard
Tune: Richard Gillard; Harm. by Betty Pulkingham, b.1929

286 I Bind My Heart

1. I bind my heart this tide to the Gal - i - le - an's side, to the

wounds of Cal - va - ry to the Christ who died for me.

2. I bind my soul this day to the broth - er far a - way to the

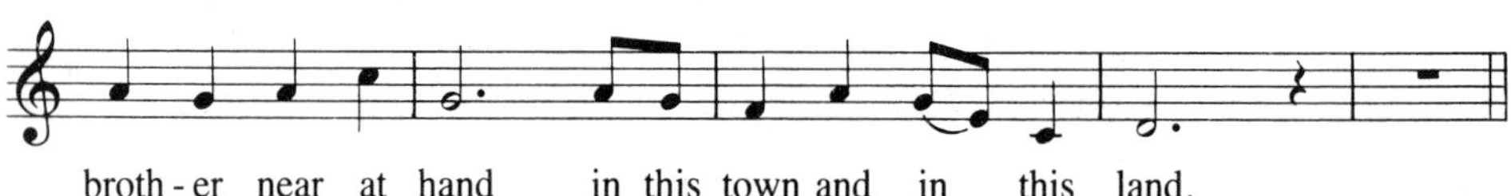

broth - er near at hand in this town and in this land.

3. I bind my heart in thrall to the God, the Lord of all, to the

God the poor one's friend, and the Christ whom he did send.

4. I bind my - self to peace, to make strife and en - vy cease; O

God, knit thou sure the cord of my thrall-dom to my Lord.

Text: "Thraldom", *The Tryst,* 1907, Lauchlan McLean Watt, 1853-1931
Tune: Suzanne Toolan, SM, b.1927,

Glorious in Majesty 287

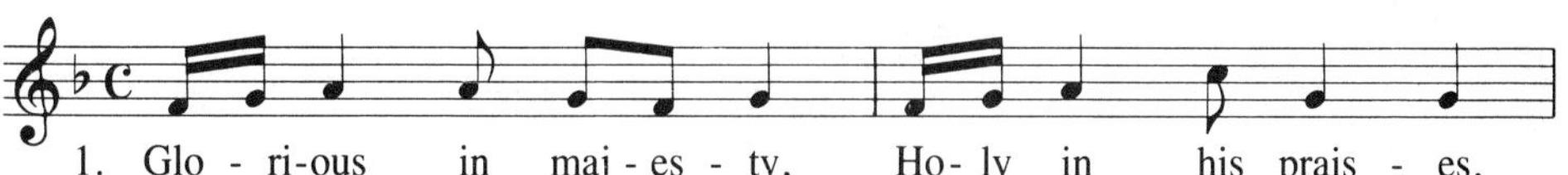

1. Glo - ri-ous in maj - es - ty, Ho- ly in his prais - es,
2. Vic - to - ry he won for us, Free-ing us from dark - ness,
3. One in love, as fam - i - ly, Liv - ing with each oth - er,

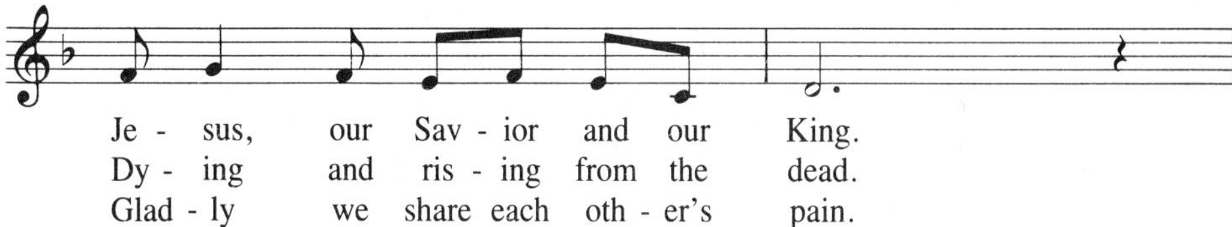

Je - sus, our Sav - ior and our King.
Dy - ing and ris - ing from the dead.
Glad - ly we share each oth - er's pain.

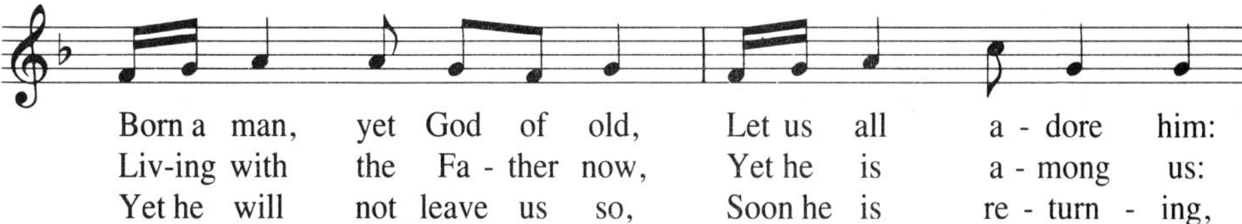

Born a man, yet God of old, Let us all a - dore him:
Liv-ing with the Fa - ther now, Yet he is a - mong us:
Yet he will not leave us so, Soon he is re - turn - ing,

Filled with his Spir - it let us sing.
We are the bod - y, he the head.
Tak - ing us back with him to reign.

Liv - ing is to love him, Serv - ing him to know his free - dom.

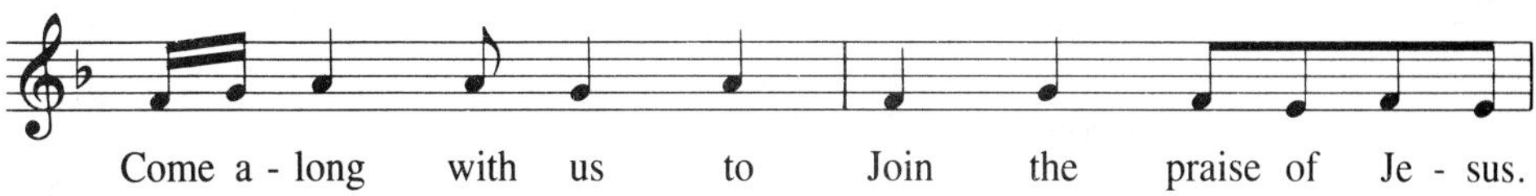

Come a - long with us to Join the praise of Je - sus.

Come to Je - sus now, Go to live his word re - joic - ing.

Text: Jeff Cothran, fl.1972
Tune: SHIBBOLET BASADEH, 7 6 7 8 D with refrain; Jewish Melody; Harm. by Jeff Cothran, fl. 1972

288 Come, My Children

Refrain

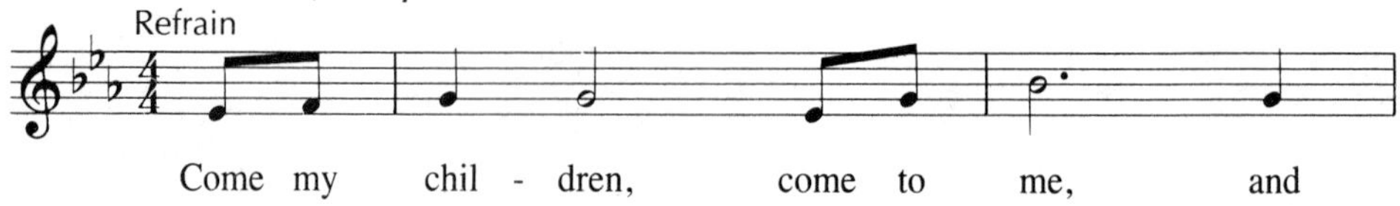
Come my chil - dren, come to me, and

you will know the fear of the Lord

Verses

1. I will bless the Lord at all times,
God's song is always on my lips.
In the Lord my soul shall make its boast,
the humble will hear and be glad.

2. Glory in the Lord with me,
may God's name always be our joy!
God answered me when I cried,
and freed me from all my fear.

3. Look to God and shine with joy!
May God free your faces from all shame!
God hears the cry of the poor
and saves all who live in their fear.

Text: Psalm 34; David Haas, b.1957
Tune: David Haas, b.1957

The Song of All Seed 289

1. To live on earth like gods, like lords and mas - ters,
2. You walk the way of ev - 'ry earth - ly crea - ture,
3. A - ban - doned to the sun and to the rain - fall,
4. We peo - ple have to die for one an - oth - er,
5. For so our God has shown him - self to be,

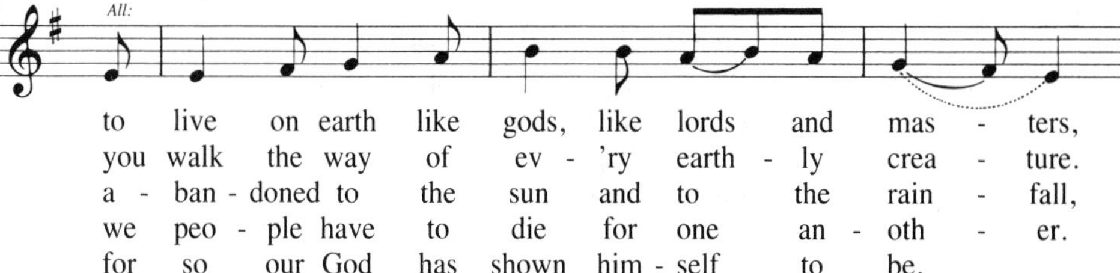

to live on earth like gods, like lords and mas - ters,
you walk the way of ev - 'ry earth - ly crea - ture.
a - ban - doned to the sun and to the rain - fall,
we peo - ple have to die for one an - oth - er.
for so our God has shown him - self to be,

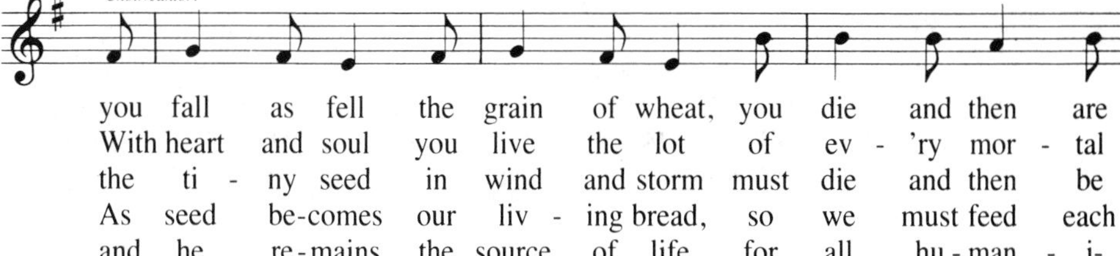

you fall as fell the grain of wheat, you die and then are
With heart and soul you live the lot of ev - 'ry mor - tal
the ti - ny seed in wind and storm must die and then be
As seed be-comes our liv - ing bread, so we must feed each
and he re-mains the source of life for all hu - man - i-

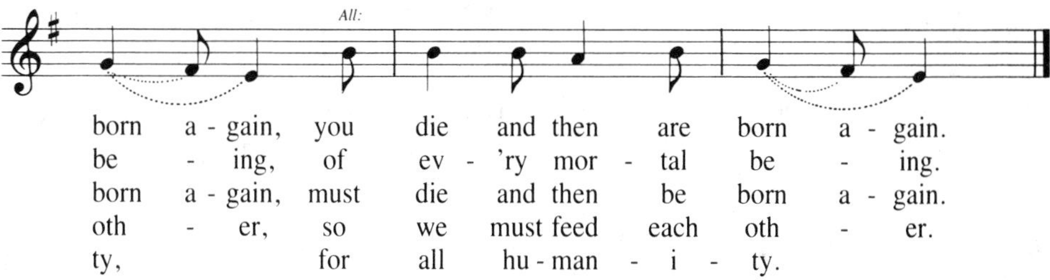

born a - gain, you die and then are born a - gain.
be - ing, of ev - 'ry mor - tal be - ing.
born a - gain, must die and then be born a - gain.
oth - er, so we must feed each oth - er.
ty, for all hu - man - i - ty.

Text: Huub Oosterhuis, b.1933; Trans. by F. Ingram, Rev. by Redmond McGoldrick
Tune: Dutch Traditional; Harm. by A. Oomen

290 Good Friday Hymn

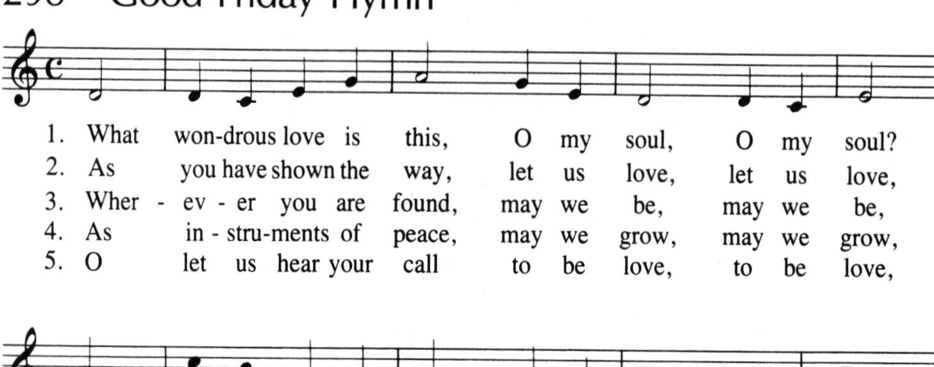
1. What won-drous love is this, O my soul, O my soul?
2. As you have shown the way, let us love, let us love,
3. Wher - ev - er you are found, may we be, may we be,
4. As in - stru-ments of peace, may we grow, may we grow,
5. O let us hear your call to be love, to be love,

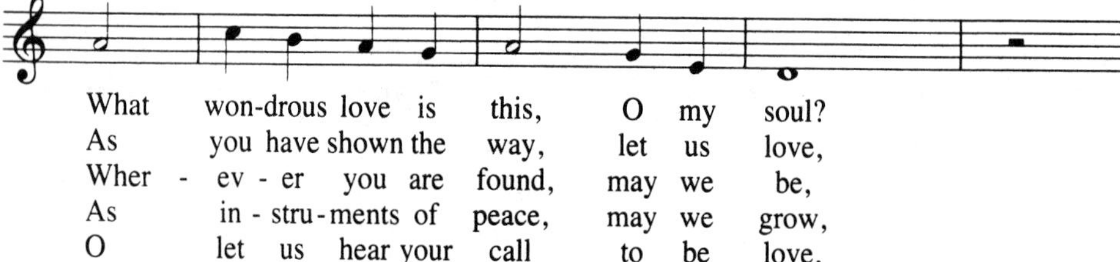
What won-drous love is this, O my soul?
As you have shown the way, let us love,
Wher - ev - er you are found, may we be,
As in - stru-ments of peace, may we grow,
O let us hear your call to be love,

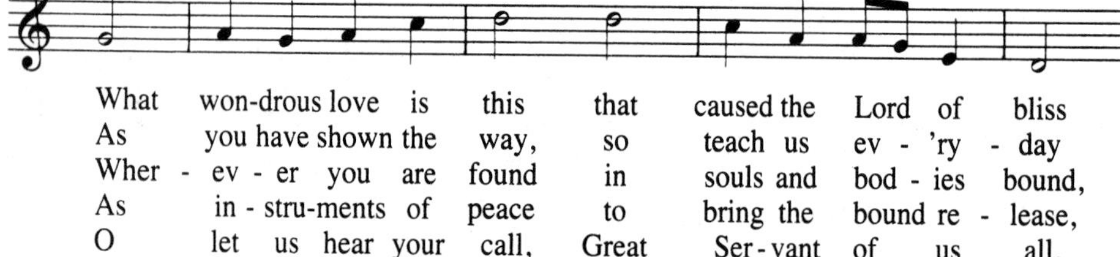
What won-drous love is this that caused the Lord of bliss
As you have shown the way, so teach us ev - 'ry - day
Wher - ev - er you are found in souls and bod - ies bound,
As in - stru-ments of peace to bring the bound re - lease,
O let us hear your call, Great Ser-vant of us all,

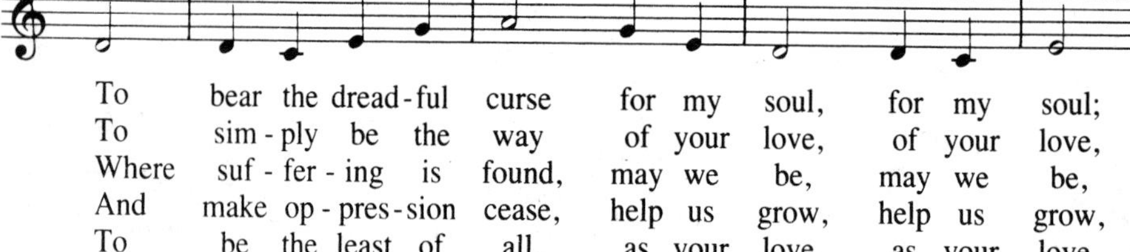
To bear the dread-ful curse for my soul, for my soul;
To sim - ply be the way of your love, of your love,
Where suf - fer - ing is found, may we be, may we be,
And make op - pres - sion cease, help us grow, help us grow,
To be the least of all, as your love, as your love,

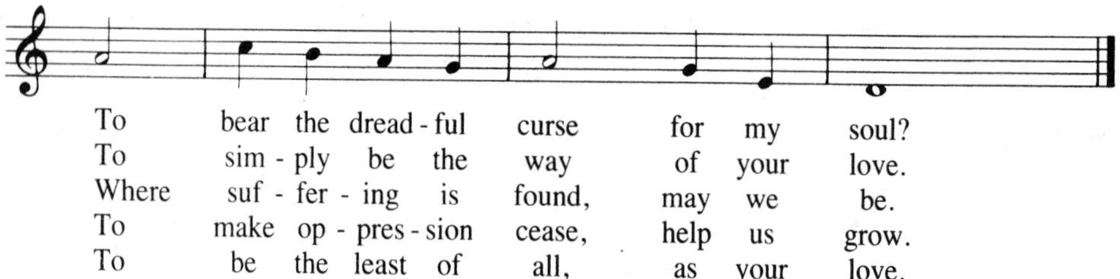
To bear the dread - ful curse for my soul?
To sim - ply be the way of your love.
Where suf - fer - ing is found, may we be.
To make op - pres - sion cease, help us grow.
To be the least of all, as your love.

Text: St. 1, Alexander Means, 1801-1853; St. 2-5, Marty Haugen, b.1950, © 1987, GIA Publications, Inc.
Tune: WONDROUS LOVE, 12 9 12 12 9; *Southern Harmony*, 1835; Acc. by Marty Haugen, b.1950, © 1987, GIA Publications, Inc.

Here I Am, Lord 291

1. I, the Lord of sea and sky, I have heard my people cry. All who dwell in dark and sin My hand will save. I who made the stars of night, I will make their darkness bright. Who will bear my light to them? Whom shall I send?

2. I, the Lord of snow and rain, I have borne my people's pain. I have wept for love of them. They turn away. I will break their hearts of stone, Give them hearts for love alone. I will speak my word to them. Whom shall I send?

3. I, the Lord of wind and flame, I will tend the poor and lame. I will set a feast for them. My hand will save. Finest bread I will provide Till their hearts be satisfied. I will give my life to them. Whom shall I send?

Here I am, Lord. Is it I, Lord? I have heard you calling in the night. I will go, Lord, if you lead me. I will hold your people in my heart.

Text: Isaiah 6; Dan Schutte
Tune: Dan Schutte; Arr. by Michael Pope, SJ, John Weissrock

292 He Has Anointed Me

1. To bring glad tid - ings to the low - ly, to
heal the bro - ken heart, he has a-
noint - ed me. To pro-claim lib - er - ty to
cap - tives, re - lease to pris - on - ers,
he has a - noint - ed me.
Refrain
The Spir - it of God is up-
on me, he has a-
noint - ed me.

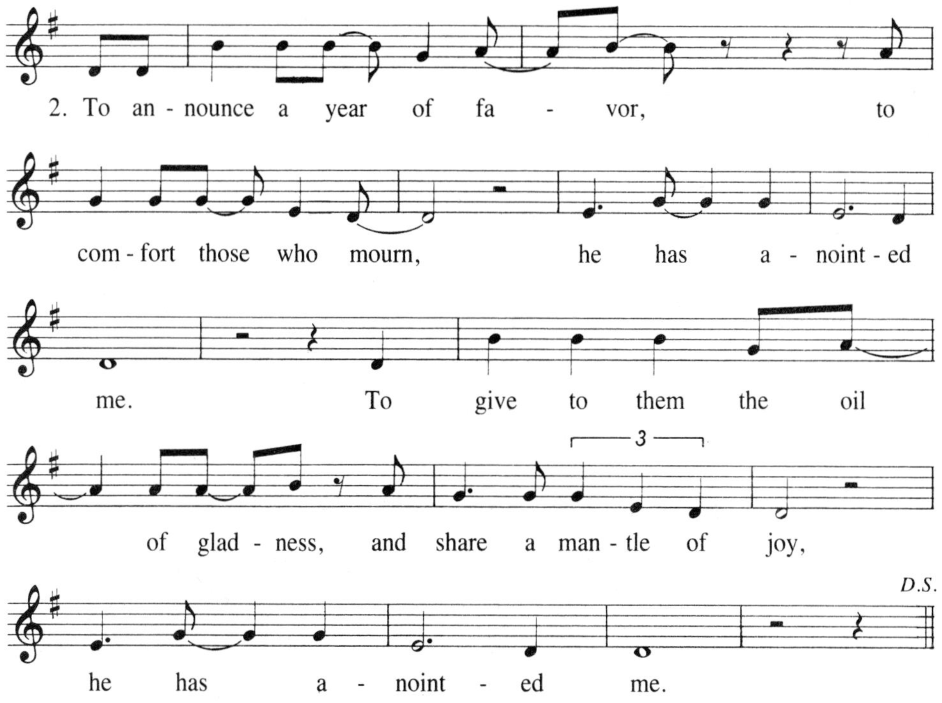

2. To an - nounce a year of fa - vor, to com - fort those who mourn, he has a - noint - ed me. To give to them the oil of glad - ness, and share a man - tle of joy, he has a - noint - ed me.

D.S.

Text: Mike Balhoff, Gary Daigle, Darryl Ducote
Tune: Mike Balhoff, Gary Daigle, Darryl Ducote; Acc. by Gary Daigle

Send Me, Jesus (Thuma Mina) 293

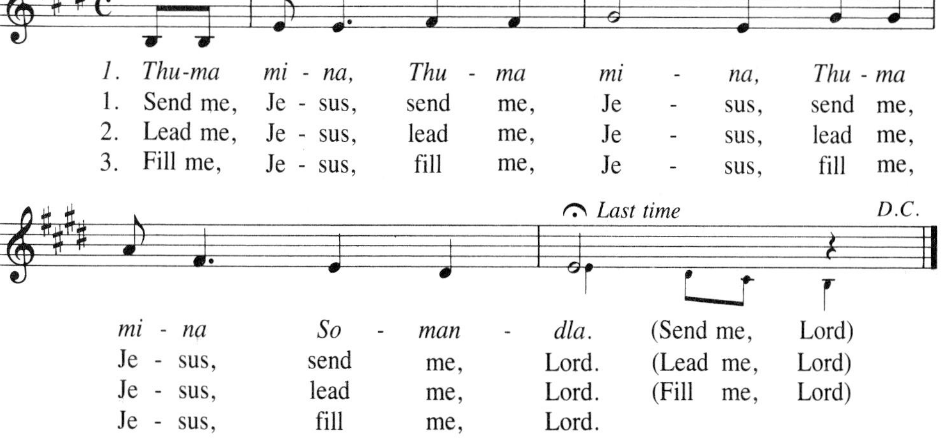
1. Thu-ma mi - na, Thu - ma mi - na, Thu - ma mi - na So - man - dla.
1. Send me, Je - sus, send me, Je - sus, send me, Je - sus, send me, Lord.
2. Lead me, Je - sus, lead me, Je - sus, lead me, Je - sus, lead me, Lord.
3. Fill me, Je - sus, fill me, Je - sus, fill me, Je - sus, fill me, Lord.
(Send me, Lord)
(Lead me, Lord)
(Fill me, Lord)
Last time
D.C.

Text: South African
Tune: THUMA MINA, South African

294 City of God

1. A-wake from your slum-ber! A-rise from your sleep!
2. We are sons of the morn-ing; we are daugh-ters of day.

A new day is dawn-ing for all those who weep.
The One who has loved us has bright-ened our way.

The peo-ple in dark-ness have seen a great light.
The Lord of all kind-ness has called us to be

The Lord of our long-ing has con-quered the night.
a light for his peo-ple to set their hearts free.

𝄋 Refrain

Let us build the cit-y of God. May our tears be turned in-to danc-ing! For the Lord our light and our love, has turned the night in-to day!

3. God is light; in him there is no

dark-ness. Let us walk in his light, his
chil - dren, one and all.
O com-fort my peo - ple; make gen-tle your words.
D.S.
Pro-claim to my cit - y the day of her birth.
4. O cit - y of glad - ness, now lift up your
voice! Pro - claim the good ti - dings
D.S.
that all may re - joice!

Text: Dan Schutte
Tune: Dan Schutte; Acc. by John Weissrock

295 The Love of the Lord

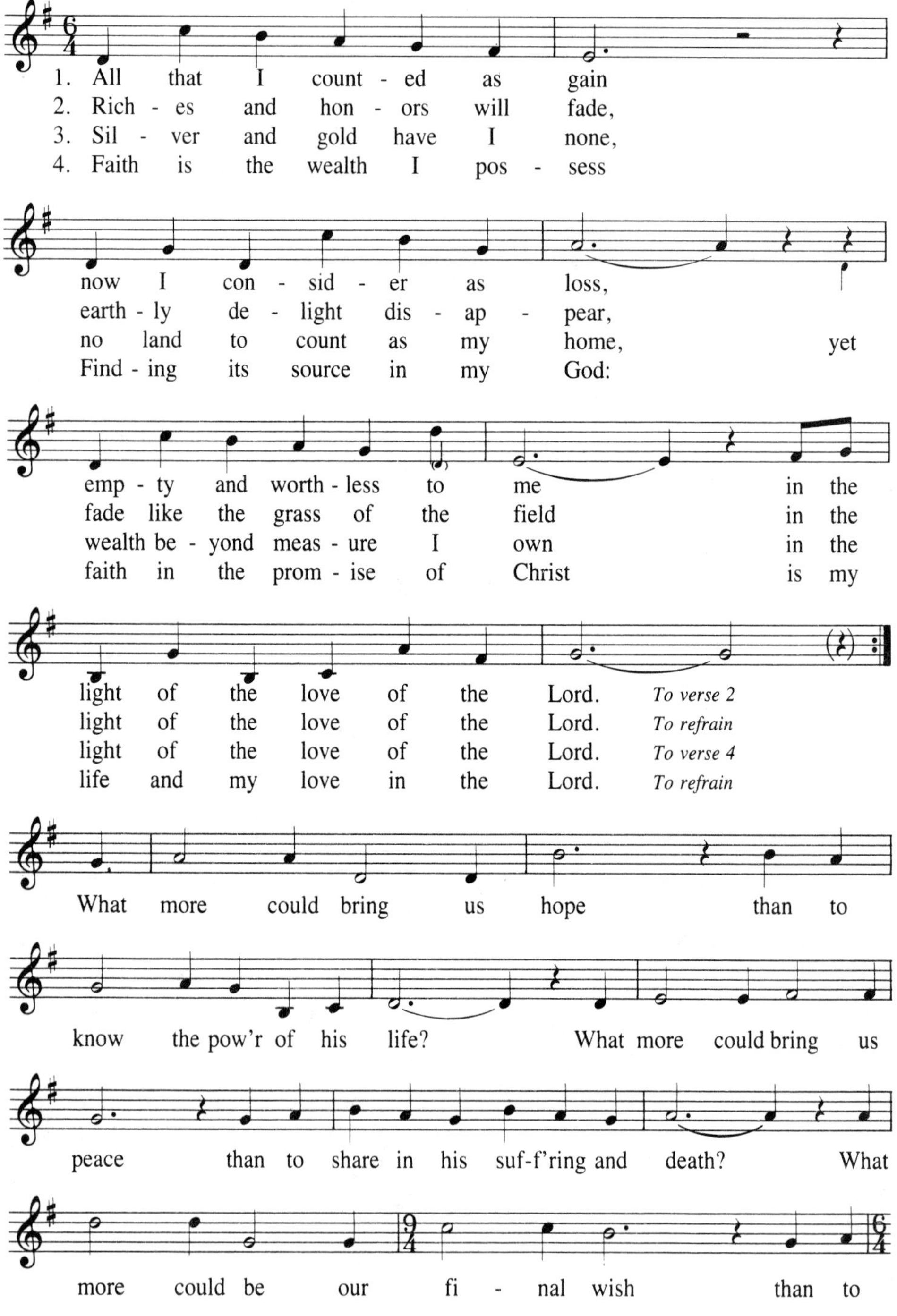
1. All that I count - ed as gain now I con - sid - er as loss, emp - ty and worth - less to me in the light of the love of the Lord. To verse 2
2. Rich - es and hon - ors will fade, earth - ly de - light dis - ap - pear, fade like the grass of the field in the light of the love of the Lord. To refrain
3. Sil - ver and gold have I none, no land to count as my home, yet wealth be - yond meas - ure I own in the light of the love of the Lord. To verse 4
4. Faith is the wealth I pos - sess Find - ing its source in my God: faith in the prom - ise of Christ is my life and my love in the Lord. To refrain
What more could bring us hope than to know the pow'r of his life? What more could bring us peace than to share in his suf-f'ring and death? What more could be our fi - nal wish than to

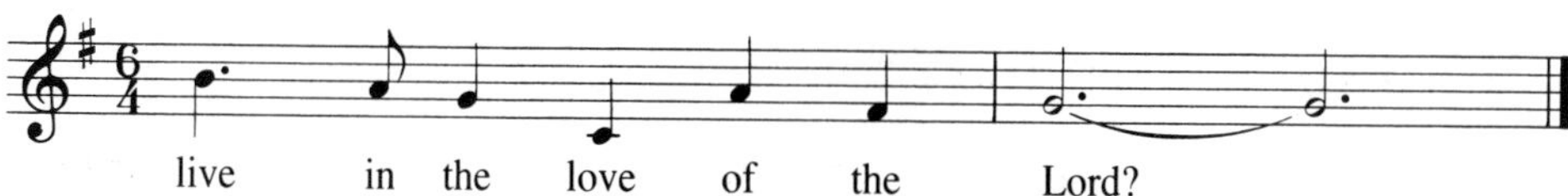
live in the love of the Lord?

Text: Philippians 3:7-11; Michael Joncas, b.1951
Tune: Michael Joncas, b.1950

We Have Been Told 296

Refrain

We have been told, we've seen his face, and heard his voice a-
live in our hearts; "Live in my love with all your heart,
as the Fa-ther has loved me, so I have loved you."

Verses

1. "I am the vine, you are the branch-es, and
all who live in me will bear great fruit." *D.C.*

2. "You are my friends, if you keep my com-mands,
no long-er slaves, I call you friends." *D.C.*

3. "No great-er love is there than this: to
lay down one's life, for a friend."

Text: David Haas, b.1957
Tune: David Haas, b.1957; Vocal arr. by David Haas, b.1957, Marty Haugen, b.1950

297 I Danced in the Morning

1. I danced in the
2. I danced for the
3. I danced on the
4. I danced on a
5. They cut me

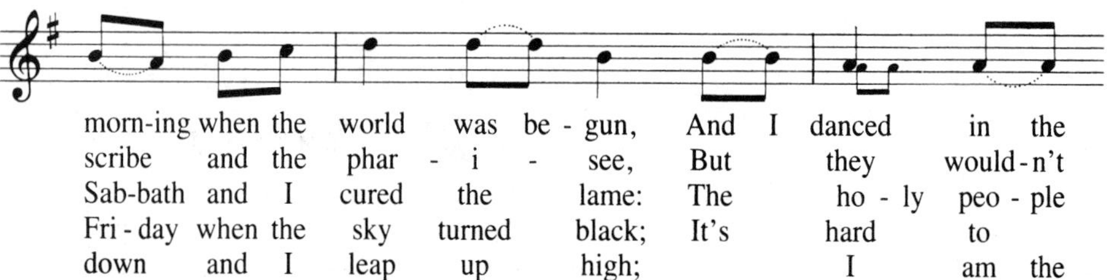
morn-ing when the world was be - gun, And I danced in the
scribe and the phar - i - see, But they would - n't
Sab-bath and I cured the lame: The ho - ly peo - ple
Fri - day when the sky turned black; It's hard to
down and I leap up high; I am the

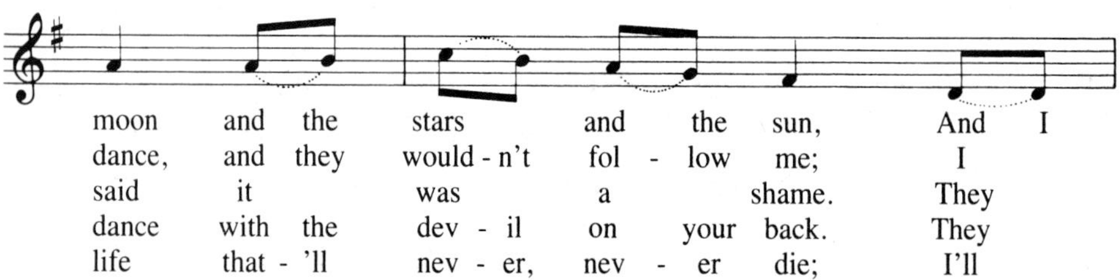
moon and the stars and the sun, And I
dance, and they would - n't fol - low me; I
said it was a shame. They
dance with the dev - il on your back. They
life that - 'll nev - er, nev - er die; I'll

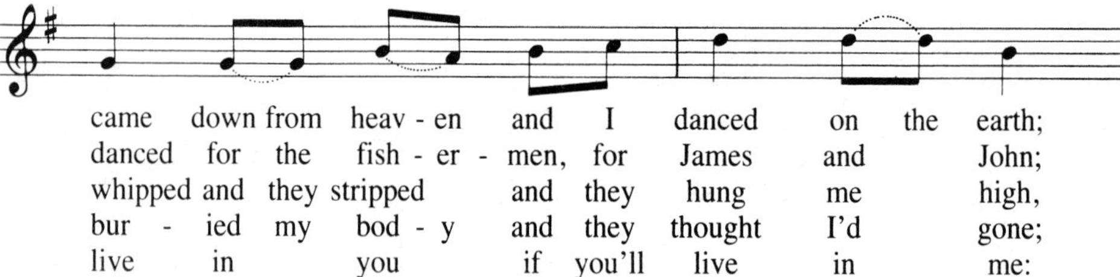
came down from heav - en and I danced on the earth;
danced for the fish - er - men, for James and John;
whipped and they stripped and they hung me high,
bur - ied my bod - y and they thought I'd gone;
live in you if you'll live in me:

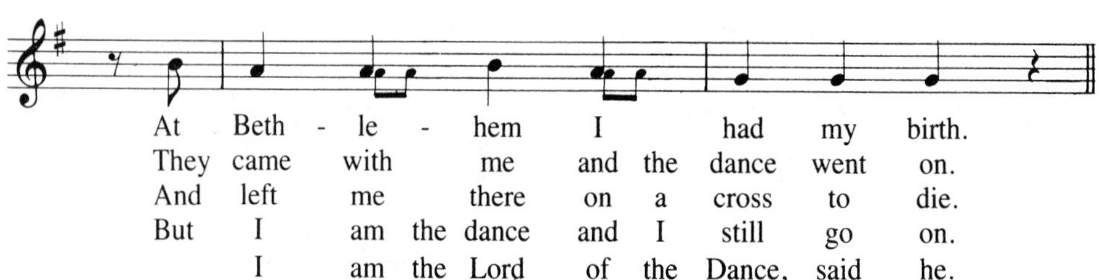
At Beth - le - hem I had my birth.
They came with me and the dance went on.
And left me there on a cross to die.
But I am the dance and I still go on.
I am the Lord of the Dance, said he.

Dance then wher - ev - er you may be; I am the Lord of the

Dance, said he, And I'll lead you all, wher - ev - er you may be,

1.-4.
5.
And I'll lead you all in the dance, said he. dance, said he.

Text: Sydney Carter, b.1915,
Tune: SHAKER SONG, Irregular; American Shaker; Harm. by Sydney Carter, b.1915,

298 Anthem

Refrain

We are called, we are cho-sen. We are Christ for one an - oth - er.

We are prom-ised to to - mor-row, while we are for him to - day.

We are sign, we are won-der. We are sow - er, we are seed.

To verses

We are har - vest, we are hun-gry. We are ques-tion, we are creed.

Last time

ques-tion, we are creed.

Verses

1. Then where can we stand jus - ti-fied? In what can we be - lieve? In no one else but he who suf - fered, noth - ing more than he who rose Who was jus - tice for the poor.
2. Then how are we to stand at all, this world of bend - ed knee? In noth - ing more than bar - ren shad-ows. No one else but he could save us. Who was jus - tice for the poor.
3. Then shall we not stand emp - ty at the al - tar of our dreams? When He prom - ised us our - selves. Who mark time a - gainst to - mor - row. Who are jus - tice for the poor.

Who was rage a - gainst the night. Who was
Who was rage a - gainst the night. Who was
Who are rage a - gainst the night. Who are
1.,2. D.C.
3. D.C.
hope for peace-ful peo - ple. Who was light.
hope for peace-ful peo - ple. Who was light.
hope for peace-ful peo - ple. Who are light.

Text: Tom Conry
Tune: Tom Conry; Arr. by Michael Joncas

299 Now We Remain

Refrain

We hold the death of the Lord deep in our hearts.

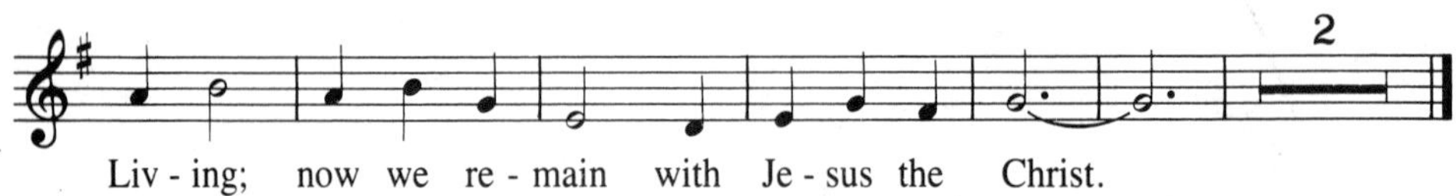
2
Liv - ing; now we re - main with Je - sus the Christ.

Verses

1. Once we were peo - ple a - fraid, lost in the night.
2. Some-thing which we have known, some-thing we've touched,
3. He chose to give of him - self, be - came our bread.
4. We are the pres - ence of God; this is our call.

Then by your cross we were saved; dead be - came
what we have seen with our eyes: this we have
Bro - ken, that we might live. Love be - yond
Now to be - come bread and wine: food for the

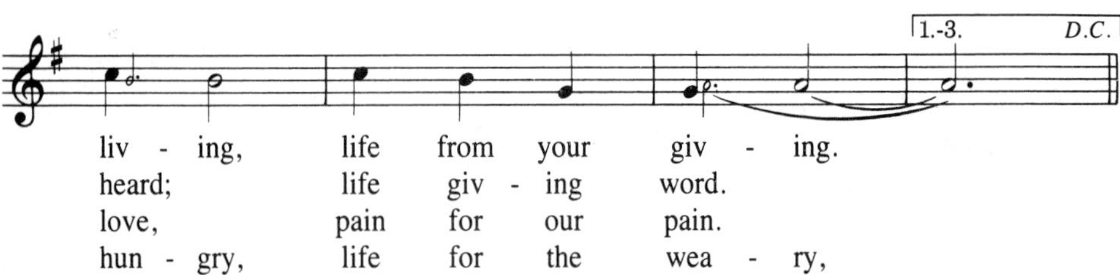
1.-3. D.C.
liv - ing, life from your giv - ing.
heard; life giv - ing word.
love, pain for our pain.
hun - gry, life for the wea - ry,

4. D.C.
for to live with the Lord, we must die with the Lord.

Text: Corinthians, 1 John, 2 Timothy; David Haas, b.1957
Tune: David Haas, b.1957

The Harvest of Justice 300

Refrain
May we find rich - ness in the har-vest of jus - tice
which Christ Je - sus has rip-ened for us.
Bread for the jour - ney, Bread for the hun - gry,
all for the glo - ry and praise of God.
Verses
1. Gath-er with pa - tience for those who have no - thing.
2. For to have mer - cy on those for - got - ten,
3. For to have lit - tle is to be in a - bun - dance. To
Leave them your rich - es, and you will re - ceive. Make
this is my true law, this is my com - mand:
give what re-mains, to give all we have, is to
room for the poor ones, make way for the stran - ger; for
Clothe the nak - ed, be home for the or - phan, be
walk with the poor ones, and be - come the stran - ger,
D.C.
I am the Lord, the Lord your God.
hope for the wid - ow, and wel-come the lost.
one with the Lord, the Lord our God.

Text: Philippians 1:11, Leviticus 19:9, 23:22, Deuteronomy 24:19; David Haas, b.1957
Tune: David Haas, b.1957

301 We Are Called

1. Come! Live in the light! Shine with the joy and the love of the Lord! We are called to be light for the kingdom to live in the freedom of the city of God!
2. Come! Open your heart! Show your mercy to all those in fear! We are called to be hope for the hopeless so all hatred and blindness will be no more!
3. Sing! Sing a new song! Sing of that great day when all will be one! God will reign, and we'll walk with each other as sisters and brothers united in love!
We are called to act with justice, we are called to love tenderly, we are called to serve one another; to walk humbly with God!

Text: Micah 6:8; David Haas, b.1957
Tune: David Haas, b.1957

Jesus Still Lives 302

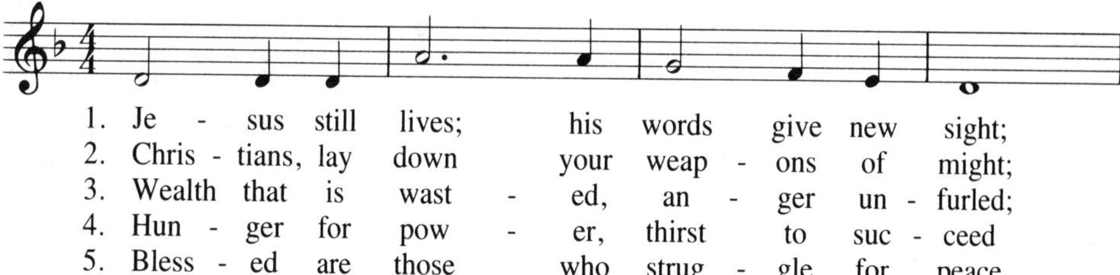
1. Je - sus still lives; his words give new sight;
2. Chris - tians, lay down your weap - ons of might;
3. Wealth that is wast - ed, an - ger un - furled;
4. Hun - ger for pow - er, thirst to suc - ceed
5. Bless - ed are those who strug - gle for peace,

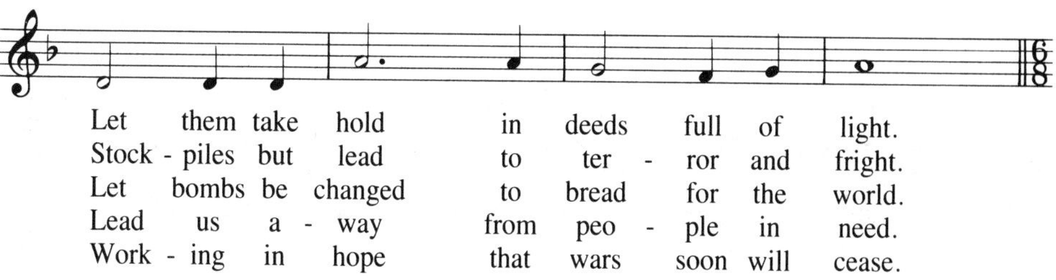
Let them take hold in deeds full of light.
Stock - piles but lead to ter - ror and fright.
Let bombs be changed to bread for the world.
Lead us a - way from peo - ple in need.
Work - ing in hope that wars soon will cease.

Je - sus still lives, a new hope to bring; Then lay fear a - side and

with him come, sing: Ho - ly, ho - ly, ho - ly Im - mor - tal One.

Text: Suzanne Toolan, SM, b.1927
Tune: Suzanne Toolan, SM, b.1927

303 My Soul Is Still

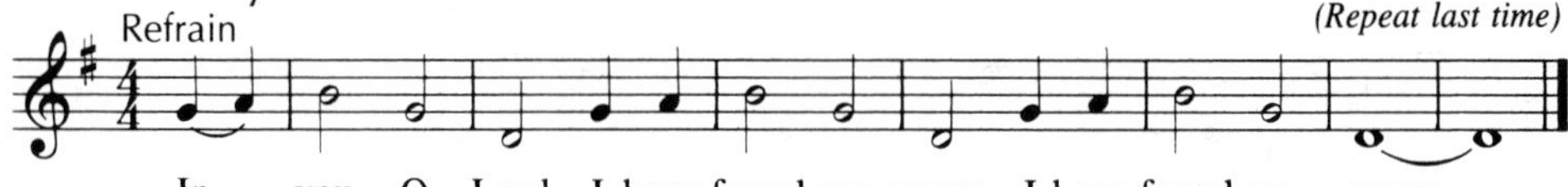
Refrain
(Repeat last time)
In you, O Lord, I have found my peace, I have found my peace.

Verses
1. My heart is not proud, my eyes not a-bove you; you fill my soul.

D.C.
I am not filled with great things, nor with thoughts be-yond me.

2. My soul is still, my soul stays qui-et, long-ing for you like a

D.C.
weened child in its moth-er's arms; so is my soul a child with you.

Text: Psalm 131; David Haas, b.1957
Tune: David Haas, b.1957

The Voice of God Speaks But of Peace 304

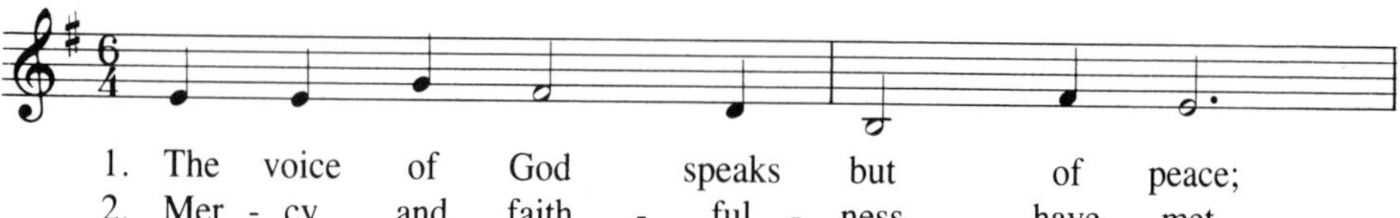

1. The voice of God speaks but of peace;
2. Mer - cy and faith - ful - ness have met,
3. The Lord shall bless our dai - ly work;

peace for all his friends.
jus - tice and peace em - braced.
earth shall yield its fruit.

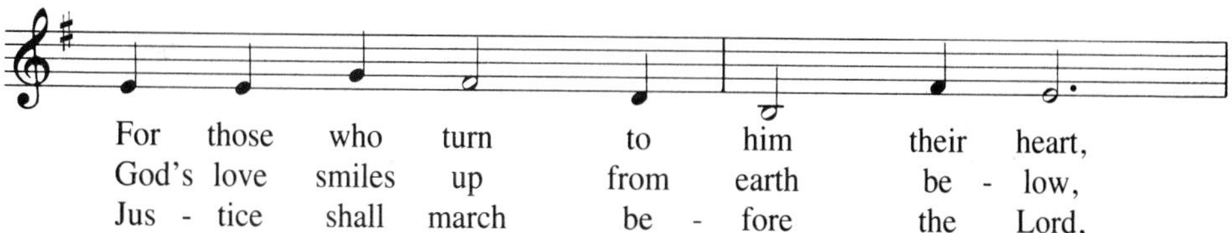

For those who turn to him their heart,
God's love smiles up from earth be - low,
Jus - tice shall march be - fore the Lord,

his help is al - ways near.
his jus - tice down from heav'n.
and peace be - hind his steps.

Re - store a - gain our life, O Lord, may

we re - joice in you! Your mer - cy let us

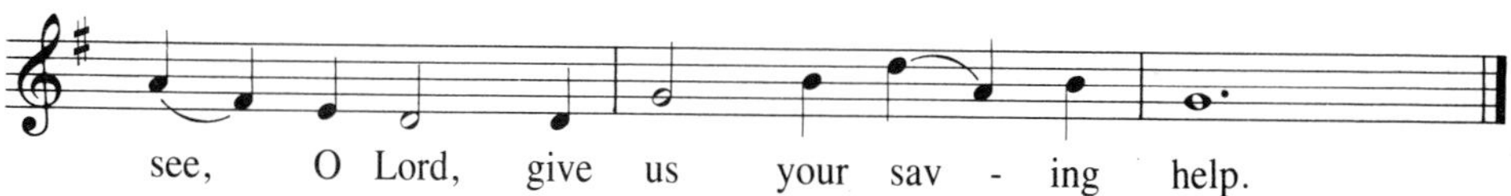

see, O Lord, give us your sav - ing help.

Text: Henry Bryan Hays, OSB
Tune: SHALOM, 8 5 8 5 with refrain ; Henry Bryan Hays

305 Prayer for Peace

1. Peace be - fore us, peace be - hind us peace
2. Love be - fore us, love be - hind us, love
3. Light be - fore us, light be - hind us, light
4. Christ be - fore us, Christ be - hind us, Christ
5. Al - le - lu - ia, al - le - lu - ia, al - le -
6. Peace be - fore us, peace be - hind us, peace

un - der our feet. Peace with - in us, peace
un - der our feet. Love with - in us, love
un - der our feet. Light with - in us, light
un - der our feet. Christ with - in us, Christ
lu - ia. Al - le - lu - ia, al - le-
un - der our feet. Peace with - in us, peace

6
o - ver us, let all a - round us be peace.
o - ver us, let all a - round us be love.
o - ver us, let all a - round us be light.
o - ver us, let all a - round us be Christ.
lu - ia, al - le - lu - ia.
o - ver us, let all a - round us be peace.

Last time
Let all a - round us be peace. Let all a - round us be peace.

Additional verses: Joy, truth, hope.

Text: Based on a Navaho Indian prayer; David Haas, b.1957
Tune: David Haas, b.1957

Peace Is Flowing Like a River 306

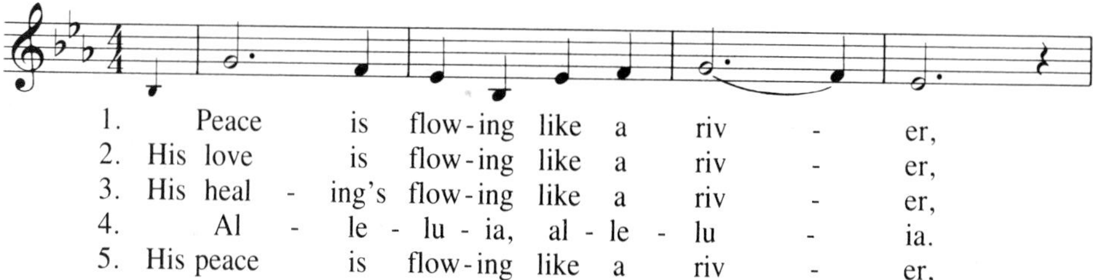
1. Peace is flow-ing like a riv - er,
2. His love is flow-ing like a riv - er,
3. His heal - ing's flow-ing like a riv - er,
4. Al - le - lu - ia, al - le - lu - ia.
5. His peace is flow-ing like a riv - er,

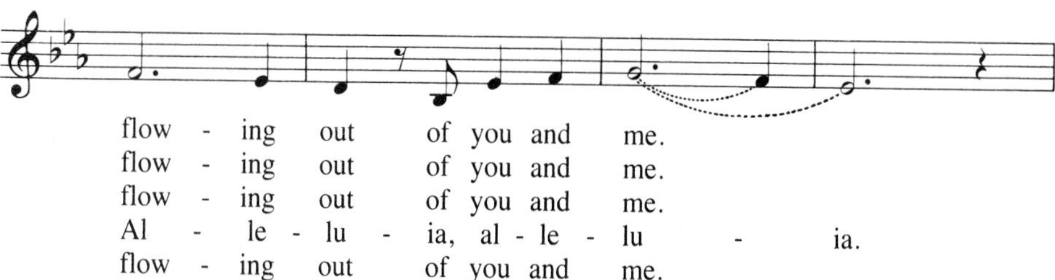
flow - ing out of you and me.
flow - ing out of you and me.
flow - ing out of you and me.
Al - le - lu - ia, al - le - lu - ia.
flow - ing out of you and me.

Flow - ing out in - to the des - ert,
Flow - ing out in - to the des - ert,
Flow - ing out in - to the des - ert,
Al - le - lu - ia, al - le - lu - ia.
Flow - ing out in - to the des - ert,

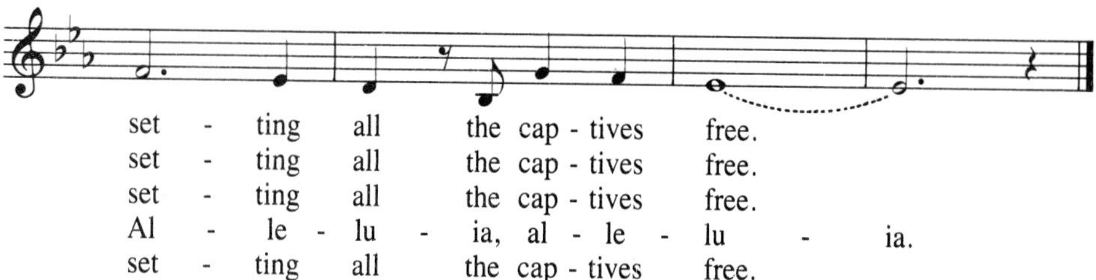
set - ting all the cap - tives free.
set - ting all the cap - tives free.
set - ting all the cap - tives free.
Al - le - lu - ia, al - le - lu - ia.
set - ting all the cap - tives free.

Text: Psalm 127; Adapt. by Carey Landry
Tune: Traditional; Adapt. by Carey Landry; Arr. by Margaret Pizzutti

307 My Peace I Leave You

My peace I leave you, my peace I give you:
trou - ble not your hearts. My peace I leave you, my
peace I give you: be not a - fraid.

Text: John 14; Taizé Community, 1984
Tune: Jacques Berthier, b.1923

Many Are the Light Beams 308

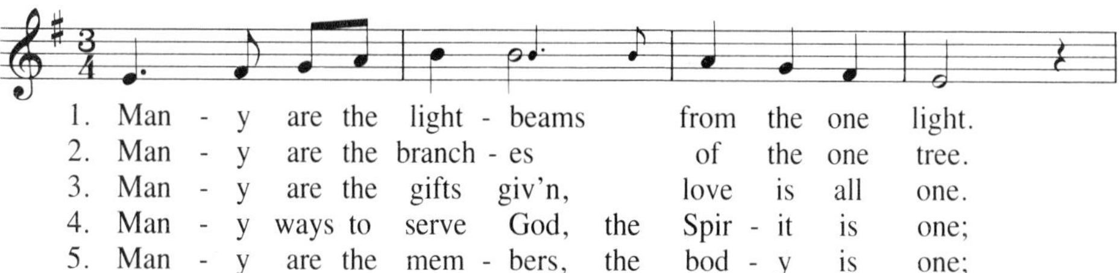
1. Man - y are the light - beams from the one light.
2. Man - y are the branch - es of the one tree.
3. Man - y are the gifts giv'n, love is all one.
4. Man - y ways to serve God, the Spir - it is one;
5. Man - y are the mem - bers, the bod - y is one;

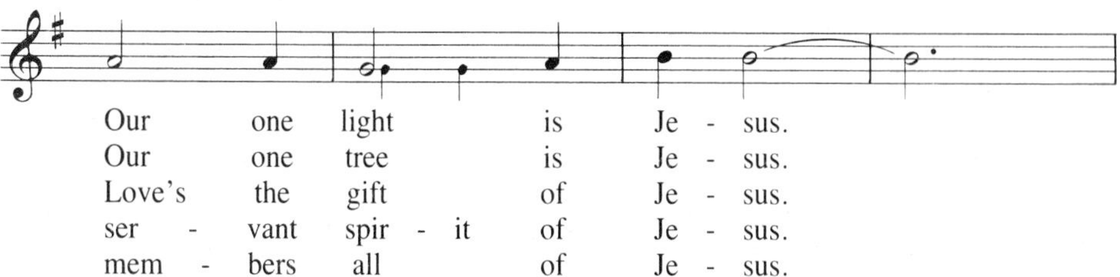
Our one light is Je - sus.
Our one tree is Je - sus.
Love's the gift of Je - sus.
ser - vant spir - it of Je - sus.
mem - bers all of Je - sus.

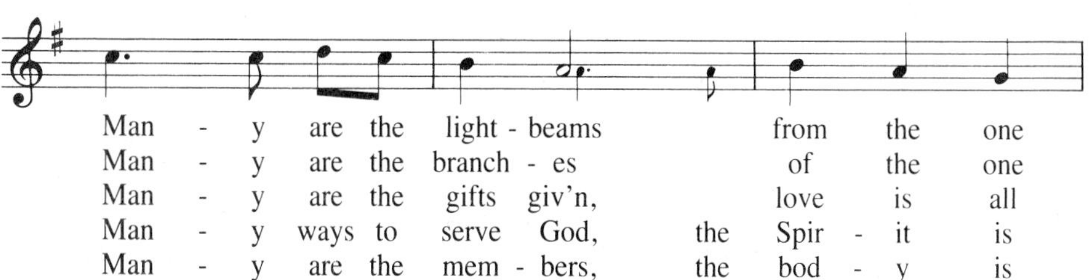
Man - y are the light - beams from the one
Man - y are the branch - es of the one
Man - y are the gifts giv'n, love is all
Man - y ways to serve God, the Spir - it is
Man - y are the mem - bers, the bod - y is

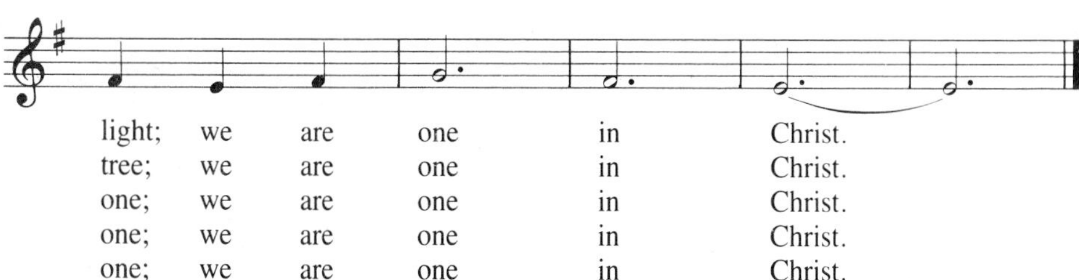
light; we are one in Christ.
tree; we are one in Christ.
one; we are one in Christ.
one; we are one in Christ.
one; we are one in Christ.

Text: *De unitate ecclesiae*, Cyprian of Carthage, 252 A.D.; Trans. by Anders Frostenson, © Verbum Forlong AB
Tune: Olle Widestrand, © Verbum Forlong AB; Acc. by Marty Haugen, b.1950, © 1987, GIA Publications, Inc.

309 Song of Gathering

Refrain
Nei-ther Greek, nor Jew, nor slave, nor free, nei-ther wo-man, nor man, but chil-dren are we, of the same God, the one Lord, the Fa-ther of all, let it be.
To verses
Last time
be. The Moth-er of all, let it be.
Verses
1. From the four winds, and the high seas, from the low-lands, and the val-leys we come to the ta-ble, to the Sav-ior, to the call.
3. From the one cup, from the one bread, at the one meal, we are all fed once more in the bod-y, in the Spir-it, in the dream.
D.C.
2. Your sons and your daugh-ters, young brides and old lov-ers, we come from the wa-ters that spring from your side.
D.C.

Text: Joe Wise
Tune: Joe Wise; Acc. by David Barrickman

We Are Many Parts 310
Refrain
We are man - y parts, we are all one bod - y,
and the gifts we have we are giv - en to share.
May the Spir - it of love make us one in - deed;
one, the love that we share, one, our hope in de-
spair, one, the cross that we bear.
Verses
1. God of all, we look to you, we would be your
2. So my pain is pain for you, in your joy is
3. All you seek - ers, great and small, seek the great - est
D.C.
ser-vants true, let us be your love to all the world.
my joy, too; all is brought to - geth - er in the Lord.
gift of all; if you love, then you will know the Lord.

Text: 1 Corinthians 12,13; Marty Haugen, b.1950
Tune: Marty Haugen, b.1950

311 Gather Us In

1. Here in this place, new light is stream - ing,
2. We are the young— our lives are a mys - t'ry,
3. Here we will take the wine and the wa - ter,
4. Not in the dark of build - ings con - fin - ing,
Now is the dark - ness, van - ished a - way,
We are the old— who yearn for your face,
Here we will take the bread of new birth,
Not in some heav - en, light years a - way, But
See, in this space, our fears and our dream - ings,
We have been sung through - out all of his - t'ry,
Here you shall call your sons and your daugh - ters,
here in this place, the new light is shin - ing,
Brought here to you in the light of this
Called to be light to the whole hu - man
Call us a - new to be salt for the
Now is the King - dom, now is the
day. Gath - er us in— the
race. Gath - er us in— the
earth. Give us to drink the
day. Gath - er us in— and
lost and for - sak - en, Gath - er us in— the
rich and the haugh - ty, Gath - er us in— the
wine of com - pas - sion, Give us to eat the
hold us for ev - er, Gath - er us in— and

blind and the lame; Call to us now, and
proud and the strong; Give us a heart so
bread that is you; Nour - ish us well, and
make us your own; Gath - er us in— all
we shall a - wak - en, We shall a - rise at the
meek and so low - ly, Give us the cour - age to
teach us to fash - ion, Lives that are ho - ly and
peo - ples to - geth - er, Fire of love in our
sound of our name.
en - ter the song.
hearts that are true.
flesh and our bone.

Text: Marty Haugen, b.1950
Tune: Marty Haugen, b.1950

312 Song over the Waters

Refrain

God, you have moved up - on the wa - ters, you have sung in the rush of wind and flame; and in your love, you have called us sons and daughters, make us peo - ple of the wa - ter and your name.

Verses

1. Come fill our wait - ing hearts with the spir - it of Je - sus, let us shine with your light and peace.
2. Give us a thirst for love, give us a hun - ger for jus-tice, make us one with the mind of Christ.
3. You are the breath of life, you are the hope of the hope-less, come and fill us with light and peace.
4. Come, o - pen ev - 'ry heart, come now and wake us to won-der, make us ves - sels of light and peace.

D.C.

Sprinkling Rite

Cantor:
All:
(Invocation)
Re - new us!

Text: Marty Haugen, b.1950
Tune: Marty Haugen, b.1950

What Is This Place 313

1. What is this place where we are meet - ing? On - ly a
2. Words from a - far, stars that are fall - ing, Sparks that are
3. And we ac - cept bread at his ta - ble, Bro - ken and

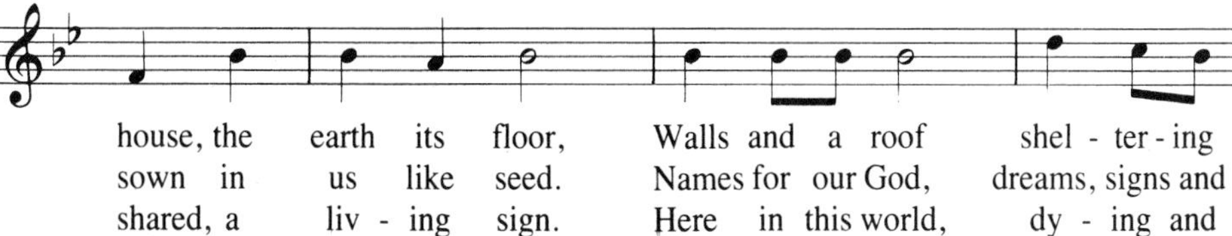

house, the earth its floor, Walls and a roof shel - ter - ing
sown in us like seed. Names for our God, dreams, signs and
shared, a liv - ing sign. Here in this world, dy - ing and

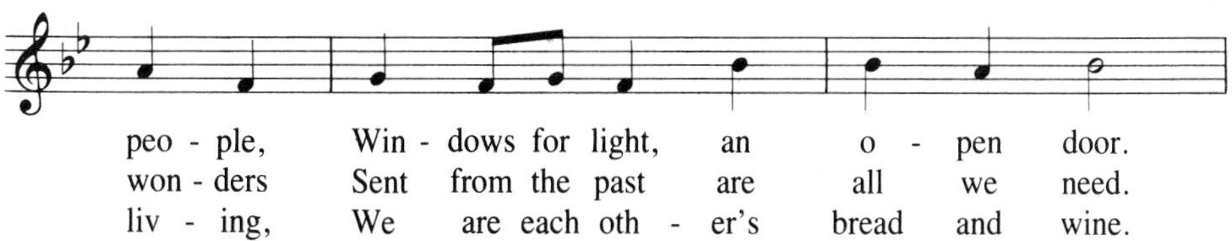

peo - ple, Win - dows for light, an o - pen door.
won - ders Sent from the past are all we need.
liv - ing, We are each oth - er's bread and wine.

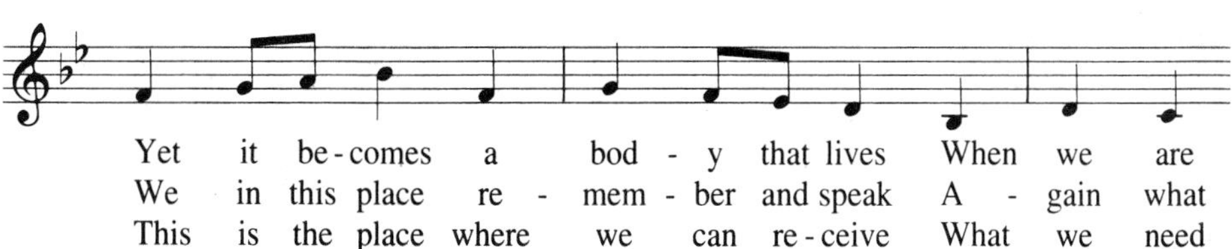

Yet it be - comes a bod - y that lives When we are
We in this place re - mem - ber and speak A - gain what
This is the place where we can re - ceive What we need

gath - ered here, And know our God is near.
we have heard: God's free re - deem - ing word.
to in - crease: God's jus - tice and God's peace

Text: *Zomaar een dak boven wat hoofen;* Huub Oosterhuis, b.1933 ; Trans. by David Smith, b.1933,
Tune: KOMT NU MET ZANG, 9 8 9 8 9 66; Valerius' *Neder-landtsche gedenck-klanck;* Acc. by Robert J. Batastini, b.1942,

314 All People Here Who Remember

(Cantor:) 1. All people here who re - mem - ber Jesus, brother and friend, all who hold to his mem - 'ry, all who keep faith in the end
(All:) 2. will live without fear or il - lu - sion, stand without anger or pride, sing without answers or end - ings, walk with - out won - ders or signs,
3. will share what we have of his King - dom, speak what we find of his word, make what we may of his jus - tice, tell of the sto - ry we've heard,
4. will eat of his bread and his si - lence, echo his call from a - far, find what we can of his kind - ness, hope to be - come who we are,
5. will live in the light of his prom - ise, die as a seed that is sown, find what we can of his fu - ture, car - ry his name as our own.
1.-4.
5.
6. All people here re- mem-ber Jesus, brother and friend, all who hold to his mem - 'ry, all who keep faith in the end,
7. who fashions our lives out of dark - ness, who

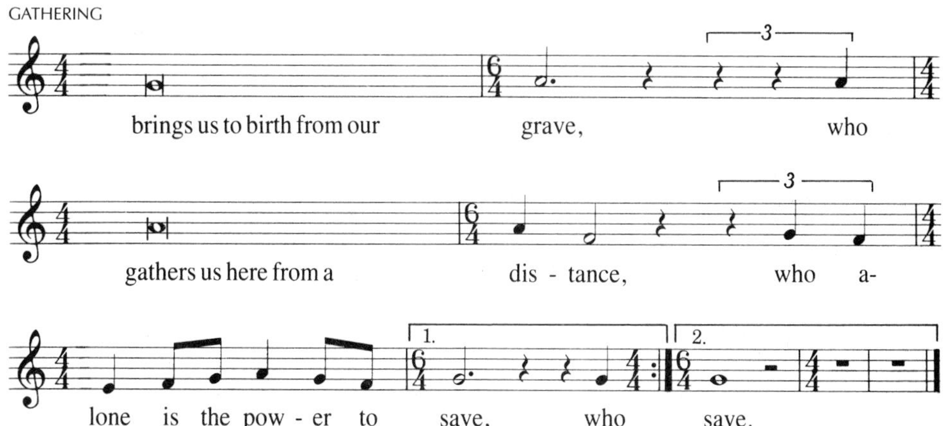
brings us to birth from our
grave,
who
gathers us here from a
dis - tance,
who a-
lone is the pow - er to
save,
who
save.
1.
2.
3

Text: Tom Conry
Tune: Tom Conry; Acc. Bernard Huijbers and Tom Conry

Jesus, Come to Us 315

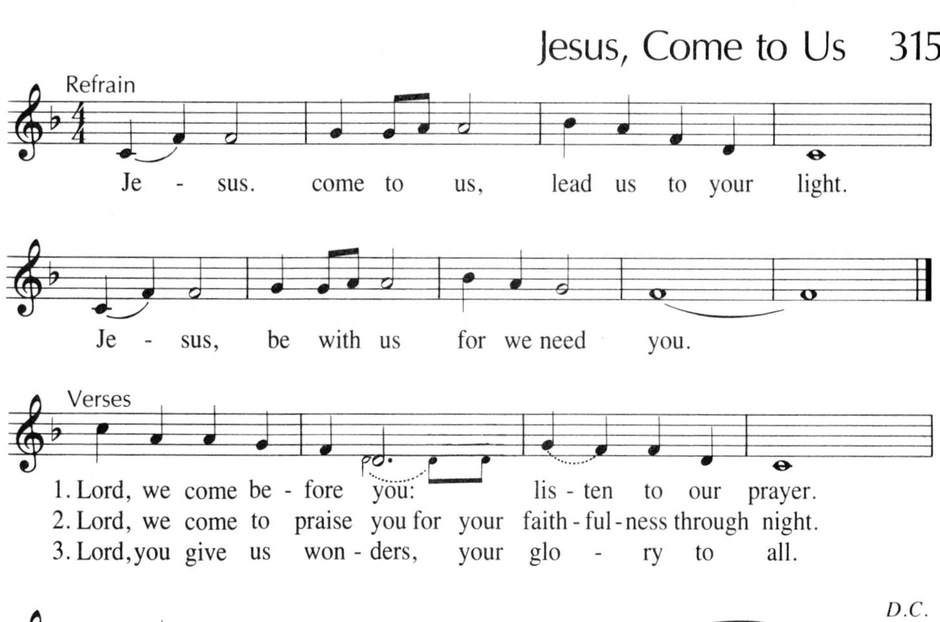
Refrain
Je - sus. come to us, lead us to your light.
Je - sus, be with us for we need you.
Verses
1. Lord, we come be - fore you: lis - ten to our prayer.
2. Lord, we come to praise you for your faith - ful - ness through night.
3. Lord, you give us won - ders, your glo - ry to all.
Fill us all with hope and your love.
You will be with me, this I know.
We be - lieve in you; come to us.
D.C.

Text: David Haas, b.1957
Tune: David Haas, b.1957

316 Canticle of Zachary

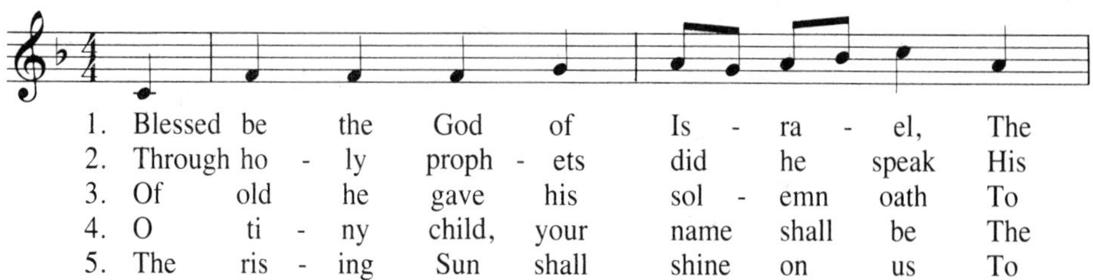
1. Blessed be the God of Is - ra - el, The
2. Through ho - ly proph - ets did he speak His
3. Of old he gave his sol - emn oath To
4. O ti - ny child, your name shall be The
5. The ris - ing Sun shall shine on us To

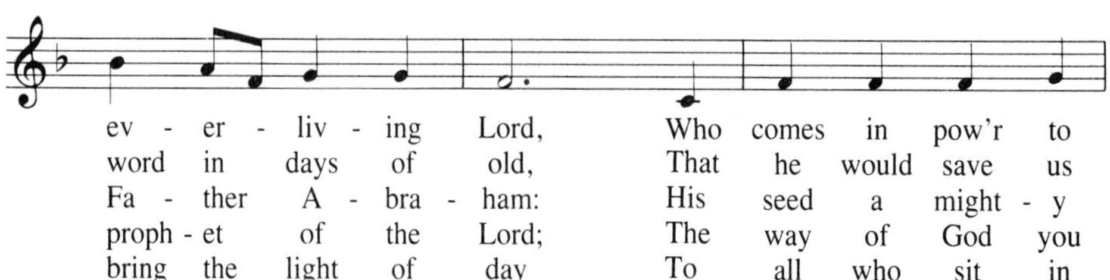
ev - er - liv - ing Lord, Who comes in pow'r to
word in days of old, That he would save us
Fa - ther A - bra - ham: His seed a might - y
proph - et of the Lord; The way of God you
bring the light of day To all who sit in

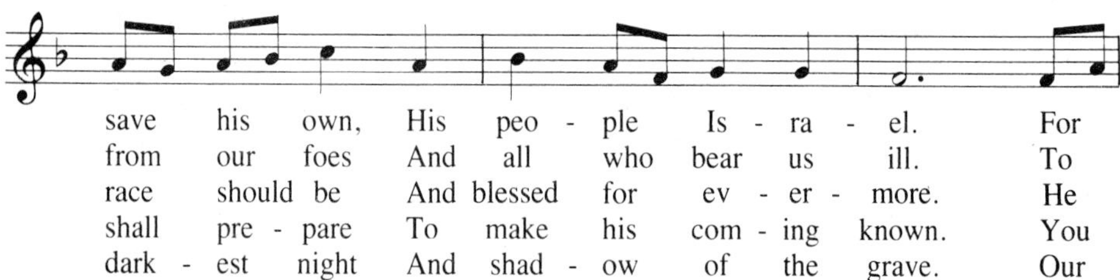
save his own, His peo - ple Is - ra - el. For
from our foes And all who bear us ill. To
race should be And blessed for ev - er - more. He
shall pre - pare To make his com - ing known. You
dark - est night And shad - ow of the grave. Our

Is - ra - el he rais - es up, Sal-
our an - ces - tors did he give His
vowed to set his peo - ple free From
shall pro - claim to Is - ra - el Sal-
foot - steps God shall safe - ly guide To

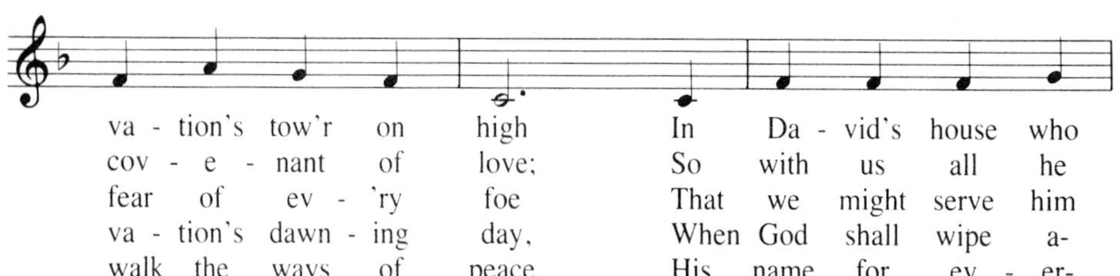
va - tion's tow'r on high In Da - vid's house who
cov - e - nant of love; So with us all he
fear of ev - 'ry foe That we might serve him
va - tion's dawn - ing day, When God shall wipe a-
walk the ways of peace. His name for ev - er-

MORNING

reigned as king And ser - vant of the Lord.
keeps his word In love that knows no end.
all our days In good - ness, love and peace.
way all sins In his re - deem - ing love.
more be blessed Who lives and loves and saves.

Text: Luke 1:67-79; Trans. by James Quinn, SJ, b.1919, © Geoffrey Chapman
Tune: FOREST GREEN, 86 86 D; Traditional English Melody; Harm. by Michael Joncas, b.1951, © 1987, GIA Publications, Inc.

Morning Has Broken 317

1. Morn-ing has bro - ken Like the first morn - ing, Black-bird has
2. Sweet the rain's new fall Sun - lit from heav - en, Like the first
3. Mine is the sun - light! Mine is the morn - ing Born of the

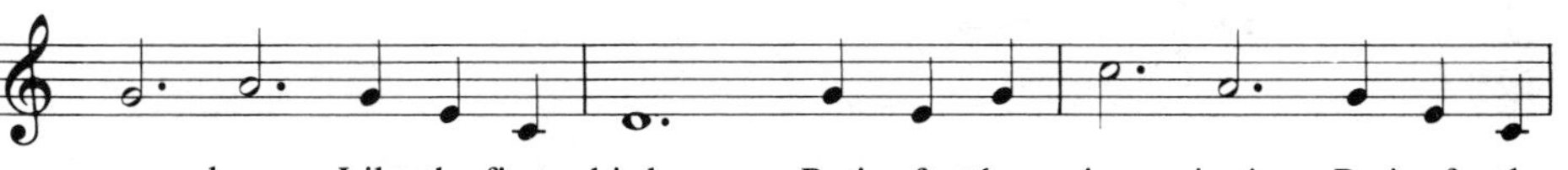

spo - ken Like the first bird. Praise for the sing - ing! Praise for the
dew - fall On the first grass. Praise for the sweet - ness Of the wet
one light E - den saw play! Praise with e - la - tion, Praise ev-'ry

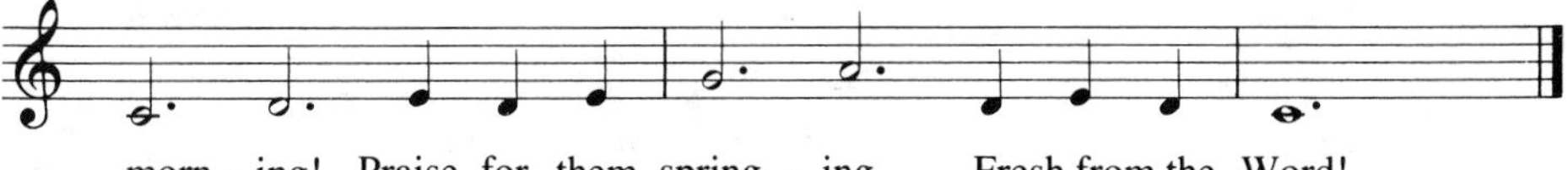

morn - ing! Praise for them, spring - ing Fresh from the Word!
gar - den, Sprung in com - plete - ness Where his feet pass.
morn - ing, God's re - cre - a - tion Of the new day!

Text: Eleanor Farjeon, 1881-1965, *The Children's Bells*, © David Higham Assoc. Ltd.
Tune: BUNESSAN, 5 5 5 4 D; Gaelic; Acc. by Marty Haugen, b.1950, © 1987, GIA Publications, Inc.

318 Joyous Light of Heavenly Glory

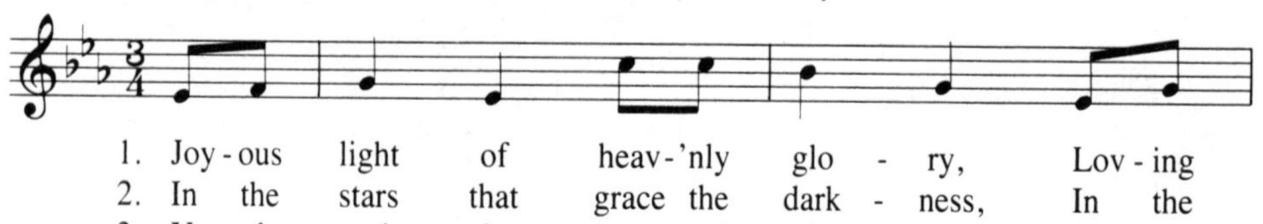

1. Joy-ous light of heav-'nly glo - ry, Lov-ing
2. In the stars that grace the dark - ness, In the
3. You who made the heav-ens's splen - dor, Ev - 'ry

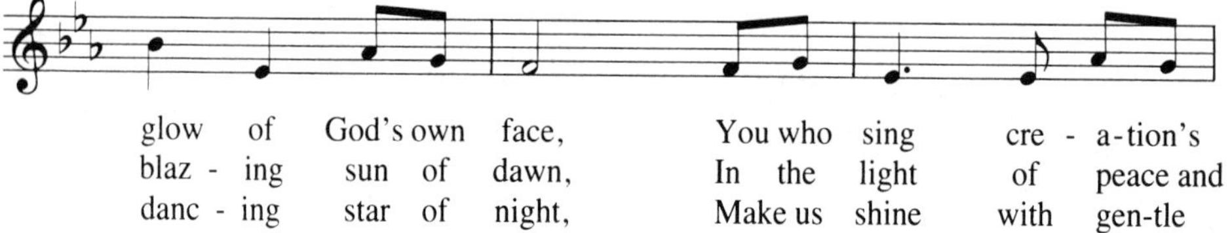

glow of God's own face, You who sing cre - a-tion's
blaz - ing sun of dawn, In the light of peace and
danc - ing star of night, Make us shine with gen-tle

sto - ry, Shine on ev - 'ry land and race. Now as
wis - dom, We can hear your qui - et song. Love that
jus - tice Let us each re - flect your light. Might-y

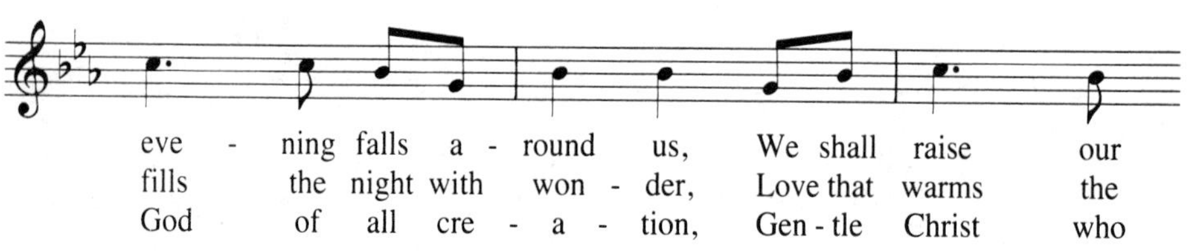

eve - ning falls a - round us, We shall raise our
fills the night with won - der, Love that warms the
God of all cre - a - tion, Gen - tle Christ who

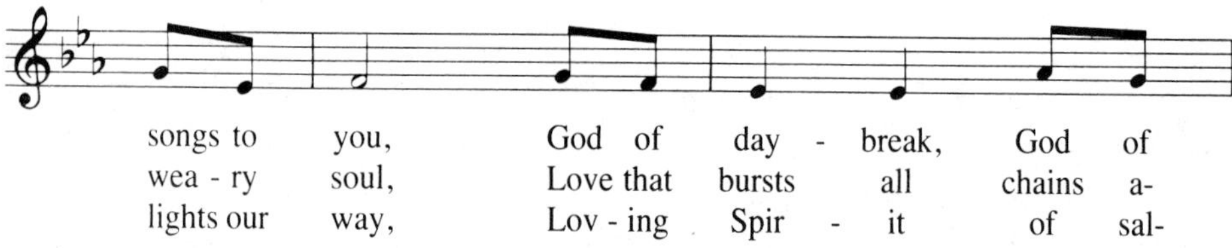

songs to you, God of day - break, God of
wea - ry soul, Love that bursts all chains a-
lights our way, Lov - ing Spir - it of sal-

shad - ows, Come and light our hearts a - new.
sun - der, Set us free and make us whole.
va - tion, Lead us on to end - less day.

Text: Marty Haugen, b.1950
Tune: JOYOUS LIGHT, 87 87 D; Marty Haugen, b.1950

God of Day and God of Darkness 319

1. God of day and God of dark - ness, Now we
2. Still the na - tions curse the dark - ness, Still the
3. Show us Christ in one an - oth - er, Make us
4. You shall be the path that guides us, You the
5. Gen - tle Fa - ther, Lov - ing Moth - er, Je - sus:
stand be - fore the night; As the shad - ows stretch and
rich op - press the poor; Still the earth is bruised and
ser - vants strong and true; Give us all your love of
light that in us burns; Shin-ing deep with - in all
Broth - er, Sav - ior, Friend; Spir - it of all grace and
deep - en, Come and make our dark - ness bright. All cre-
bro - ken By the ones who still want more. Come and
jus - tice So we do what you would do. Let us
peo - ple, Yours the love that we must learn, For our
pow - er, May we praise you with - out end. Grant us
a - tion still is groan - ing For the dawn - ing of your
wake us from our sleep - ing, So our hearts can - not ig-
call all peo - ple ho - ly, Let us pledge our lives a-
hearts shall wan - der rest - less 'Til they safe to you re-
all a peace - ful rest - ing, Let each mind and bod - y
might, When the Sun of peace and jus - tice Fills the
nore, All your peo - ple lost and bro - ken, All your
new, Make us one with all the low - ly, Let us
turn; Find-ing you in one an - oth - er, We shall
mend, So we rise re - freshed to - mor - row, Hearts re-
earth with ra - diant light.
chil - dren at our door.
all be one in you.
all your face dis - cern.
newed to King - dom tend.

Text: Marty Haugen, b.1950
Tune: BEACH SPRING, 87 87 D; *The Sacred Harp*, 1844; Harm. by Marty Haugen, b.1950

320 At Evening

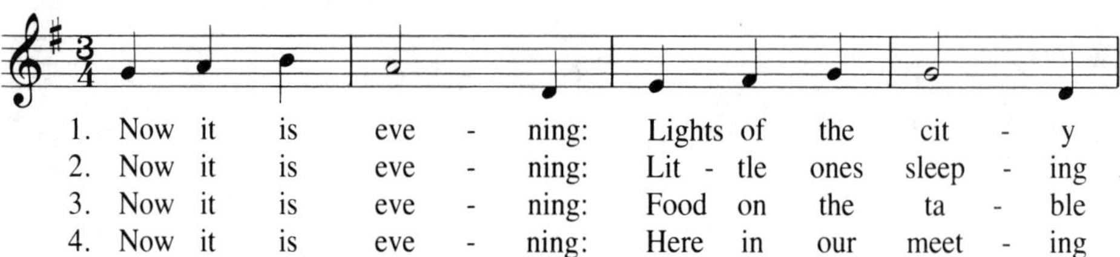
1. Now it is eve - ning: Lights of the cit - y
2. Now it is eve - ning: Lit - tle ones sleep - ing
3. Now it is eve - ning: Food on the ta - ble
4. Now it is eve - ning: Here in our meet - ing

Bid us re - mem - ber Christ is our Light.
Bid us re - mem - ber Christ is our Peace.
Bids us re - mem - ber Christ is our Life.
May we re - mem - ber Christ is our Friend.

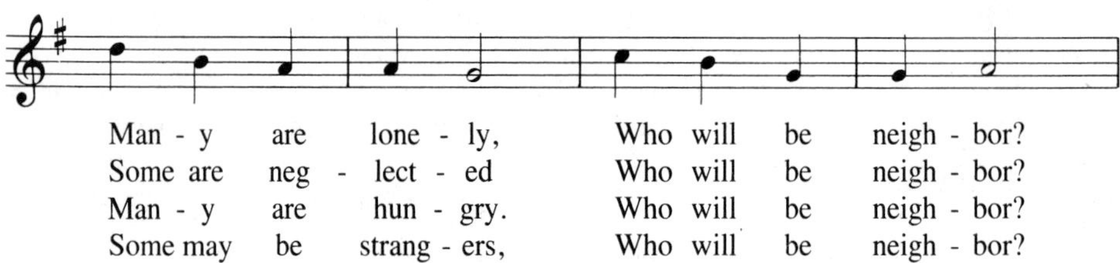
Man - y are lone - ly, Who will be neigh - bor?
Some are neg - lect - ed Who will be neigh - bor?
Man - y are hun - gry. Who will be neigh - bor?
Some may be strang - ers, Who will be neigh - bor?

Where there is car - ing Christ is our Light.
Where there is car - ing Christ is our Peace.
Where there is shar - ing Christ is our Life.
Where there's a wel - come Christ is our Friend.

Text: *Now It Is Evening,* Fred Pratt Green, b.1903, © 1974, Hope Publishing Co.
Tune: EVENING HYMN, 5 5 5 4; David Haas, b.1957, © 1985, GIA Publications Inc.

We Shall Rise Again 321

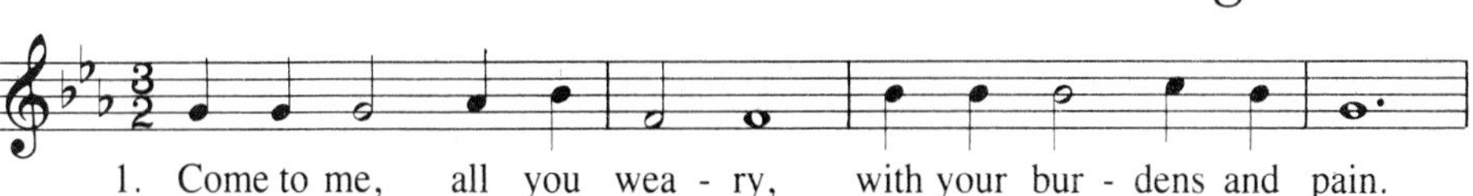

1. Come to me, all you wea - ry, with your bur - dens and pain.
2. Though we walk through the dark-ness, e - vil we do not fear.
3. We de - pend on God's mer - cy, mer - cy which nev - er fades.
4. Do not fear death's do - min - ion, look be - yond earth and grave.
5. At the door there to greet us, mar-tyrs, an - gels and saints,

Take my yoke on your shoul - ders and learn from me:
You are walk - ing be - side us with your rod and your staff.
We re-mem - ber our cov - e - nant and the prom - ise Je - sus made:
See the bright-ness of Je - sus shin-ing out to light our way.
And our fam - 'ly and loved ones, ev - 'ry - one freed from their chains.

I am gen - tle and hum - ble, and your soul will find rest,
On-ly good - ness and kind - ness fol-low us all our lives.
If we die with Christ Je - sus, we shall live with him,
Lov-ing Fa - ther and Spir - it, lov-ing Je - sus the Son,
We shall feel their ac - cept - ance, and the joy of new life.

For my yoke is eas - y and my bur - den is light.
We shall dwell in the Lord's house for so man - y years to come!
And if we are faith - ful, we shall reign with him!
All God's peo - ple to - geth - er, we shall live on as one!
We shall join in the gath - er - ing, re - u - nit - ed in God's love!

We shall rise a-gain on the last day with the faith - ful rich and

poor. Com-ing to the house of Lord Je - sus, we will

find an o - pen door there, we will find an o - pen door.

Text: Psalm 23, John 11, 2 Timothy 2; Jeremy Young
Tune: RESURRECTION; Irregular with refrain; Jeremy Young

322 The River Will Rise

1. God of all liv - ing and our light, are we not
pre-cious in your sight? Born of your spir - it, born of your
breath. Who set the sun and moon and stars, who sets us
dream-ing from a - far, great-er than griev - ing, more than our
death. With-in our hearts, with - in our-selves,
ech-oes the name - less voice that cries; this world will hear,
deep in the night, when the riv - er will rise.
Refrain
And the riv - er will rise, deep and free; we our-selves,

we shall see: on the day when the Lord will wipe

a - way all of the tears from the peo-ple's eyes, then

peace will flow like a riv - er, and the riv - er will rise.

2. Hear, then, the cry - ing of your own, who call your

name so far from home, Lord of the light - ning, God of the poor.

Who counts the tears from day to day, who knows our wan-

d'rings and our way? God of the des - ert, Lord of the shore.

You in your dis - tance, you in our midst, you of the name - less voice

SECOND COMING

D.S.
that cries, this world will hear, deep in the night, when the riv-er will rise.

3. Ev-'ry moun-tain, ev-'ry plain, ev-'ry val - ley shall pro-claim,

tell of the jus - tice God may be-gin. Then let your name

at last be known, that name that no one calls a - lone,

break-ing the si - lence, burn-ing with-in. Lad-en with laugh-

ter, bur-dened with tears, name of the name - less voice that cries:

D.S.
this world will hear, deep in the night, when the riv - er will rise.

Text: Tom Conry
Tune: Tom Conry; Acc. by Patrick Loomis

Freedom Is Coming 323

O Free - dom, O Free - dom, O
(know) Free-dom is com-ing. Free-dom is
Free - dom. O
com - ing. Free-dom is com - ing. O yes, I
yes, I know. O yes, I know. O yes, I know.
know. O yes, I know. O yes, I know.
O yes, I know. O yes, I know. O
O yes, I know. O yes, I know.
O
O yes, I know. O yes. I yes, I know.

O Jesus, O Jesus,
O Jesus, Jesus is coming.
O yes, I know.
O yes, I know.

Text: South African
Tune: South African

324 Lord of Glory

Refrain

Leap-ing the moun-tains, bound-ing the hills, see how our God has come to meet us. His voice is lift-ed; his face is joy. Now is the sea-son to sing our song on high. 2. He

Verses

1. Come, then, O Lord of glo-ry, show us your face. Speak, for we know your words are life. *D.C.*

pas-tures his flock a-mong the wild flow'rs and leads them to the moun-tain of his love.

3. All through the day, all through the night,

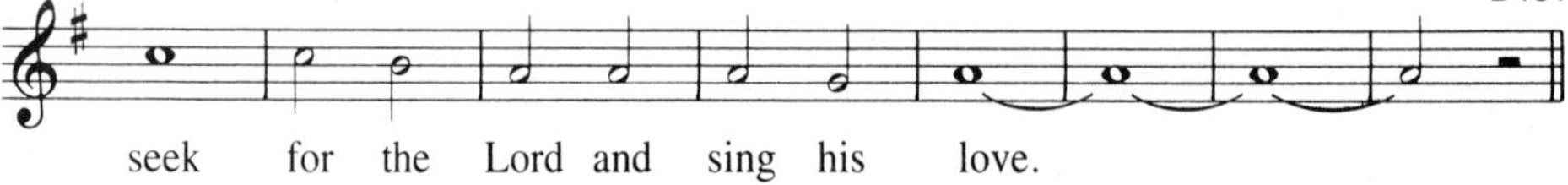

seek for the Lord and sing his love. *D.C.*

Text: The Song of Songs; Tim Manion
Tune: Tim Manion; Acc. by Sr. Theophane Hytrek, OSF

In the Lord, I'll Be Thankful 325

In the Lord I'll be ev - er thank - ful, in the
Lord I will re - joice! Look to him, do
not be a - fraid; in him re - joic - ing: the Lord is
near, in him re - joic - ing: the Lord is near.

Text: Taizé Community
Tune: Jacques Berthier, b.1923

326 All Who Claim the Faith of Jesus

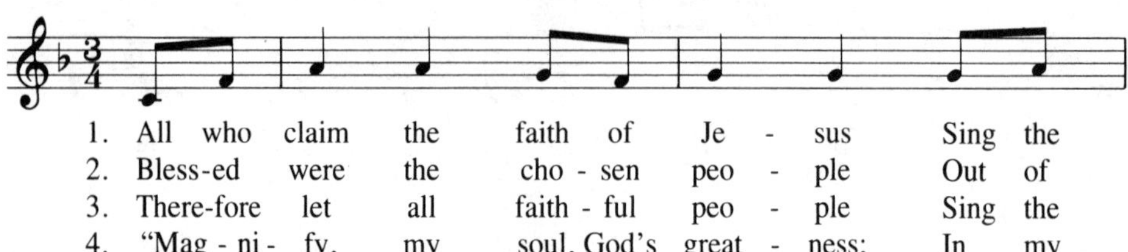
1. All who claim the faith of Je - sus Sing the
2. Bless-ed were the cho - sen peo - ple Out of
3. There-fore let all faith - ful peo - ple Sing the
4. "Mag - ni - fy, my soul, God's great - ness; In my

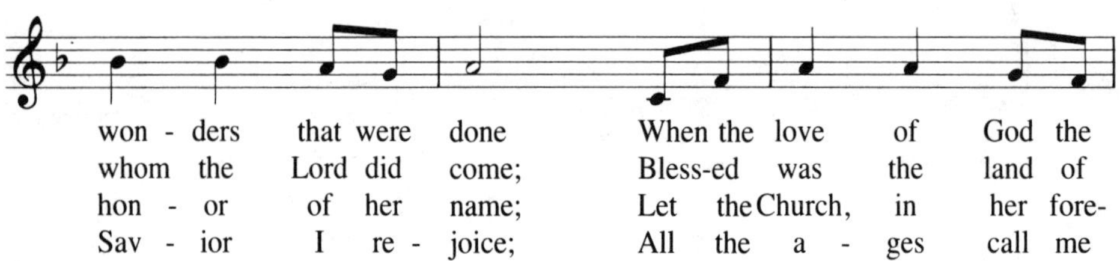
won - ders that were done When the love of God the
whom the Lord did come; Bless-ed was the land of
hon - or of her name; Let the Church, in her fore-
Sav - ior I re - joice; All the a - ges call me

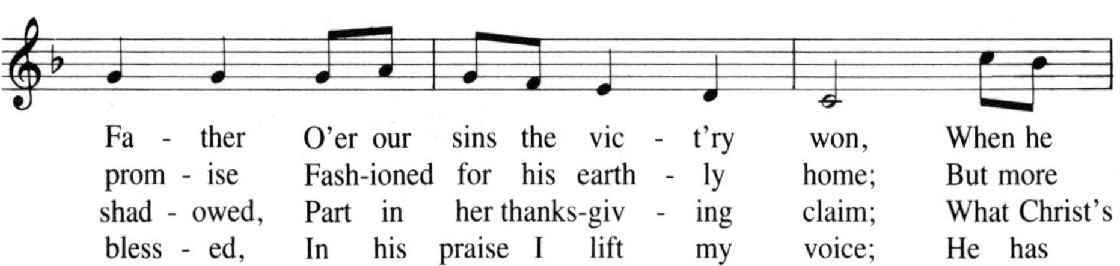
Fa - ther O'er our sins the vic - t'ry won, When he
prom - ise Fash-ioned for his earth - ly home; But more
shad - owed, Part in her thanks-giv - ing claim; What Christ's
bless - ed, In his praise I lift my voice; He has

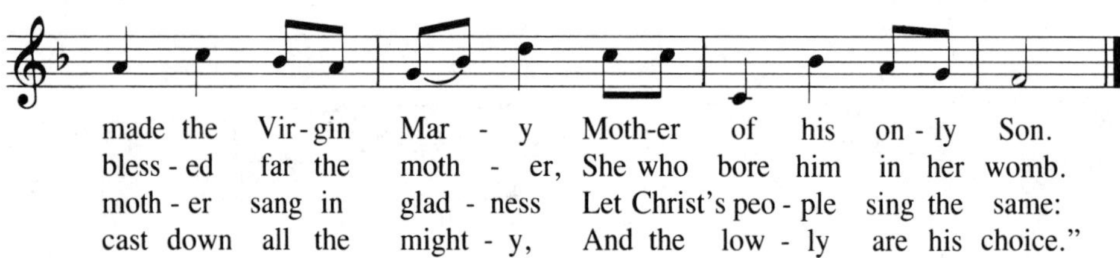
made the Vir - gin Mar - y Moth-er of his on - ly Son.
bless - ed far the moth - er, She who bore him in her womb.
moth - er sang in glad - ness Let Christ's peo - ple sing the same:
cast down all the might - y, And the low - ly are his choice."

Text: Vincent Stuckey Stratton Coles, 1845-1929, alt.; St. 4, F. Bland Tucker, 1895-1984
Tune: TILLFLYKT, 87 87 87; *Sionstoner,* 1889; Harm. by Marty Haugen, b.1950,

I Sing a Maid 327

1. I sing a maid of ten - der years To
2. She watched him grow to man - hood's strength To
3. And if the song had end - ed then, Our

whom an an - gel came, And knelt, as to a
meet his des - tin - y, And when the dan - ger
eyes would fill with tears, But ah! the song had

might - y queen, And bowed his wings of flame: A
of his truth Brought him to Cal - va - ry, She
just be - gun To ech - o down the years! Now

na - tion's hope in her re - ply, This maid of match - less
stood by him all pow - er - less To ease his dy - ing
lift your voic - es, hearts and souls, To sing with one ac-

grace; For God's own son be - came her child,
pain, 'Til in the dark - est hour of all,
cord To hon - or Mar - y, Moth - er of

And she his rest - ing place.
She held her son a - gain.
The Christ, the Ris - en Lord!

Text: M.D. Ridge
Tune: THE FLIGHT OF THE EARLS; 14 14 14 14; Celtic Traditional; Harm. by Michael Joncas, b.1951

328 Give Thanks to God on High

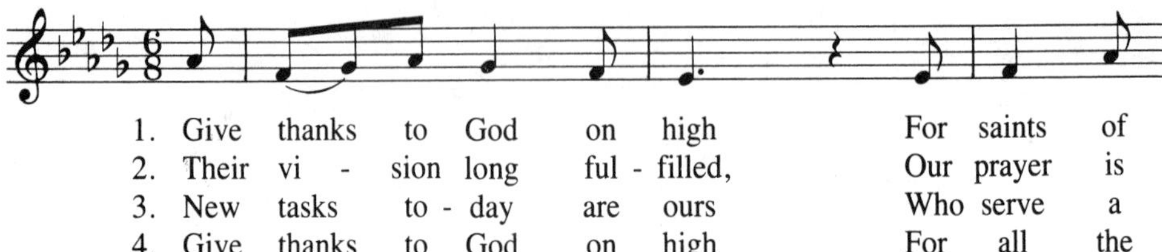
1. Give thanks to God on high For saints of
2. Their vi - sion long ful - filled, Our prayer is
3. New tasks to - day are ours Who serve a
4. Give thanks to God on high For all the

oth - er days, Whose hope it was to
still the same; Up - on their work of
world of pain, New calls to chal - lenge
fu - ture sends, In praise of Christ to

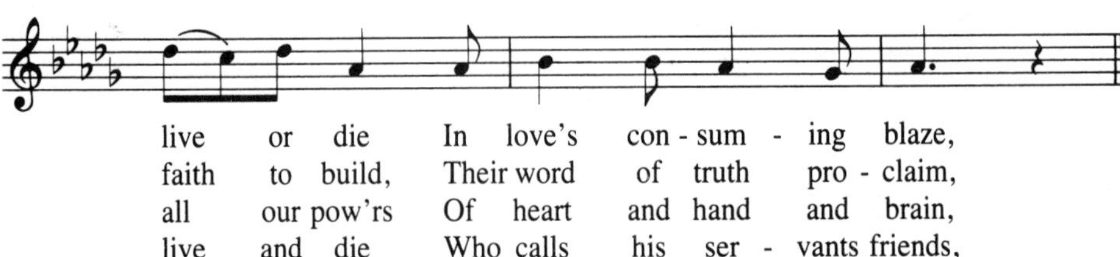
live or die In love's con - sum - ing blaze,
faith to build, Their word of truth pro - claim,
all our pow'rs Of heart and hand and brain,
live and die Who calls his ser - vants friends,

2
2
For Christ and his king-dom, His glo - ry and his praise.
For Christ and his king-dom, And for his ho - ly name.
For Christ and his king-dom, While life and breath re-main.
For Christ and his king-dom, Whose glo - ry nev - er ends.

Text: Timothy Dudley-Smith, b.1926, © 1985, Hope Publishing Co.
Tune: BALDWIN, 66 86 66; James J. Chepponis, b. 1956, © 1987, GIA Publications, Inc.

Wonder of Wonders 329

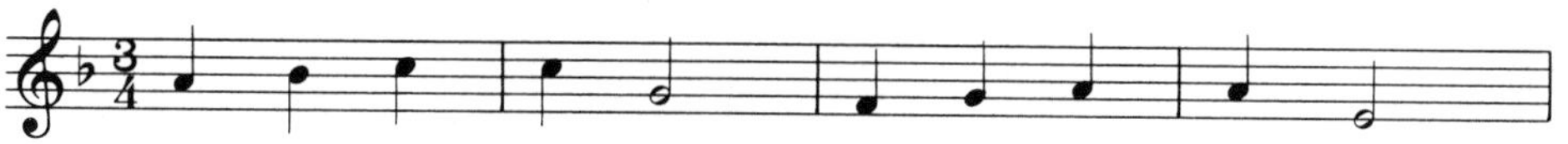

1. Won - der of won - ders, Life is be - gin - ning,
2. Now with re - joic - ing, Make cel - e - bra - tion;
3. Lord of cre - a - tion, Dy - ing and liv - ing,

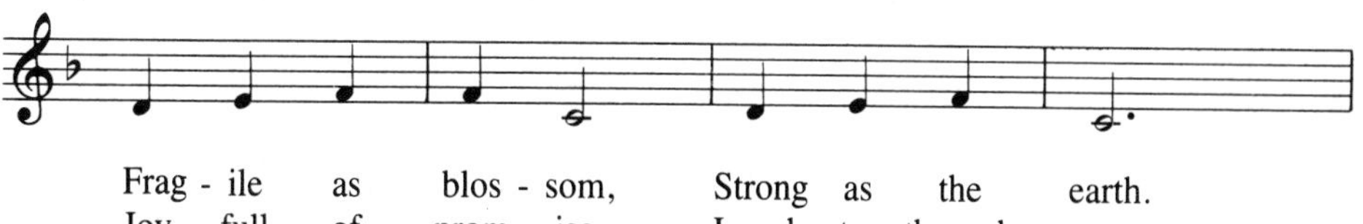

Frag - ile as blos - som, Strong as the earth.
Joy full of prom - ise, Laugh - ter through tears.
Fa - ther and moth - er, Part - ner and friend.

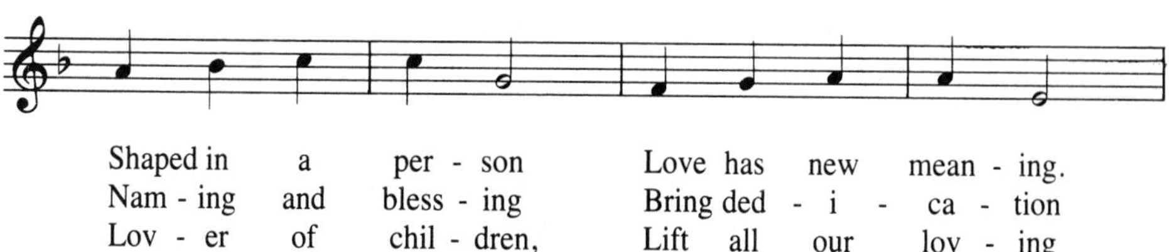

Shaped in a per - son Love has new mean - ing.
Nam - ing and bless - ing Bring ded - i - ca - tion
Lov - er of chil - dren, Lift all our lov - ing

Par - ents and peo - ple Sing at their birth.
Hum - ble in pur - pose O - ver the years.
In - to your king - dom World with - out end.

Text: Brian Wren, b.1936, © 1983, Hope Publishing Co.
Tune: VIKTORA, 55 54, D; David Haas, b.1957, Acc. by Jeanne Cotter, © 1988, GIA Publications, Inc.

330 Awake, O Sleeper

Refrain
A - wake, O sleep - er, a - rise from death, a-
ban - don the shad - ows of night; the wind of the
spir - it shall be your breath, and Christ, will
fill you with light.
Verses
1. Once you were dark - ness, once you were lost in the
2. Live as God's peo - ple, live as God's jus - tice and
shad - ows. Once you were dark-ness,
mer - cy, filled with com - pas - sion,
D.C.
now you are chil - dren of light.
filled with the pow - er of love.
3. Shine out with the splen - dor of love,

shine with jus - tice and right - eous - ness.

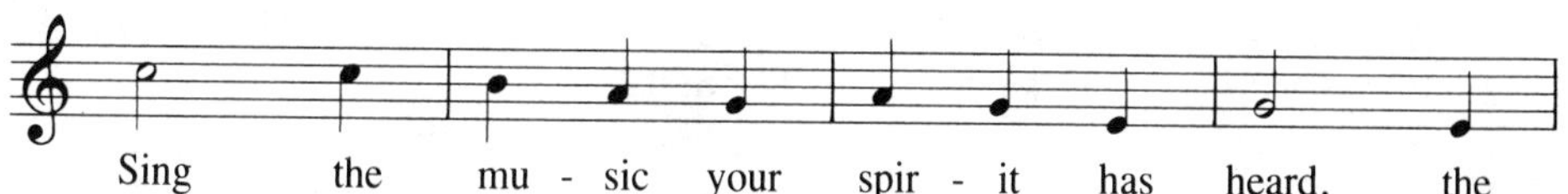
Sing the mu - sic your spir - it has heard, the

D.C.
songs of glo - ry and light.

Text: Ephesians 5; Marty Haugen, b.1950
Tune: Marty Haugen, b.1950

You Are God's Work of Art 331

Refrain
You are God's work of art, cre - a - ted in Je - sus the Christ.
Verses
1. You have been en - light - ened by the Lord.
2. Keep the flame of faith in your heart, and
3. Bless - ed be our God, who
D.C.
Walk as chil - dren of the light.
may you meet him when he comes.
chose you in the light of Christ.

Text: Ephesians 1:4, 2:10, Rite of Baptism; David Haas, b.1957
Tune: David Haas, b.1957

332 Baptized in Water

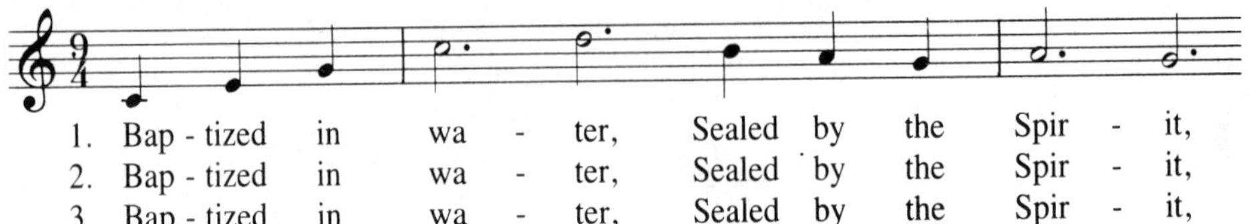
1. Bap - tized in wa - ter, Sealed by the Spir - it,
2. Bap - tized in wa - ter, Sealed by the Spir - it,
3. Bap - tized in wa - ter, Sealed by the Spir - it,

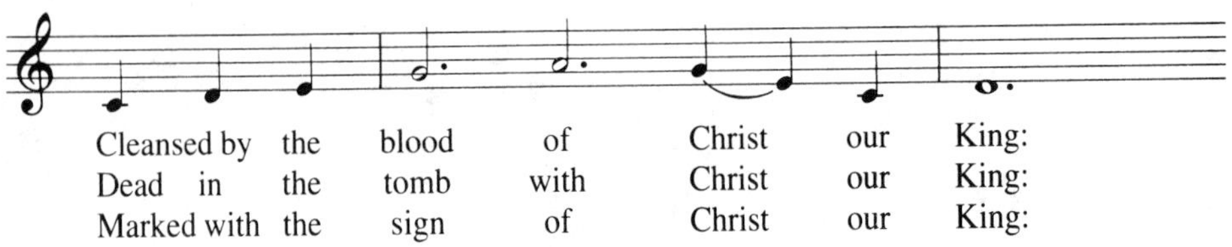
Cleansed by the blood of Christ our King:
Dead in the tomb with Christ our King:
Marked with the sign of Christ our King:

Heirs of sal - va - tion, Trust - ing his prom - ise,
One with his ris - ing, Freed and for - giv - en,
Born of one Fa - ther, We are his chil - dren,

Faith - ful - ly now God's praise we sing.
Thank-ful - ly now God's praise we sing.
Joy - ful - ly now God's praise we sing.

Text: Michael Saward, b.1932, © 1982, Hope Publishing Co.
Tune: BUNESSAN, 5 5 8 D; Gaelic; Acc. by Marty Haugen, b.1950, © 1987, GIA Publications, Inc.

The Water I Give 333

Refrain
All who drink the wa - ter I give will nev - er thirst,

the wa-ter I give will be a foun-tain with - in you, giv-ing life.

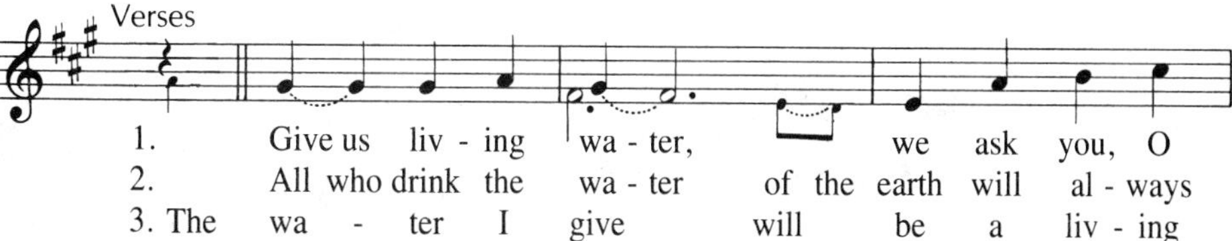
Verses
1. Give us liv - ing wa - ter, we ask you, O
2. All who drink the wa - ter of the earth will al - ways
3. The wa - ter I give will be a liv - ing

D.C.
Lord, so that we may nev - er thirst a - gain.
thirst. Drink of me and nev - er thirst a - gain.
spring, leap- ing up to give e - ter - nal life.

Text: David Haas, b.1957
Tune: David Haas, b.1957

334 I Have Loved You

I have loved you with an ev - er - last - ing love, I have

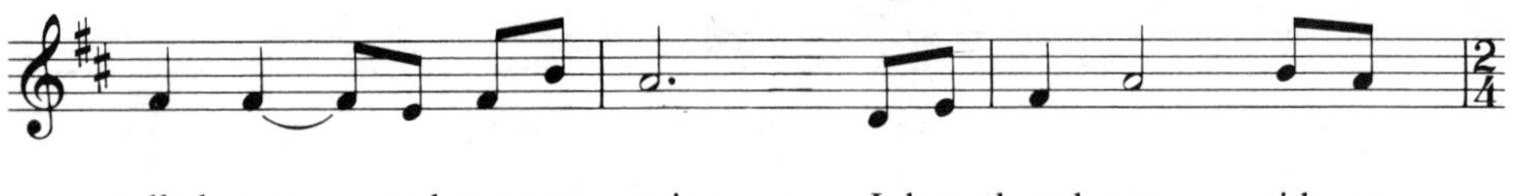

called you and you are mine; I have loved you with an

ev - er - last-ing love, I have called you and you are mine.

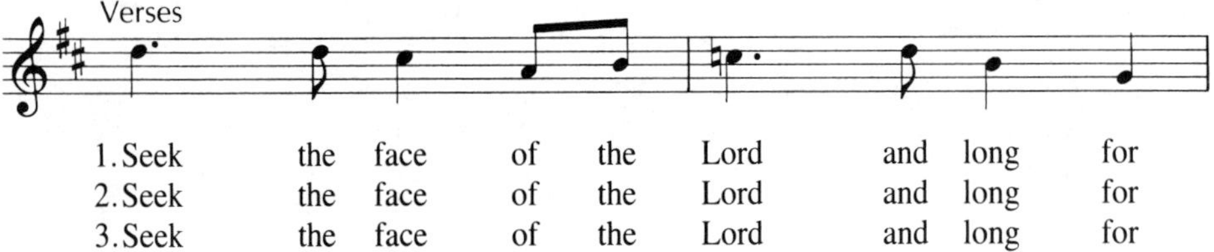

1. Seek the face of the Lord and long for
2. Seek the face of the Lord and long for
3. Seek the face of the Lord and long for

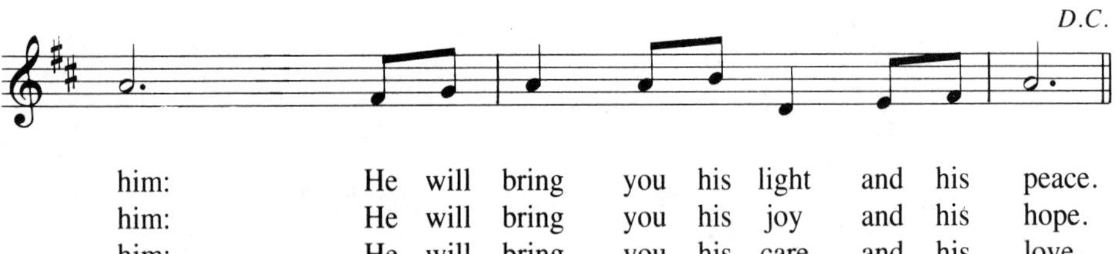

him: He will bring you his light and his peace.
him: He will bring you his joy and his hope.
him: He will bring you his care and his love.

Text: Jeremiah 31:3, Psalm 24:3; Michael Joncas, b.1951
Tune: Michael Joncas, b.1951

Jesus, Wine of Peace 335

Refrain
Je - sus, wine of peace, wine of love, may we drink of

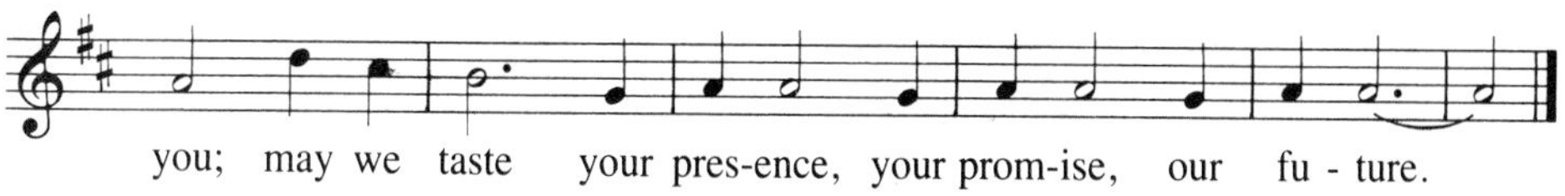
you; may we taste your pres-ence, your prom-ise, our fu - ture.

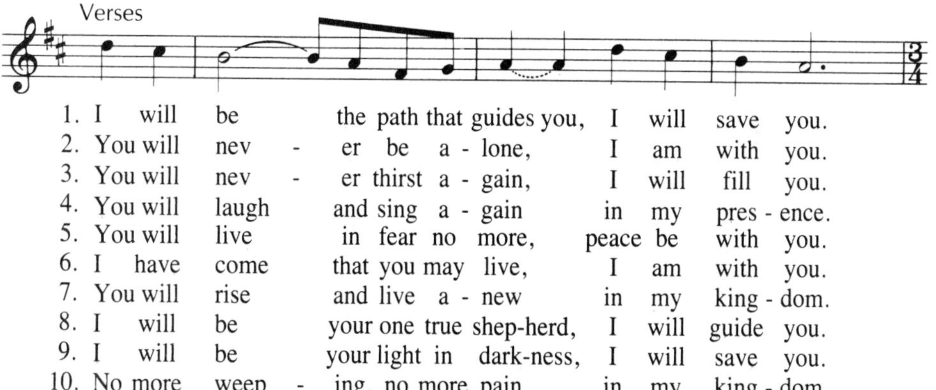
Verses
1. I will be the path that guides you, I will save you.
2. You will nev - er be a - lone, I am with you.
3. You will nev - er thirst a - gain, I will fill you.
4. You will laugh and sing a - gain in my pres - ence.
5. You will live in fear no more, peace be with you.
6. I have come that you may live, I am with you.
7. You will rise and live a - new in my king - dom.
8. I will be your one true shep-herd, I will guide you.
9. I will be your light in dark-ness, I will save you.
10. No more weep - ing, no more pain in my king - dom.

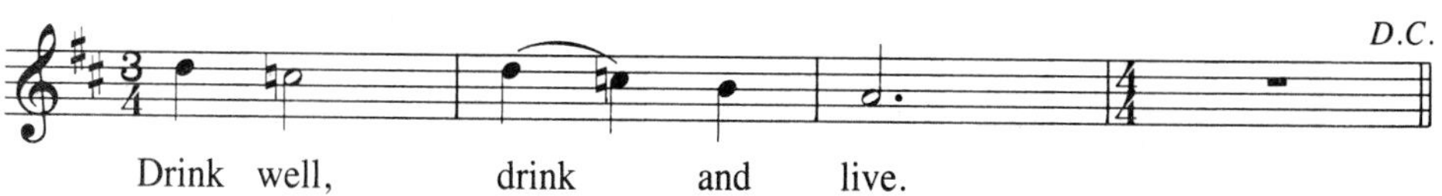
D.C.
Drink well, drink and live.

Text: David Haas, b.1957
Tune: David Haas, b.1957

336 Now in This Banquet

Refrains
1.
2.
Now in this ban-quet, Christ is our bread; Here shall all hun-gers be fed. Bread that is bro-ken, wine that is poured, Love is the sign of our Lord.
*Advent: God of our jour-neys, day-break to night; Lead us to jus-tice and light. Grant us com-pas-sion, strength for the day, Wis-dom to walk in your way.
*Lent: Lord, you can o-pen hearts that are stone; Live in our flesh and our bone; Lead us to won-der, mys-t'ry and grace, One in your lov-ing em-brace.
Verses
1. You who have touched us and graced us with love, make us your peo-ple of good-ness and light.
2. Let our hearts burn with the fire of your love; o-pen our eyes to the glo-ry of God.
D.C.
3. God who makes the blind to see, God who makes the lame to walk, bring us danc-ing in-to day, lead your peo-ple in your way.
D.C.
4. Hope for the hope-less, light for the blind,

*Alternate refrains

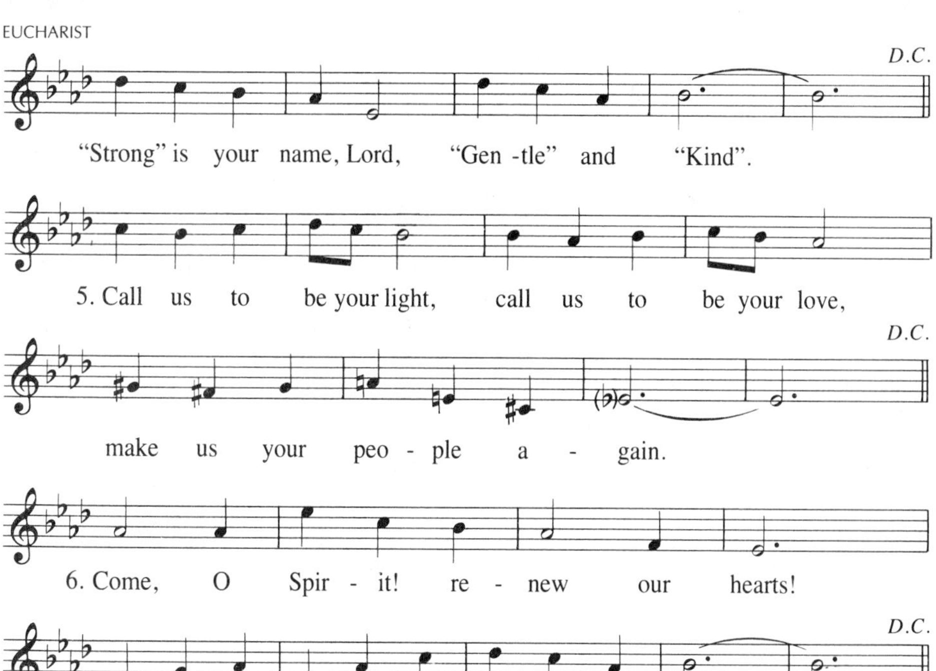
D.C.
"Strong" is your name, Lord, "Gen -tle" and "Kind".
5. Call us to be your light, call us to be your love,
D.C.
make us your peo - ple a - gain.
6. Come, O Spir - it! re - new our hearts!
D.C.
We shall a - rise to be chil - dren of light.

Text: Marty Haugen, b.1950
Tune: Marty Haugen, b.1950

337 I Am the Bread of Life

1. I am the Bread of life. You who
2. The bread that I will give is my
3. Un - less you eat of the
4. I am the Res - ur - rec - tion,
5. Yes, Lord, I be - lieve that
come to me shall not hun - ger; and who be-
flesh for the life of the world, and if you
flesh of the Son of Man and
I am the life. If you be-
you are the Christ, the
lieve in me shall not thirst. No one can come to
eat of this bread, you shall live for
drink of his blood, and drink of his
lieve in me, e - ven though you
Son of God, who have
me un - less the Fa - ther beck - ons.
ev - er, you shall live for ev - er.
blood, you shall not have life with - in you.
die, you shall live for ev - er.
come in - to the world.
And I will raise you up, and I will raise you
up, and I will raise you up on the last day.

Text: John 6; Suzanne Toolan, SM, b.1927
Tune: BREAD OF LIFE, Irregular with refrain; Suzanne Toolan, b.1927

Taste and See 338

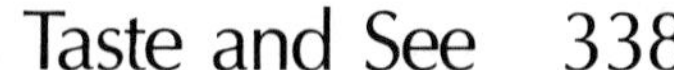

Refrain
Taste and see, taste and see the good - ness of the Lord. O taste and see, taste and see the good - ness of the Lord, of the Lord.
Verses
1. I will bless the Lord at all times. His praise shall al-ways be on my lips; my soul shall glo - ry in the Lord for he has been so good to me.
2. Glo-ri - fy the Lord with me To-geth-er let us all praise his name. I called the Lord and he an - swered me; from all my trou-bles he set me free.
3. Wor-ship the Lord, all you peo-ple. You'll want for noth-ing if you ask. Taste and see that God is good; in him we need put all our trust.
D.C.

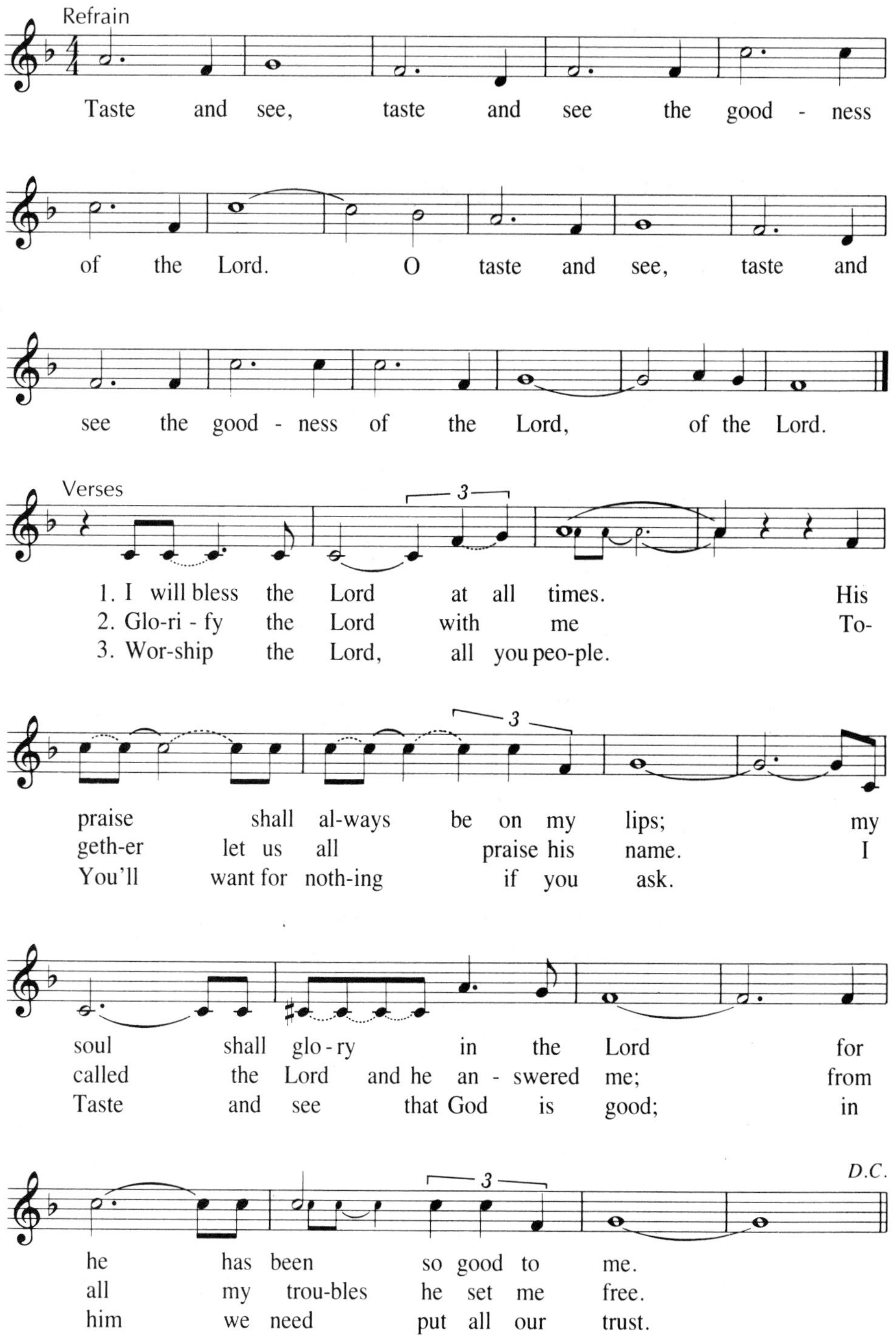

Text: Psalm 34; James E. Moore, Jr.
Tune: James E. Moore, Jr.

339 Life-Giving Bread, Saving Cup

Refrain
Life - giv - ing bread, sav - ing cup, we
of - fer in thanks-giv-ing, O God. Life - giv-ing bread,
sav - ing cup, we of - fer as a sign of our love.
Verses
1. For bread that is bro - ken, we give thanks.
2. We thank you, O Fa - ther, for your name
3. Cre - a - tor of all, we of - fer thanks.
4. Re - mem - ber your Church which sings your praise.
For wine that is poured, we give praise.
which you give to dwell in our hearts.
You give us a share in your life.
Per - fect it in truth and in love.
For life and for knowl-edge of the King - dom,
You bring us to - geth - er as one fam - 'ly:
You strength - en our bod - y and our spir - it:
And gath - er your peo - ple all to - geth - er
D.C.
all praise to you un - til the end of time!
all praise to you un - til the end of time!
all praise to you un - til the end of time!
to praise you un - til the end of time!

Text: Adapted from the *Didache*, 2nd C.; James J. Chepponis, b.1956
Tune: James J. Chepponis, b.1956

In the Breaking of Bread 340

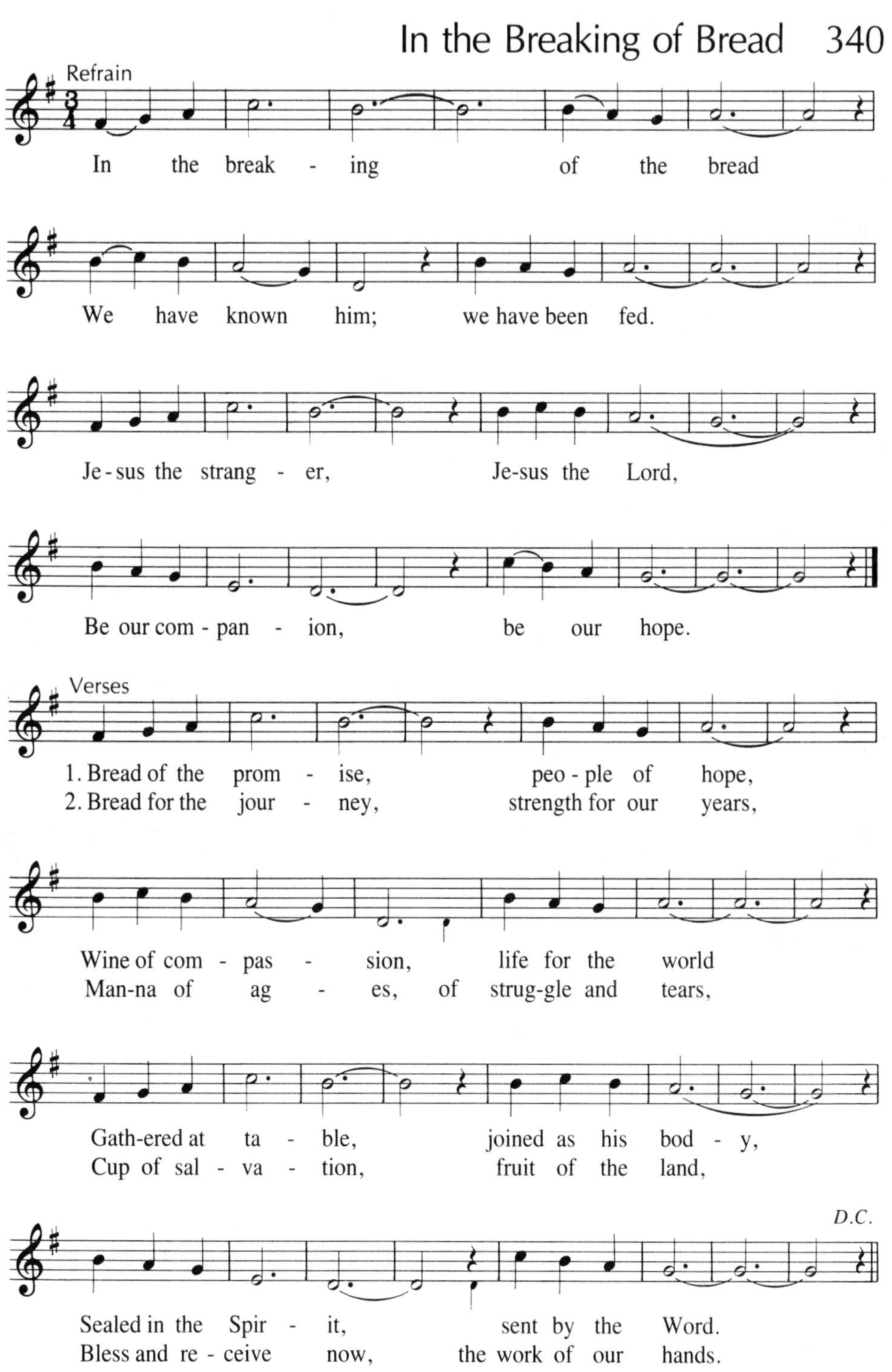

Refrain
In the break - ing of the bread
We have known him; we have been fed.
Je-sus the strang - er, Je-sus the Lord,
Be our com-pan - ion, be our hope.
Verses
1. Bread of the prom - ise, peo-ple of hope,
2. Bread for the jour - ney, strength for our years,
Wine of com - pas - sion, life for the world
Man-na of ag - es, of strug-gle and tears,
Gath-ered at ta - ble, joined as his bod - y,
Cup of sal - va - tion, fruit of the land,
D.C.
Sealed in the Spir - it, sent by the Word.
Bless and re - ceive now, the work of our hands.

Text: Bob Hurd, © 1984
Tune: Bob Hurd, © 1984; Acc. by Dominic MacAller, © 1984, Oregon Catholic Press

341 Eat This Bread

Eat this bread, drink this cup,
come to me and nev - er be hun - gry. Eat this bread,
drink this cup, trust in me and you will not thirst.

Text: John 6; Adapt. by Robert J. Batastini, b.1942, and the Taizé Community, 1984
Tune: Jacques Berthier, b.1923

The Name of God 342

Refrain
I will take the cup of life, I will call God's name all my days.

Verses
1. How can I make a re - turn for the good - ness of
2. The dy - ing of those who keep faith is pre-cious to our
3. To you I will of - fer my thanks and call up - on your

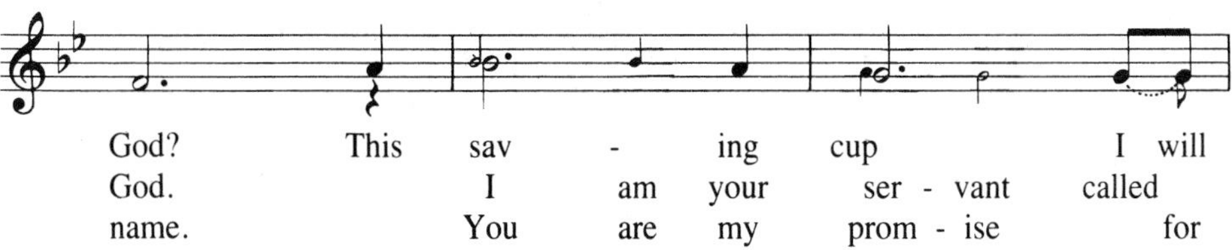
God? This sav - ing cup I will
God. I am your ser - vant called
name. You are my prom - ise for

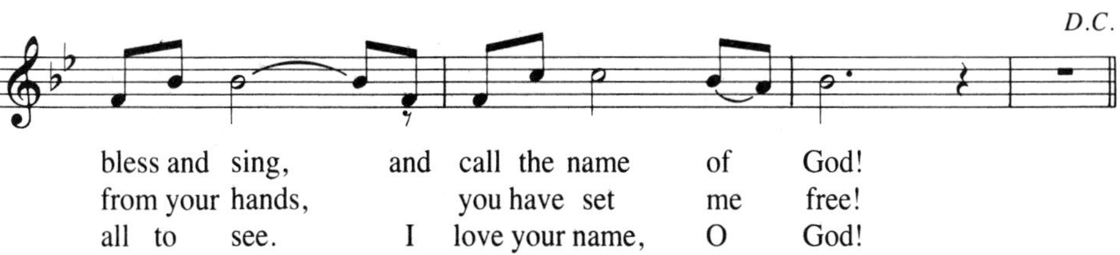
D.C.
bless and sing, and call the name of God!
from your hands, you have set me free!
all to see. I love your name, O God!

Text: Psalm 116; David Haas, b.1957
Tune: David Haas, b.1957

343 Look Beyond

Refrain

Look be-yond the bread you eat; See your Sav-ior and your Lord.

Look be-yond the cup you drink; See his love poured out as blood.

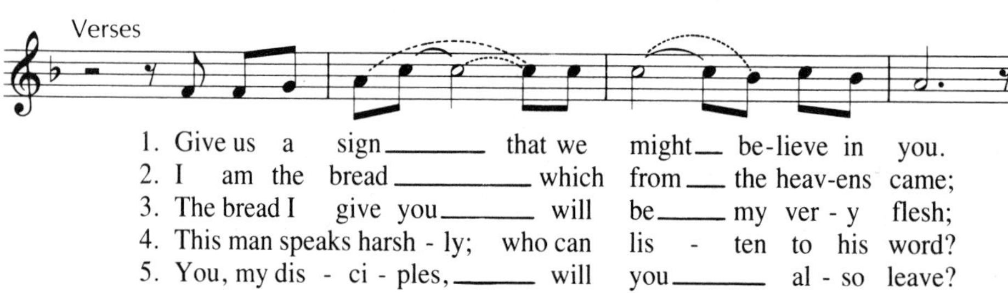
Verses
1. Give us a sign that we might be-lieve in you.
2. I am the bread which from the heav-ens came;
3. The bread I give you will be my ver-y flesh;
4. This man speaks harsh-ly; who can lis-ten to his word?
5. You, my dis-ci-ples, will you al-so leave?

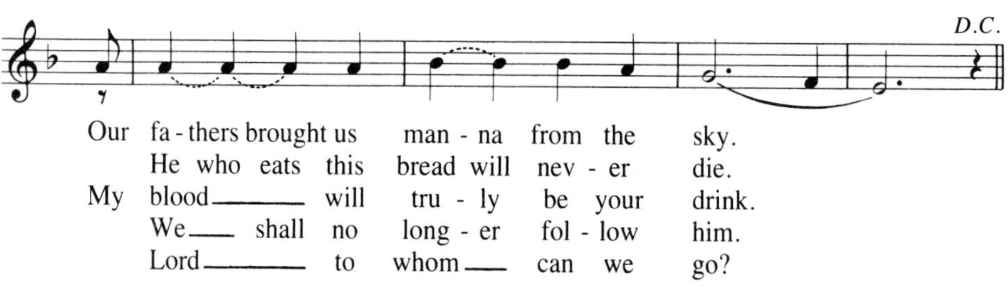
D.C.
Our fa-thers brought us man-na from the sky.
He who eats this bread will nev-er die.
My blood will tru-ly be your drink.
We shall no long-er fol-low him.
Lord to whom can we go?

Text: Darryl Ducote
Tune: Darryl Ducote

Behold the Lamb 344

1. Those who were in the dark are thank-ful for the sun - light;
2. Peace-ful now, those whose hearts are blessed with un-der-stand-ing
3. Gen-tle one, Child of God, join with us at this ta - ble.
4. Lord of all, give us light. De - liv - er us from e - vil.

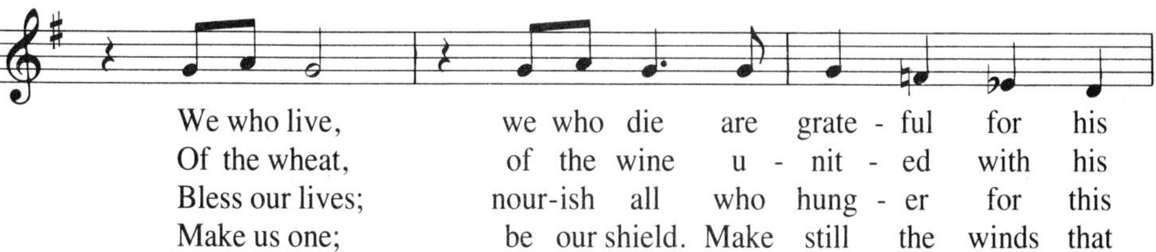

We who live, we who die are grate - ful for his
Of the wheat, of the wine u - nit - ed with his
Bless our lives; nour-ish all who hung - er for this
Make us one; be our shield. Make still the winds that

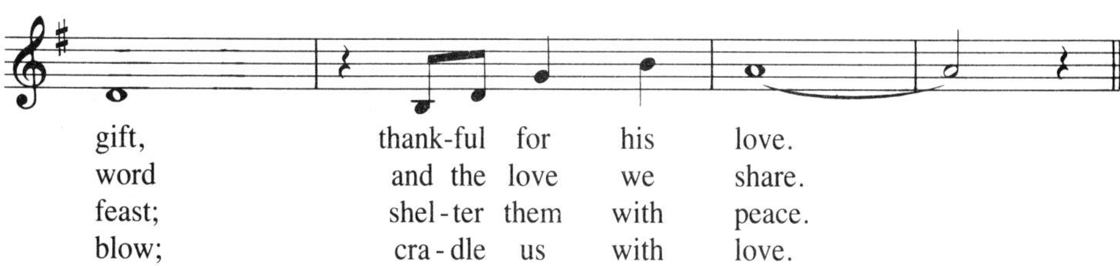

gift, thank-ful for his love.
word and the love we share.
feast; shel-ter them with peace.
blow; cra-dle us with love.

Be - hold, be - hold the Lamb of God. All who eat,

all who drink shall live; and all, all who dwell in

God shall come to know his glo-ry!

Text: Martin Willett
Tune: Martin Willett; Acc. by Craig S. Kingsbury

345 We Who Once Were Dead

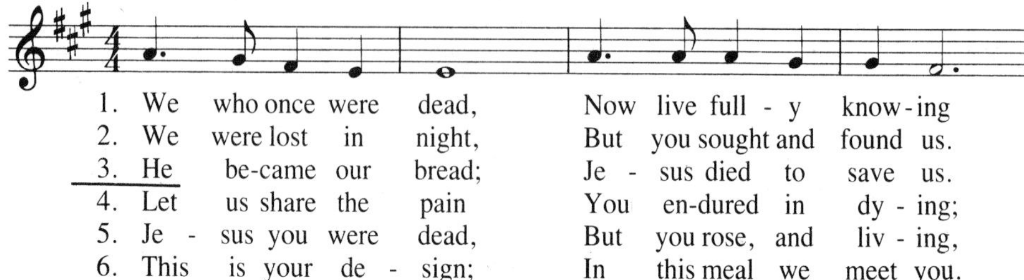
1. We who once were dead, Now live full - y know - ing
2. We were lost in night, But you sought and found us.
3. He be-came our bread; Je - sus died to save us.
4. Let us share the pain You en-dured in dy - ing;
5. Je - sus you were dead, But you rose, and liv - ing,
6. This is your de - sign; In this meal we meet you.

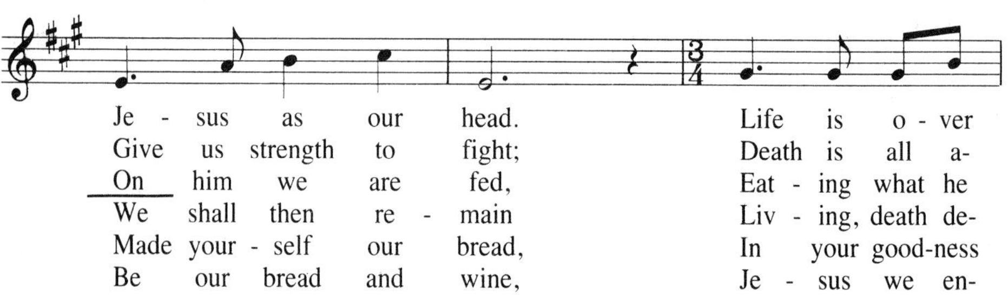
Je - sus as our head. Life is o - ver
Give us strength to fight; Death is all a-
On him we are fed, Eat - ing what he
We shall then re - main Liv - ing, death de-
Made your - self our bread, In your good-ness
Be our bread and wine, Je - sus we en-

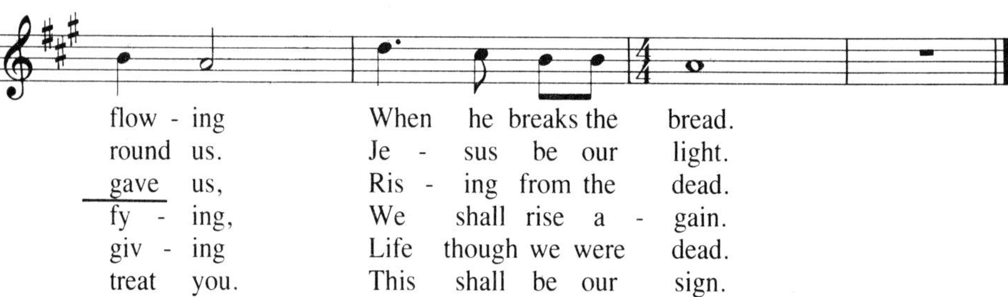
flow - ing When he breaks the bread.
round us. Je - sus be our light.
gave us, Ris - ing from the dead.
fy - ing, We shall rise a - gain.
giv - ing Life though we were dead.
treat you. This shall be our sign.

One Bread, One Body 346

Refrain

One bread, one bod - y, one Lord of all, one cup of bless - ing which we bless. And we, though man - y, through-out the earth, we are one bod - y in this one Lord.

Verses

1. Gen-tile or Jew, ser - vant or free,
2. Man-y the gifts, man - y the works,
3. Grain for the fields, scat-tered and grown,

D.C.
wom-an or man no more.
one in the Lord of all.
gath-ered to one for all.

Text: I Corinthians 10:16, 17, 12:4, Galatians 3:28, The Didache 9; John Foley, SJ
Tune: John Foley, SJ

347 Our Blessing-Cup

Refrain
Our bless-ing - cup is a com - mun - ion in the blood of Christ. Christ.
1. 2.
Verses
1. How shall I make a re - turn to the Lord for all the good he has done for me? The cup of sal - va - tion I will take up, and I will call up - on the name of the Lord.
D.C.
2. Taste and see, taste and see the sweet - ness of the Lord, the

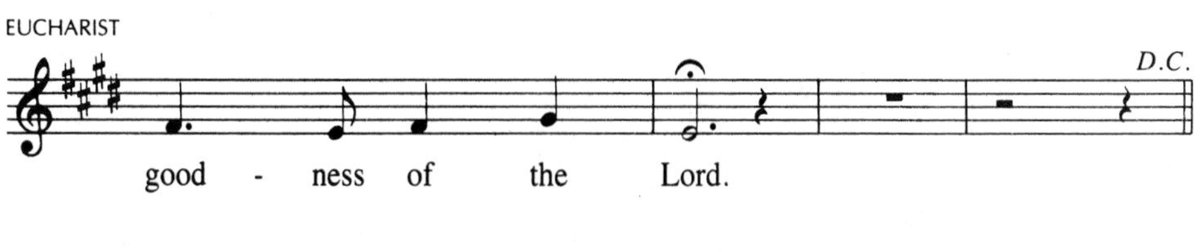
D.C.
good - ness of the Lord.

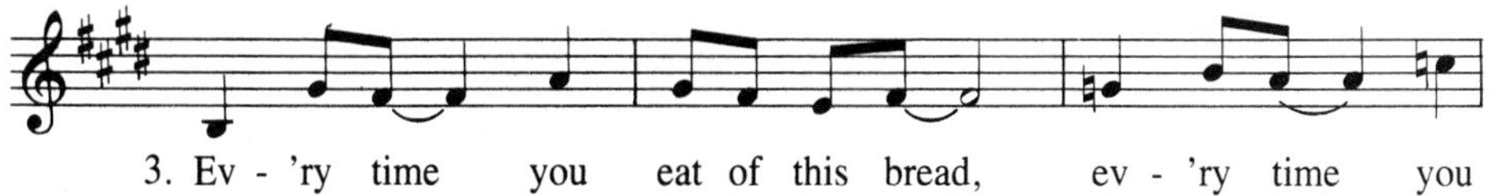
3. Ev - 'ry time you eat of this bread, ev - 'ry time you

drink of this cup you pro - claim the

D.C.
death of the Lord un - til he comes.

Text: I Corinthians 10:16, 11:26, Psalm 116:12, 13, Psalm 34:9a; Michael Joncas, b.1951
Tune: Michael Joncas, b.1951

348 Seed, Scattered and Sown

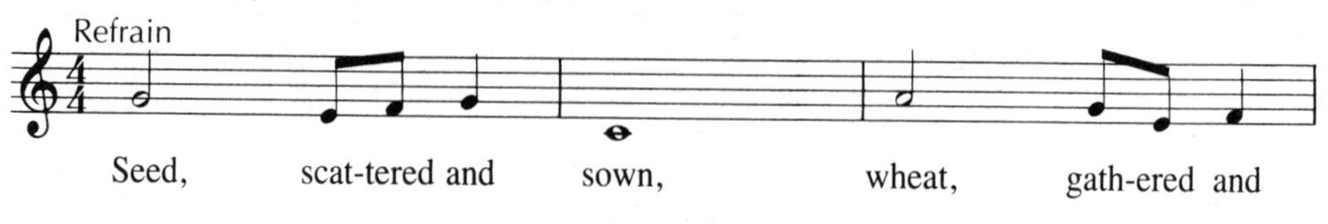
Refrain
Seed, scat-tered and sown, wheat, gath-ered and

grown, bread, bro-ken and shared as one, the

Liv - ing Bread of God. Vine, fruit of the

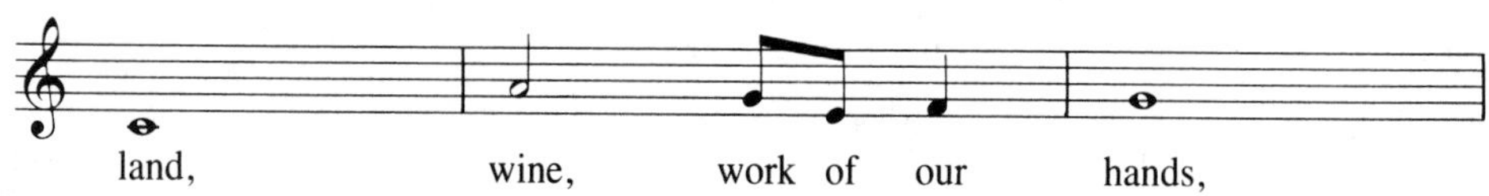
land, wine, work of our hands,

one cup that is shared by all; the Liv - ing Cup, the

Liv - ing Bread of God.

Verses
1. Is not the bread we break, a
2. The seed which falls on rock will
3. As wheat up - on the hills was

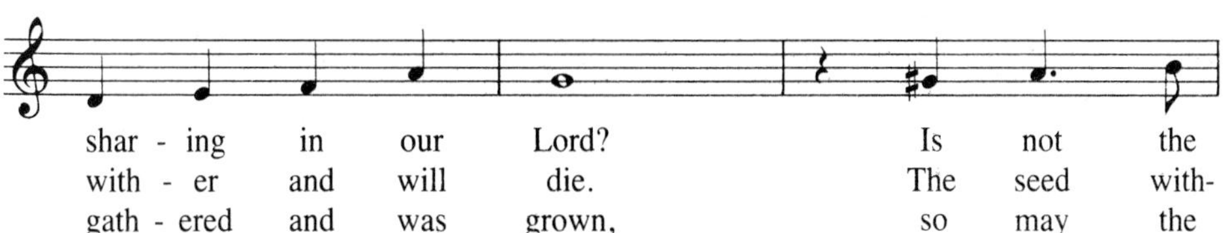
shar - ing in our Lord? Is not the
with - er and will die. The seed with-
gath - ered and was grown, so may the

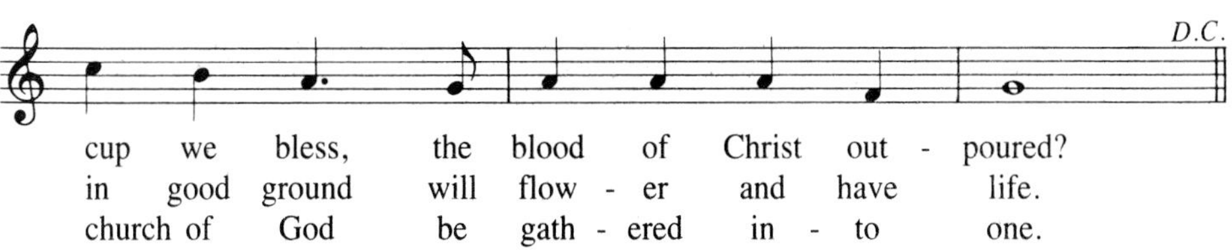
D.C.
cup we bless, the blood of Christ out - poured?
in good ground will flow - er and have life.
church of God be gath - ered in - to one.

Text: Didache 9, 1 Corinthians 10:16-17, Mark 4:3-6; Dan Feiten, EKKLESIA
Tune: Dan Feiten: Keyboard arr. by Eric Gunnison, R.J. Miller

349 Song of Farewell

Refrain
Dy - ing you de - stroyed our death! Ris - ing you re - stored our life!
Lord Je - sus, Lord Je - sus, come in glo - ry!
Verses
1. May Christ who died for you lead you in - to his king-dom;
may Christ who died for you lead you this day in - to Par-a - dise.
D.C.
2. May Christ, the Good Shep-herd, lead you home to - day and
(alternate child's verse):
May Christ, the Good Shep-herd, take you on his shoul-ders and
give you a place with - in his flock.
bring you home, bring you home to - day.
D.C.
3. May the an - gels lead you in - to Par - a - dise; may the
mar-tyrs come to wel-come you and take you to the Ho - ly

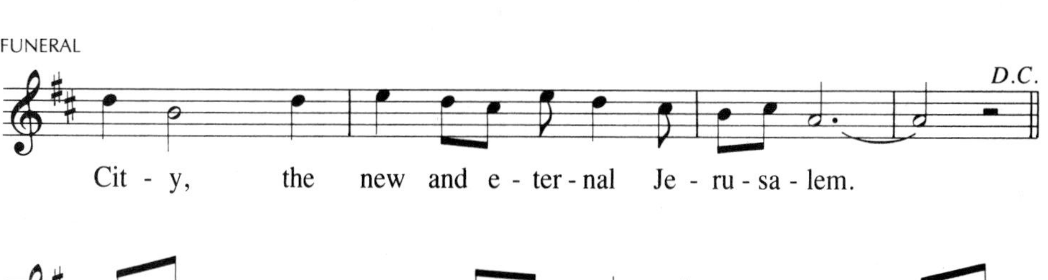
D.C.
Cit - y, the new and e - ter - nal Je - ru - sa - lem.

4. May the choirs of an - gels come to meet you, may the

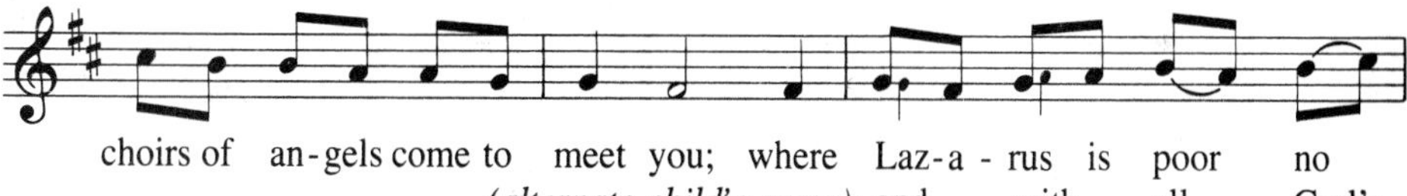
choirs of an-gels come to meet you; where Laz-a - rus is poor no
(alternate child's verse): and with all God's

D.C.
long - er may you have e - ter - nal life in Christ.
chil-dren

Text: Memorial Acclamation, © 1973, ICEL; *In paradisum;* Michael Marchal
Tune: Michael Joncas, b.1951

350 We Will Rise Again

1. Like a shep-herd I will feed you; I will gath - er you with
2. I am strength to the wear - y, to the weak I am new

care. I will lead you and hold you close to my heart.
life. Though the young may grow wear - y; I will be their hope.

Refrain
We will run and not grow wea - ry, for our God will be our

strength, and we will fly like the ea - gle, we will rise a - gain.

3. Lift up your eyes, and see who made the stars. I
4. Fear not, I am with you, I am your God. I will

D.S.
lead you, and I know you, I call you each by name.
strength-en you, and help you; up hold you with my hand.

Text: Isaiah 40:11, 26, 29-30, 41:10; David Haas, b.1957
Tune: David Haas, b.1957

When Love Is Found 351

1. When love is found and hope comes home, Sing and be
2. When love has flow'red in trust and care, Build both each
3. When love is tried as loved-ones change, Hold still to
4. When love is torn and trust be - trayed, Pray strength to
5. Praise God for love, praise God for life, In age or

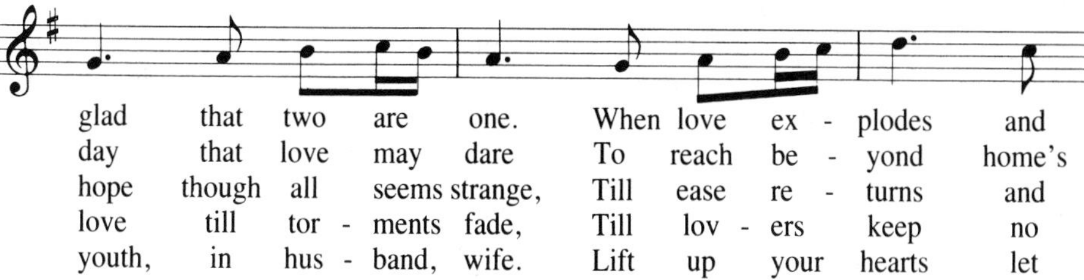

glad that two are one. When love ex - plodes and
day that love may dare To reach be - yond home's
hope though all seems strange, Till ease re - turns and
love till tor - ments fade, Till lov - ers keep no
youth, in hus - band, wife. Lift up your hearts let

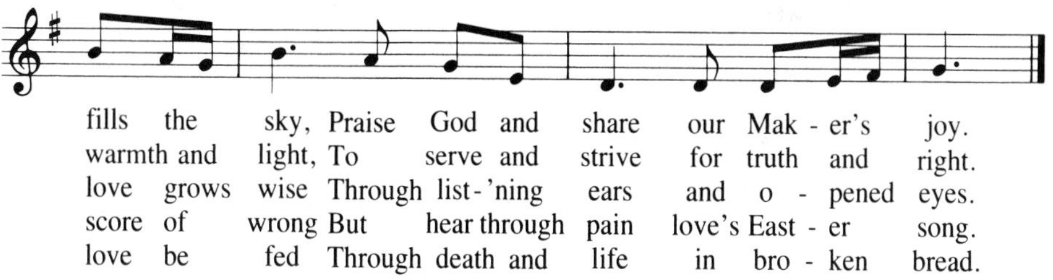

fills the sky, Praise God and share our Mak - er's joy.
warmth and light, To serve and strive for truth and right.
love grows wise Through list-'ning ears and o - pened eyes.
score of wrong But hear through pain love's East - er song.
love be fed Through death and life in bro - ken bread.

Text: Brian Wren, b.1936
Tune: O WALY WALY, LM; Traditional English Melody; Harm. by Martin West, b.1929

352 Your Love, O God

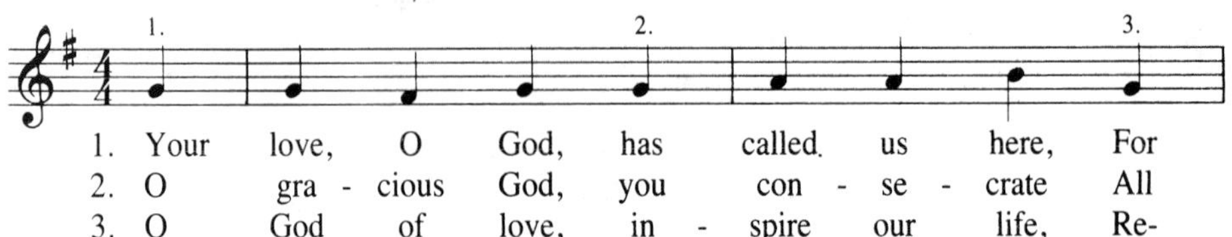
1. 2. 3.
1. Your love, O God, has called us here, For
2. O gra - cious God, you con - se - crate All
3. O God of love, in - spire our life, Re-

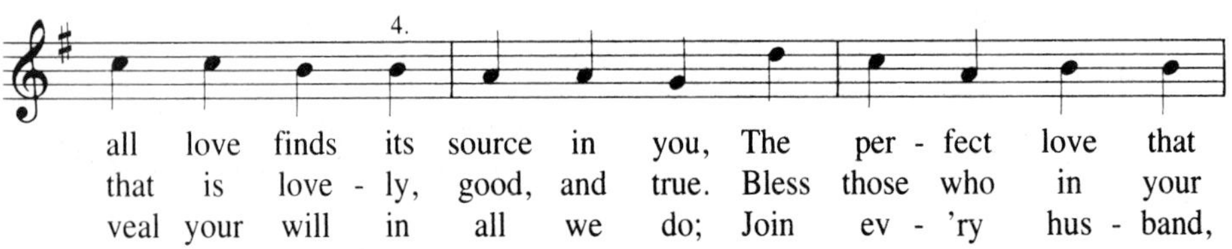
4.
all love finds its source in you, The per - fect love that
that is love - ly, good, and true. Bless those who in your
veal your will in all we do; Join ev - 'ry hus - band,

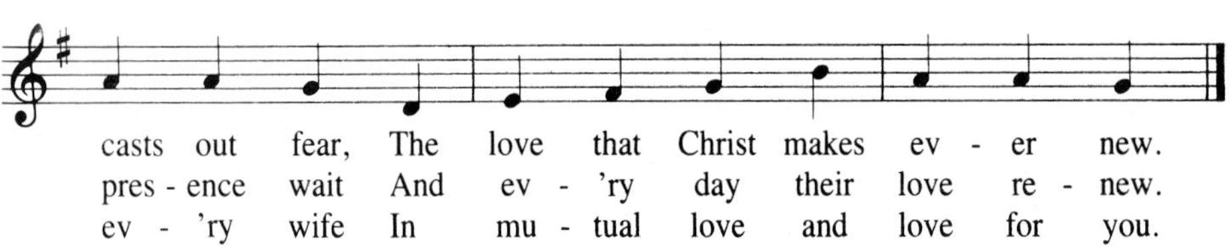
casts out fear, The love that Christ makes ev - er new.
pres - ence wait And ev - 'ry day their love re - new.
ev - 'ry wife In mu - tual love and love for you.

Text: Russell Schulz-Widmar, b.1944, © 1982
Tune: TALLIS' CANON, LM; Thomas Tallis, 1505?-1585

Balm in Gilead 353

Refrain

There is a balm in Gil - e - ad To
make the wound - ed whole, There is a balm in
Gil - e - ad To heal the sin - sick soul.

Verses

1. Some - times I feel dis - cour - aged And
2. If you can - not preach like Pe - ter, If you
3. Don't ev - er feel dis - cour - aged For

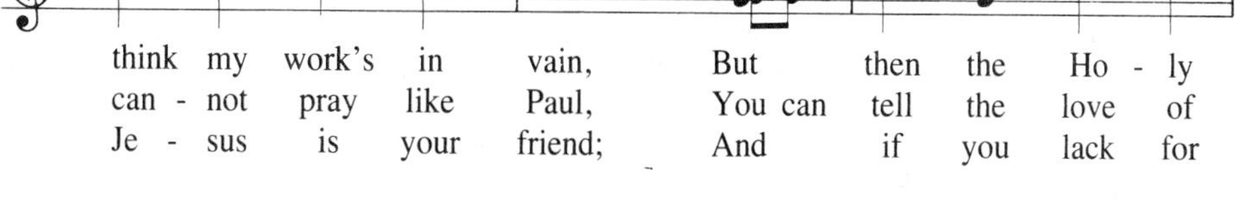
think my work's in vain, But then the Ho - ly
can - not pray like Paul, You can tell the love of
Je - sus is your friend; And if you lack for

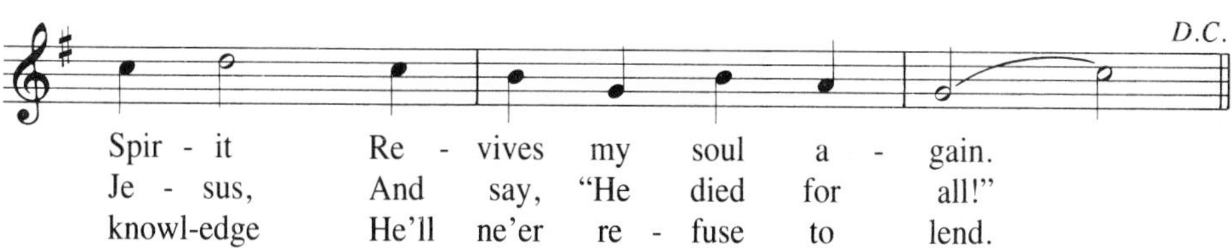
D.C.
Spir - it Re - vives my soul a - gain.
Je - sus, And say, "He died for all!"
knowl-edge He'll ne'er re - fuse to lend.

Text: Jeremiah 8:22; Afro-American Spiritual
Tune: BALM IN GILEAD, Irregular; Afro-American Spiritual; Acc. by Robert J. Batastini, b.1942,

354 Jesus, Heal Us

Refrain
Je - sus, heal us; Je - sus. Je - sus, hear us now.

Verses
1. All who fear the Lord: Wait for his mer - cy.
2. All who fear the Lord: Fol - low in his ways.

D.C.
All who love the Lord: Come, he will fill you.
All who love the Lord: Hope in his good - ness.

3. All who fear the Lord: Keep your hearts pre - pared All who
4. All who trust the Lord: He will up - hold you. Let us

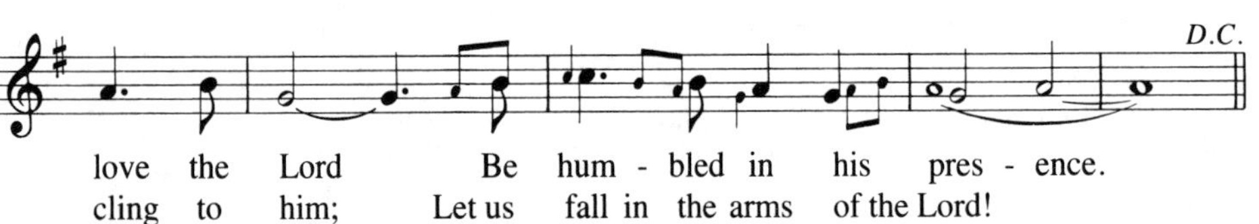
D.C.
love the Lord Be hum - bled in his pres - ence.
cling to him; Let us fall in the arms of the Lord!

Text: David Haas, b.1957
Tune: David Haas, b.1957

Return to Me 355

Refrain
Re - turn to me; I meet you more than half-way,

long - ing to gath - er you to my - self.

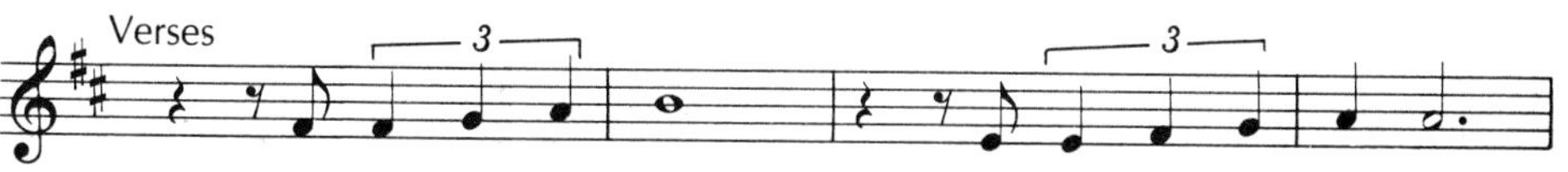
Verses
3
3
1. The more that I call, the far - ther you wan - der.
2. How could I for - get, for - get my be - lov - ed?
3. And when the sheep strays, the shep-herd will fol - low,

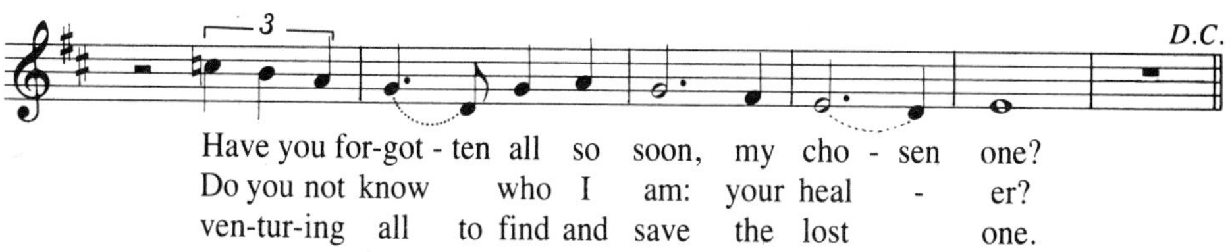
3
D.C.
Have you for-got - ten all so soon, my cho - sen one?
Do you not know who I am: your heal - er?
ven-tur-ing all to find and save the lost one.

Text: Hosea 11, Matthew 18:10-14; Adapt. by Bob Hurd © 1984
Tune: Bob Hurd, © 1984; Arr. by Craig Kingsbury, © 1984, Oregon Catholic Press

356 Remember Your Mercy, O Lord

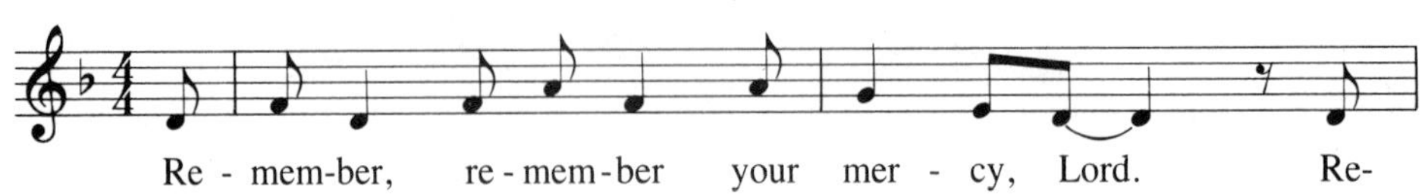
Re - mem-ber, re - mem - ber your mer - cy, Lord. Re-

mem-ber, re-mem-ber your mer - cy, Lord. Hear your peo-ple's prayer

as they call to you: re-mem-ber, re-mem-ber your mer-cy, Lord. 2. Re-
3. The

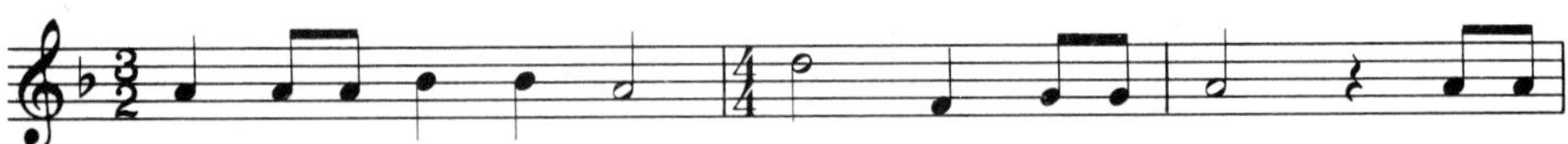
1. Lord, make me know your ways. Lord, teach me your paths. Make me

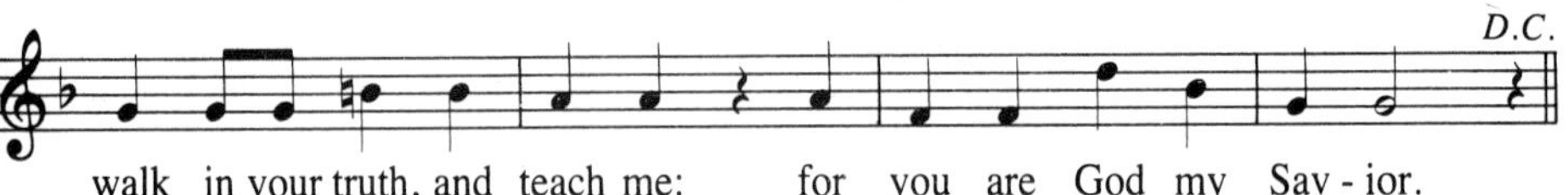
D.C.
walk in your truth, and teach me: for you are God my Sav - ior.

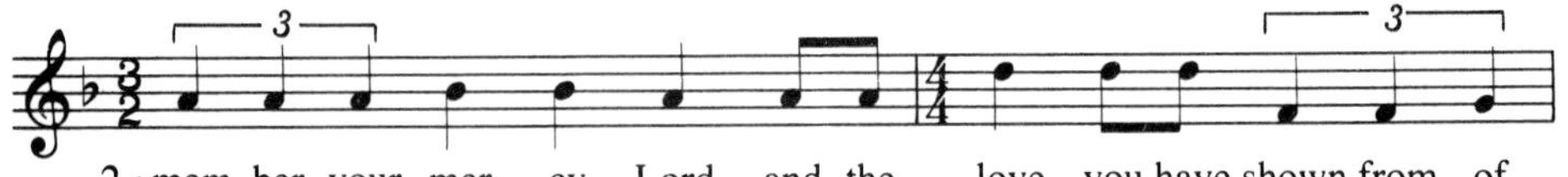
2. mem-ber your mer - cy, Lord, and the love you have shown from of

old. Do not re - mem-ber the sins of my youth.

In your love, re - mem-ber me, in your love, re-

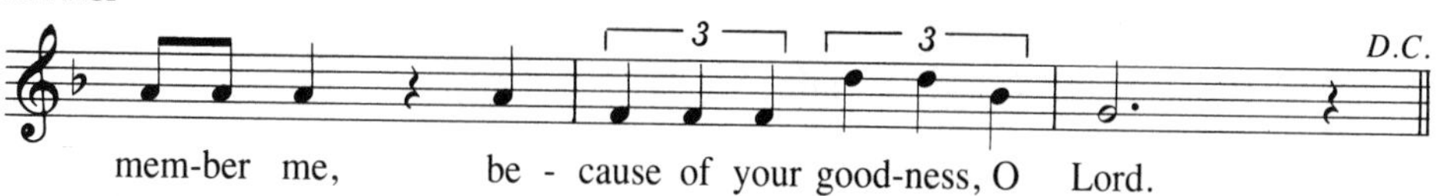
3
3
D.C.
mem-ber me, be - cause of your good-ness, O Lord.

3. Lord is good and up - right. He shows the path to all who

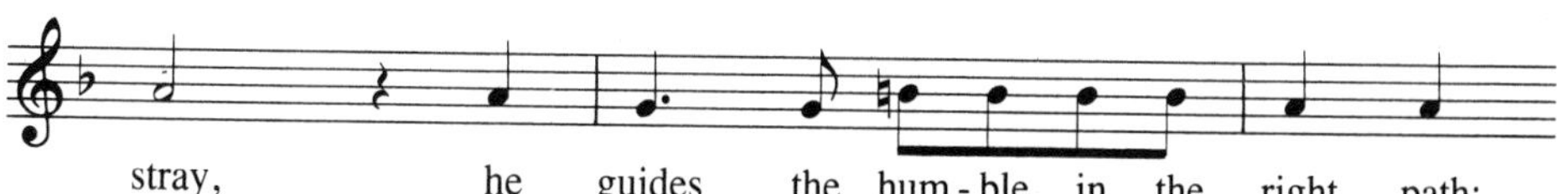
stray, he guides the hum - ble in the right path;

3
D.C.
he teach - es his way to the poor.

Text: Psalm 25:4-9; © 1963, The Grail, GIA Publications, Inc., alt.
Tune: Paul Inwood, © 1987

357 Healer of Our Every Ill

Refrain

Heal - er of our ev - 'ry ill, light of each to - mor - row,

give us peace be - yond our fear, and hope be-yond our sor - row.

Verses

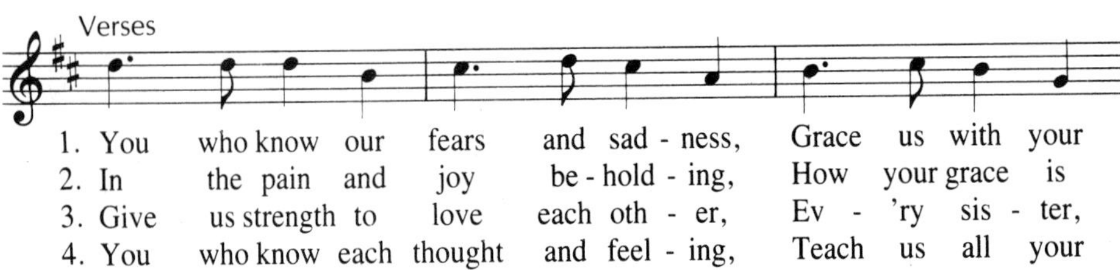
1. You who know our fears and sad - ness, Grace us with your
2. In the pain and joy be - hold - ing, How your grace is
3. Give us strength to love each oth - er, Ev - 'ry sis - ter,
4. You who know each thought and feel - ing, Teach us all your

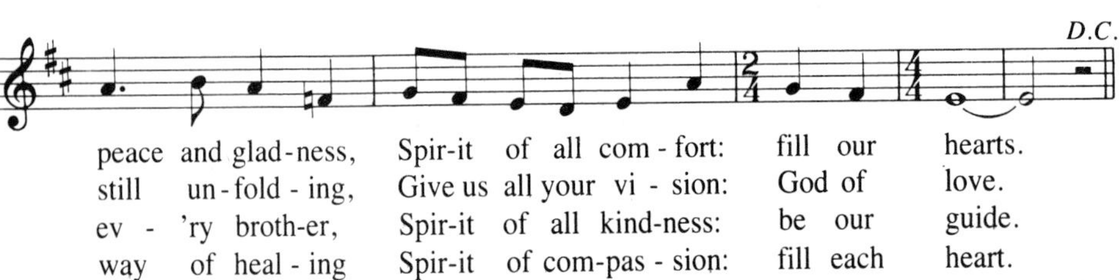
D.C.
peace and glad-ness, Spir-it of all com - fort: fill our hearts.
still un-fold - ing, Give us all your vi - sion: God of love.
ev - 'ry broth-er, Spir-it of all kind-ness: be our guide.
way of heal - ing Spir-it of com-pas - sion: fill each heart.

Text: Marty Haugen, b.1950
Tune: Marty Haugen, b.1950

358 Acknowledgements

MORNING PRAISE AND EVENSONG

All music and texts found from nos. 1 to 17 is copyright by GIA Publications, Inc., with the exception of those items specified below.

SERVICE MUSIC

All music found from nos. 65 to 135 is copyright by GIA Publications, Inc. with the exception of those items specified below.

5 Text: © 1969, James Quinn, SJ. By Permission of Geoffrey Chapman, a division of Cassell Ltd.
10 Text: © William G. Storey.
12 Verses: © 1963, The Grail, England. GIA Publications, Inc., agent.
18 Music and adaptation of verses: © 1983, GIA Publications, Inc. Refrain: © 1969, ICEL.
19 Music and adaptation of verses: © 1983, GIA Publications, Inc. Refrain: © 1969, ICEL.
20 Text and Music: © 1986, GIA Publications, Inc.
21 Music and adaptation of verses: © 1982, GIA Publications, Inc. Refrain: © 1969, ICEL.
22 Music and adaptation of verses: © 1985, North American Liturgy Resources. Refrain: © 1969, ICEL.
23 Music and adaptation of text: © 1983, GIA Publications, Inc.
24 Text of the verses: © 1963, 1986, The Grail, GIA Publications, Inc., agent. Music: © 1985, Paul Inwood. Published in England by St. Thomas More Centre, London. Published and distributed in North America by OCP Publications, Portland, OR 97213.
25 Music, adaptation of verses and refrain 2: © 1987, GIA Publications, Inc. Refrain 1: © 1969, ICEL.
26 Text and Music: © 1978, John B. Foley, SJ and North American Liturgy Resources.
27 Music and adaptation of verses: © 1980, GIA Publications, Inc. Refrain: © 1969, ICEL.
28 Text and Music: © 1980, GIA Publications, Inc.
29 Text and Music: © 1983, GIA Publications, Inc.
30 Music and adaptation of verses: © 1983, GIA Publications, Inc. Refrain: © 1969, ICEL.
31 Text and Music: © 1987, GIA Publications, Inc.
32 Text and Music: © 1987, GIA Publications, Inc.
33 Music: © 1985, North American Liturgy Resources. Verses: © 1963, 1986, The Grail, England, GIA Publications, Inc., agent. Refrain: © 1969, ICEL.
34 Music and Refrain: © 1987, GIA Publications, Inc. Versus: © 1970, New American Bible.
35 Text and Music: © 1982, GIA Publications, Inc.
36 Text and Music: © 1987, GIA Publications, Inc.
37 Text and Music: © 1982, GIA Publications, Inc.
38 Text and Music: © 1979, North American Liturgy Resources.
39 Text and Music: © 1987, GIA Publications, Inc.
40 Music and adaptation of verses: © 1983, GIA Publications, Inc. Refrain: © 1969, ICEL.
41 Music and adaptation of verses: © 1987, GIA Publications, Inc. Refrain: © 1969, ICEL.
42 Text and Music: © 1980, GIA Publications, Inc.
43 Music: © 1983, GIA Publications, Inc. Verses: © 1963, 1986, The Grail, England, GIA Publications, Inc., agent. Refrain: © 1969, ICEL.
44 Text and Music: © 1983, GIA Publications, Inc.
45 Text and Music: © 1983, GIA Publications, Inc.
46 Music and adaptation of verses: © 1983, GIA Publications, Inc. Refrain: © 1969, ICEL.
47 Music and adaptation of verses: © 1985, GIA Publications, Inc. Refrain: © 1969, ICEL.
48 Text and Music: © 1983, GIA Publications, Inc.
49 Music: © 1979, GIA Publications, Inc. Verses: © 1963, 1986, The Grail, England, GIA Publications, Inc., agent. Refrain: © 1969, ICEL.
50 Music and adaptation of verses: © 1983, GIA Publications, Inc. Refrain: © 1969, ICEL.
51 Text and Music: © 1987, GIA Publications, Inc.
52 Music: © 1979, GIA Publications, Inc. Verses: © 1963, 1986, The Grail, England, GIA Publications, Inc., agent.
53 Music and adaptation of verses: © 1987, GIA Publications, Inc. Refrain: © 1969, ICEL.
54 Music: © 1987, Paul Inwood. Published in England by St. Thomas More Centre, London. Published and distributed in North America by OCP Publications, Portland, OR 97213. Verses: © 1963, 1986, The Grail, England, GIA Publications, Inc., agent. Refrain: © 1969, ICEL.
55 Text and Music: © 1988, GIA Publications, Inc.
56 Music and adaptation of verses: © 1983, GIA Publications, Inc. Refrain: © 1969, ICEL.
57 Text and Music: © 1983, North American Liturgy Resources.
58 Text and Music: © 1987, GIA Publications, Inc.
59 Text and Music: © 1987, GIA Publications, Inc.
61 Music and Text: © 1987, GIA Publications, Inc.
62 Music and text of the refrain: © 1979, GIA Publications, Inc. Verses: © 1963, 1986, The Grail, England, GIA Publications, Inc., agent.
63 Text and Music: © 1964, World Library Publications, Inc.
65 Text: © 1984, GIA Publications, Inc.
71 Text: © 1984, GIA Publications, Inc.
104 Text: © 1987, GIA Publications, Inc.
114 Text: © 1987, GIA Publications, Inc.
115 Music: ©, Verbum Forlong AB, Sweden.
116 Text and Music: © 1973, Joe Wise, GIA Publications, Inc., agent.
117 Text and Music: © 1985, Fintan O'Carroll and Christopher Walker. Published in England by St. Thomas More Centre, London. Published and distributed in North America by OCP Publications, Portland, OR 97213.
118 Music: © 1982, 1983, 1984, Les Presses de Taizé, GIA Publications, Inc., agent.
121 Text: © 1983, GIA Publications, Inc.
122 Text and Music: © 1979, Joe Wise, GIA Publications, Inc., agent.
123 Text and Music: © 1984, Bob Hurd. Arrangement © 1984, OCP Publications, Portland, OR 97213.
124 Text: © 1987, GIA Publications, Inc.
125 Music: © 1978, 1980, 1981, Les Presses de Taizé, GIA Publications, Inc., agent.
129 Adaptation: © 1980, The Church Pension Fund.
132 Music: © 1971, 1972, Joe Wise. GIA Publications, Inc., agent.
133 Music: © 1984, Paul Inwood. Published in England by St. Thomas More Centre, London. Published and distributed in North America by OCP Publications, Portland, OR 97213.
135 Music: © 1977, St. Vincent Archabbey, Latrobe, PA 15650.
136 Text and Music: © 1984, TEAM Publications, OCP Publications, Portland, OR 97213, agent.
137 Text and Music: © 1982, GIA Publications, Inc.
138 Text and Tune: © 1971, The United Church Press. Reprinted from *A New Song 3*. Accompaniment: © 1987, GIA Publications, Inc.
139 Text and Music: © 1984, Les Presses de Taizé, GIA Publications, Inc., agent.
140 Text and Music: © 1983, GIA Publications, Inc.
141 Text and Music: © 1979, OCP Publications, Portland, OR 97213.
142 Text and Music: © 1982, Bernadette Farrell. Published in England by St. Thomas More Centre, London. Published and distributed in North America by OCP Publications, Portland, OR 97213.
143 Text and Music: © 1987, GIA Publications, Inc.

Acknowledgements/*continued*

144 Text and Music: © 1985, TEAM Publications, OCP Publications, Portland, OR 97213, agent.
145 Text: © 1980, Hope Publishing Company, Carol Stream, IL 60188. All Rights Reserved. Used by Permission. Music: © 1985, GIA Publications, Inc.
146 Text and Music: © 1984, GIA Publications, Inc.
148 Tune: © 1968, Joe Wise, GIA Publications, Inc., agent. Accompaniment: © 1968, Saul Stirks.
149 Text and Music: © 1979, 1988, Les Presses de Taizé, GIA Publications, Inc., agent.
150 Text and Music: © 1987, GIA Publications, Inc.
151 Text and Music: © 1983, GIA Publications, Inc.
152 Text and Music: © 1987, GIA Publications, Inc.
153 Harmonization: © 1987, GIA Publications, Inc.
154 Text: © 1984, TEAM Publications, OCP Publications, Portland, OR 97213, agent. Music: © 1986, GIA Publications, Inc.
155 Text and Music: © 1987, GIA Publications, Inc.
156 Harmonization: © 1987, GIA Publications, Inc.
157 Text and Music: © 1978, Damean Music.
158 Text and Music: © 1978, Damean Music.
159 Text and Music: © 1987, GIA Publications, Inc.
160 Text: © 1982, Thomas H. Cain. Music: © 1988, GIA Publications, Inc.
161 Text and Music: © 1988, GIA Publications, Inc.
162 Text: © 1972, James Quinn, SJ. By permission of Geoffrey Chapman, a division of Cassell Ltd. Music: © 1984, The Church Pension Fund.
163 Text and Music: © 1984, GIA Publications, Inc.
164 Music: © 1984, GIA Publications, Inc.
165 Text and Music: © 1987, GIA Publications, Inc.
166 Text and Music: © 1984, Les Presses de Taizé, GIA Publications, Inc., agent.
167 Text and Music: © 1981, Les Presses de Taizé, GIA Publications, Inc., agent.
168 Text and adaptation of tune: © 1969, Hope Publishing Company, Carol Stream, IL 60188. International Copyright Secured. All Rights Reserved. Harmonization: © 1987, GIA Publications, Inc.
169 Arrangement: © 1987, GIA Publications, Inc.
170 Text and Music: © 1984, Les Presses de Taizé, GIA Publications, Inc., agent.
171 Harmonization: © 1987, GIA Publications, Inc.
173 Text and Music: © 1978, North American Liturgy Resources.
174 Text: © 1966, *The Jerusalem Bible*. Music: © 1979, St. Meinrad Archabbey, St. Meinrad, IN 47557.
175 Text: From the *Oxford Book of Carols* by permission of Oxford University Press. Accompaniment: © 1987, GIA Publications, Inc.
176 Text and Music: © 1978, Les Presses de Taizé, GIA Publications, Inc., agent.
177 Text and Music: © 1984, Les Presses de Taizé, GIA Publications, Inc., agent.
178 Text and Music: © 1983, GIA Publications, Inc.
179 Text and Music: © 1987, GIA Publications, Inc.
180 Text and Arrangement: © 1986, GIA Publications, Inc.
181 Text and Music: © 1987, GIA Publications, Inc.
182 Harmonizations: From *The Oxford Book of Carols* used by permission of Oxford University Press.
183 Text: © 1975, Hope Publishing Company, Carol Stream, IL 60188. All Rights Reserved. Used by Permission. Accompaniment: © 1987, GIA Publications, Inc.
184 Text: © 1956, Hymns Ancient and Modern, Ltd. Stanza 5, © 1971, Walton Music Corporation. Accompaniment: © 1987, GIA Publications, Inc.
185 Harmonization: © 1984, Jack W. Burnham.
186 Text and Music: © 1984, Les Presses de Taizé, GIA Publications, Inc., agent.
187 Text and Music: © 1984, TEAM Publications. OCP Publications, Portland, OR 97213, agent.
188 Text and Music: © 1983, GIA Publications, Inc.
189 Text and Music: © 1981, 1982, David Haas, GIA Publications, Inc., agent.
190 Text: © 1968, Hope Publishing Company, Carol Stream, IL 60188. All Rights Reserved. Used by Permission. Music: © 1987, GIA Publications, Inc.
191 Text and Music: © 1987, GIA Publications, Inc.
192 Text and Adaptation: © 1969, Hope Publishing Company, Carol Stream, IL 60188. International Copyright Secured. All Rights Reserved. Used by Permission. Accompaniment: © 1987, GIA Publications, Inc.
193 Text and Music: © 1979, Les Presses de Taizé, GIA Publications, Inc., agent.
194 Text and Music: © 1984, TEAM Publications, OCP Publications, Portland, OR 97213, agent.
195 Text: © 1983, Hope Publishing Company, Carol Stream, IL 60188. All Rights Reserved. Used by Permission. Music: © 1987, GIA Publications, Inc.
196 Text and Music: © 1987, GIA Publications, Inc.
197 Text and Music: © 1980, GIA Publications, Inc.
198 Text and Music: © 1985, GIA Publications, Inc.
199 Text and Music: © 1975, Saint Joseph Abbey, Saint Benedict, LA 70457.
200 Text and Music: © 1986, GIA Publications, Inc.
201 Text: © 1981, Hope Publishing Company, Carol Stream, IL 60188. All Rights Reserved. Used by Permission. Music: © 1987, GIA Publications, Inc.
202 Text and Music: © 1978, John B. Foley and North American Liturgy Resources.
203 Text and Music: © 1984, TEAM Publications. OCP Publications, Portland, OR 97213, agent.
204 Text and Music: © 1982, 1988, GIA Publications, Inc.
205 Text and Tune: © 1978, 1979, Greg Hayakawa. Accompaniment: © 1985, OCP Publications, Portland, OR 97213, agent.
206 Music: © 1987, GIA Publications, Inc.
207 Music: © 1987, GIA Publications, Inc.
208 Text and Tune: © 1970, 1975, Celebration, administered by Maranatha! Music. Accompaniment: © 1987, GIA Publications, Inc.
209 Text and Music: © 1988, GIA Publications, Inc.
210 Text and Music: © 1986, Bernadette Farrell. Published in England by St. Thomas More Centre, London. Published and distributed in North America by OCP Publications, Portland, OR 97213.
211 Text and Music: © 1986, GIA Publications, Inc.
212 Text and Music: © 1983, GIA Publications, Inc.
213 Text and Music: © 1974, 1975, Celebration, administered by Maranatha! Music.
214 Text and Music: © 1983, GIA Publications, Inc.
215 Text and Music: © 1985, GIA Publications, Inc.
216 Text and Music: © 1980, Les Presses de Taizé, GIA Publications, Inc., agent.
217 Text and Tune: © 1981, Ernest Sands. Accompaniment: © 1986, Paul Inwood. Descant: © 1984, Christopher Walker. Published in England by St. Thomas More Centre, London. Published and distributed in North America by OCP Publications, Portland, OR 97213.
218 Text and Music: © 1973, Hope Publishing Company, Carol Stream, IL 60188. All Rights Reserved. Used by Permission.
219 Text and Music: © 1972, GIA Publications, Inc.
220 Text and Music: © 1981, GIA Publications, Inc.
221 Text and Music: © 1979, Les Presses de Taizé, GIA Publications, Inc., agent.
222 Text and Music: © 1983, 1987, GIA Publications, Inc.
223 Text and Music: © 1979, Les Presses de Taizé, GIA Publications, Inc., agent.
224 Text and Music: © 1978, Damean Music.
225 Text and Tune: © 1984, Bob Hurd. Accompaniment: © 1984, OCP Publications, Portland, OR 97213.
226 Text and Music: © 1980, GIA Publications, Inc.
227 Text and Music: © 1976, Robert F. O'Connor and North American Liturgy Resources.
228 Text: © 1969, James Quinn, SJ. By permission of Geoffrey Chapman, a division of Cassell Ltd. Music: © 1979, GIA Publications, Inc.
229 Text and Music: © 1979, North American Liturgy Resources.
230 Text and Music: © 1972, Daniel L. Schutte and North American Liturgy Resources.
231 Text and Music: © 1981, Robert F. O'Connor, SJ and North American Liturgy Resources.
232 Text and Music: © 1985, Daniel L. Schutte and North American Liturgy Resources.
233 Text and Music: © 1976, Daniel L. Schutte and North American Liturgy Resources.

Acknowledgements/*continued*

234 Text and Music: © 1975, Robert J. Dufford, SJ and North American Liturgy Resources.
235 Text and Music: © 1981, John Foley, SJ and North American Liturgy Resources.
236 Text and Music: © 1988, GIA Publications, Inc.
237 Text and Music: © 1982, Les Presses de Taizé, GIA Publications, Inc., agent.
238 Text and Music: © 1985, Damean Music.
239 Text and Music: © 1978, Les Presses de Taizé, GIA Publications, Inc., agent.
240 Text and Music: © 1982, Les Presses de Taizé, GIA Publications, Inc., agent.
241 Text and Music: © 1985, TEAM Publications, OCP Publications, Portland, OR 97213, agent.
242 Arrangement: © 1982, GIA Publications, Inc.
243 Text and Music: © 1966, Joe Wise, GIA Publications, Inc., agent.
244 Text and Music: © 1985, GIA Publications, Inc., agent.
245 Text: © 1979, Stainer and Bell. Music: © 1987, GIA Publications, Inc.
246 Text and Tune: © 1983, Word Music, a division of Word, Inc. All Rights Reserved. Accompaniment: © 1985, OCP Publications, Portland, OR 97213.
247 Text and Music: © 1986, GIA Publications, Inc.
248 Text and Music: © 1982, GIA Publications, Inc.
249 Text and Music: © 1980, GIA Publications, Inc.
250 Text and Music: © 1988, GIA Publications, Inc.
251 Text: © 1963, 1986, The Grail, England, GIA Publications, Inc., agent. Refrain and Music: © 1985, Paul Inwood. Published in England by St. Thomas More Centre, London. Published and distributed in North America by OCP Publications, Portland, OR 97213.
252 Music: © 1984, GIA Publications, Inc.
253 Text and Music: © 1985, Jeffrey Keyes and Vineyard Pastoral Music Ministry. Taken from *A Gentle Strength* published by Resource Publications, Inc. All Rights Reserved.
254 Text and Music: © 1974, TEAM Publications, OCP Publications, Portland, OR 97213, agent.
255 Text and Music: © 1982, Dennis Vessels.
256 Text and Music: © 1974, TEAM Publications, OCP Publications, Portland, OR 97213, agent.
257 Text and Music: © 1969, Damean Music.
258 Text and Tune: © 1986, Bob Hurd. Accompaniment: © 1986, OCP Publications, Portland, OR 97213.
259 Text and Tune: © 1978, Damean Music.
260 Harmonization: © 1987, GIA Publications, Inc.
261 Text and Music: © 1979, North American Liturgy Resources.
262 Text and Music: © 1975, Daniel L. Schutte and North American Liturgy Resources.
263 Text and Music: © 1975, Robert J. Dufford, SJ, and North American Liturgy Resources.
264 Text and Music: © 1976, 1979, Daniel L. Schutte and North American Liturgy Resources.
265 Text and Music: © 1979, North American Liturgy Resources.
266 Text and Music: © 1981, North American Liturgy Resources.
267 Text and Music: © 1961, 1962, World Library Publications, Inc.
268 Text and Music: © 1983, GIA Publications, Inc.
269 Text and Music: © 1988, GIA Publications, Inc.
270 Text and Music: © 1987, GIA Publications, Inc.
271 Text and Music: © 1979, Les Presses de Taizé, GIA Publications, Inc., agent.
272 Text: © 1980, Robert Trupia. Music: © 1980, Bob Hurd. Arrangement: © 1985, OCP Publications, Portland, OR 97213.
273 Text: © 1985, Hope Publishing Company, Carol Stream, IL 60188. All Rights Reserved. Used by Permission. Music: © 1988, GIA Publications, Inc.
274 Text and Tune: © 1979, Joe Wise, GIA Publications, Inc., agent. Accompaniment: © 1987, GIA Publications, Inc.
275 Text and Music: © 1982, GIA Publications, Inc.
276 Text and Tune: © 1984, Bob Hurd. Harmonization: © 1984, OCP Publications, Portland, OR 97213.
277 Text and Music: © 1982, GIA Publications, Inc.
278 Text and Music: © 1984, Les Presses de Taizé, GIA Publications, Inc., agent.
279 Text and Music: © 1985, Christopher Walker. Published in England by St. Thomas More Centre, London. Published and distributed in North America by OCP Publications, Portland, OR 97213.
280 Text and Music: © 1986, GIA Publications, Inc.
281 Text and Music: © 1984, TEAM Publications, OCP Publications, Portland, OR 97213, agent.
282 Acompaniment: © 1987, GIA Publications, Inc.
283 Text and Music: © 1983, GIA Publications, Inc.
284 Text and Music: © 1985, GIA Publications, Inc.
285 Text and Music: © 1977, Scripture in Song, administered by Maranatha! Music.
286 Music: © 1979, Resource Publications, Inc. All Rights Reserved.
287 Text and Music: © 1972, GIA Publications, Inc.
288 Text and Music: © 1987, GIA Publications, Inc.
289 Text and Music: © 1972, TEAM Publications, OCP Publications, Portland, OR 97213, agent.
290 Text for stanzas 2-5 and Accompaniment: © 1987, GIA Publications, Inc.
291 Text and Music: © 1981, Daniel L. Schutte and North American Liturgy Resources.
292 Text and Music: © 1981, Damean Music.
293 Text and Music: © 1984, Utryck. Used by Permission of Walton Music Corporation.
294 Text and Music: © 1981, Daniel L. Schutte and North American Liturgy Resources.
295 Text and Music: © 1988, GIA Publications, Inc.
296 Text and Music: © 1983, GIA Publications, Inc.
297 Text and Harmonization: © 1963, Galliard Publications, Inc.
298 Text and Music: © 1978, North American Liturgy Resources.
299 Text and Music: © 1983, GIA Publications, Inc.
300 Text and Music: © 1985, GIA Publications, Inc.
301 Text and Music: © 1987, GIA Publications, Inc.
302 Text and Music: © 1985, World Library Publications, Inc.
303 Text and Music: © 1985, GIA Publications, Inc.
304 Text and Music: © 1979, The Order of St. Benedict, Inc. Published by The Liturgical Press, Collegeville, MN.
305 Text and Music: © 1987, GIA Publications, Inc.
306 Text and Music: © 1975, Carey Landry and North American Liturgy Resources.
307 Text and Music: © 1984, Les Presses de Taizé, GIA Publications, Inc., agent.
308 Text and Tune: ©, Verbum Forlong AB. Sweden. Accompaniment: © 1987, GIA Publications, Inc.
309 Text and Music: © 1982, Joe Wise, GIA Publications, Inc., agent.
310 Text and Music: © 1980, 1986, GIA Publications, Inc.
311 Text and Music: © 1982, GIA Publications, Inc.
312 Text and Music: © 1987, GIA Publications, Inc.
313 Text: © 1984, TEAM Publications, OCP Publications, Portland, OR 97213, agent. Accompaniment: © 1987, GIA Publications, Inc.
314 Text and Music: © 1981, North American Liturgy Resources.
315 Text and Music: © 1981, 1982, David Haas, OCP Publications, Portland, OR 97213, agent.
316 Text: © 1975, James Quinn, SJ. By permission of Geoffrey Chapman, a division of Cassell Ltd. Harmonization: © 1987, GIA Publications, Inc.
317 Text: From "The Children's Bells", published by Oxford University Press. ©, David Higham Assoc., Ltd. Accompaniment: © 1987, GIA Publications, Inc.
318 Text and Music: © 1987, GIA Publications, Inc.
319 Text and Harmonization: © 1985, GIA Publications, Inc.
320 Text: © 1974, Hope Publishing Company, Carol Stream, IL 60188. All Rights Reserved. Used by Permission. Music: © 1985, GIA Publications, Inc.
321 Text and Music: © 1987, GIA Publications, Inc.
322 Text and Music: © 1985, TEAM Publications, OCP Publications, Portland, OR 97213, agent.
323 Text and Music: © 1984, Utryck, Used by Permission of Walton Music Corporation.
324 Text and Music: © 1976, Timothy Manion and North American Liturgy Resources.
325 Text and Music: © 1986, Les Presses de Taizé, GIA Publications, Inc., agent.
326 Harmonization: © 1987, GIA Publications, Inc.

Acknowledgements/*continued*

327 Text and Harmonization: © 1987, GIA Publications, Inc.
328 Text: © 1985, Hope Publishing Company, Carol Stream, IL 60188. All Rights Reserved. Used by Permission. Music: © 1987, GIA Publications, Inc.
329 Text: © 1983, Hope Publishing Company, Carol Stream, IL 60188. All Rights Reserved. Used by Permission. Music: © 1987, GIA Publications, Inc.
330 Text and Music: © 1987, GIA Publications, Inc.
331 Music: © 1987, GIA Publications, Inc.
332 Text: © 1982, Hope Publishing Company, Carol Stream, IL 60188. All Rights Reserved. Used by Permission. Music: © 1987, GIA Publications, Inc.
333 Text and Music: © 1987, GIA Publications, Inc.
334 Text and Music: © 1979, North American Liturgy Resources.
335 Text and Music: © 1985, GIA Publications, Inc.
336 Text and Music: © 1986, GIA Publications, Inc.
337 Text and Music: © 1970, 1985, GIA Publications, Inc.
338 Text and Music: © 1983, GIA Publications, Inc.
339 Text and Music: © 1987, GIA Publications, Inc.
340 Text and Tune: © 1984, Bob Hurd. Accompaniment: © 1984, OCP Publications, Portland, OR 97213, agent.
341 Text and Music: © 1984, Les Presses de Taizé, GIA Publications, Inc., agent.
342 Text and Music: © 1987, GIA Publications, Inc.
343 Text and Music: © 1969, 1979, Damean Music.
344 Text and Music: © 1982, Oregon Catholic Press.
345 Text: © 1963, Gooi en Sticht n.v. Hilversum, The Netherlands. Music: © 1987, GIA Publications, Inc.
346 Text and Music: © 1978, John B. Foley SJ and North American Liturgy Resources.
347 Text and Music: © 1979, North American Liturgy Resources.
348 Text and Music: © 1987, EKKLESIA MUSIC, INC., P.O. Box 22967, Denver, CO 80222. All Rights Reserved. From the recording and Songbook, "Seed, Scattered and Sown" by EKKLESIA.
349 Text: © 1973, ICEL. Compilation of text and music: © 1988, GIA Publications, Inc.
350 Text and Music: © 1985, David Haas, OCP Publications, Portland, OR 97213, agent.
351 Text and Harmonization: © 1983, Hope Publishing Company, Carol Stream, IL 60188. All Rights Reserved. Used by Permission.
352 Text: © 1982, Russell Schulz-Widmar.
353 Accompaniment: © 1987, GIA Publications, Inc.
354 Text and Music: © 1987, GIA Publications, Inc.
355 Text and Tune: © 1984, Bob Hurd. Arrangement: © 1984, OCP Publications, Portland, OR 97213.
356 Text: © 1963, The Grail, England, GIA Publications, Inc., agent. Music: © 1987, Paul Inwood. Published in England by St. Thomas More Centre, London. Published and distributed in North America by OCP Publications, Portland, OR 97213.
357 Text and Music: © 1987, GIA Publications, Inc.

359 Scripture Passages Related to Hymns

GENESIS

1:	Song over the Waters 312
18:	This Is the Day 226
28:12-13	Calvary 172

EXODUS

13:21	Eternal Lord of Love 160
	Singing Songs of Expectation 282
15:1-6,11	The Song of Moses 219
34:	I Will Not Die 281

DEUTERONOMY

30:19	Gift of Love 272

RUTH

1:16	Wherever You Go 174

JOB

38:	Born of Peace 144

PSALMS

16:	Center of My Life 251
	You Will Show Me the Path of Life 277
17:6-9	Shelter Me, O God 276
19:	Psalm 19 - Lord, You Have the Words 18
	The Stars Declare His Glory 201
19:2	Canticle of the Sun 197
22:	From My Mother's Womb 258
	Psalm 22 - My God, My God, Why Have You Abandoned Me? 19
23:	Because the Lord Is My Shepherd 279
	Psalm 23 - Shepherd Me, O God 20
	The Lord Is My Shepherd 274
	We Shall Rise Again 321
25:	Psalm 25 - To You, O Lord 21
	Psalm 25 - To You, O Lord 22
25:4-9	Remember Your Mercy, Lord 356
25:5	My Soul in Stillness Waits 137
27:	Psalm 27 - The Lord Is My Light 23
	The Lord Is Near 265
27:1, 7-8	Remember Your Love 158
27:1, 4, 13-14	The Lord Is My Life 209
27:14	Wait for the Lord 139
30:	Psalm 30 - I Will Praise You, Lord 24
31:	My Refuge 255
33:	Psalm 33 - Let Your Mercy Be on Us 25
	Psalm 33 - The Earth Is Full of the Goodness 25
34:	Psalm 34 - Taste and See 27
	Psalm 34 - The Cry of the Poor 26
	Come, My Children 288
	Jesus, Heal Us 354
	Taste and See 338
34:9	Our Blessing Cup 347
36:	Lift Up Your Hearts 231
37:34	Wait for the Lord 139
39:8	My Soul in Stillness Waits 137
39:13	O Lord, Hear My Prayer 240
42:	Psalm 42 - Song of the Exile 28
47:	Psalm 47 - God Mounts His Throne 29
51:	Psalm 51 - Be Merciful, O Lord, for We Have Sinned 30
	Psalm 51 - Create in Me 31
62:	Psalm 62 - In God Alone 32
62:6	My Soul in Stillness Waits 137
63:	I Will Lift Up My Eyes 203
	Psalm 63 - As Morning Breaks 33
	Psalm 63 - My Soul Is Thirsting for You, O Lord, My God 34
	Your Love Is Finer Than Life 248
63:2-9	Psalm 63 - In the Shadow of Your Wings 3
65:	Glory and Praise to Our God 233
66:	Glory and Praise to Our God 233
	Psalm 66 - Let All the Earth 35
72:	Psalm 72 - Lord, Every Nation on Earth Will Adore You 36
80:	Psalm 80 - Lord, Make Us Turn to You 37
80:9, 15-16	We Praise You 224
80:15	Maranatha 141
84:	Psalm 84 - Happy Are They Who Dwell in Your House 39
	Psalm 84 - How Lovely Is Your Dwelling Place 38

Scripture Passages Related to Hymns/*continued*

85:	Psalm 85 - Lord, Let Us See Your Kindness 40
	The Voice of God But Speaks of Peace 304
85:11-12	The Day Is Near 136
85:11-12	Maranatha 141
89:	Psalm 89 - Forever I Will Sing the Goodness of the Lord 41
90:2	Remember Your Love 158
91:	Blest Be the Lord 264
	On Eagle's Wings 261
	Psalm 91 - Be with Me 42
95:	My Soul in Stillness Waits 137
	Psalm 95 - If Today You Hear His Voice 43
96:1	A New Song 214
97:1	Lord, Today 157
98:	Psalm 98 - All the Ends of the Earth 44
	Sing a New Song 230
	Sing a New Song to the Lord 218
98:7-9	Let the Heavens Be Glad 148
100:	In Praise of His Name 227
	Jubilate, Servite 223
	Lift Up Your Hearts 231
	Psalm 100 - We Are His People 45
	Sing of the Lord's Goodness 217
	To God with Gladness Sing 228
	With Drums and Dancing 232
102:2	O Lord, Hear My Prayer 240
103:	Bless the Lord 246
	Jesus, Heal Us 354
	Praise the Lord, My Soul 220
	Psalm 103 - The Lord Is Kind and Merciful 46
103:5	Our Help Is in the Name of the Lord 254
104:	Blessed Be God 236
	God of All Creation 196
	Psalm 104 - Lord, Send Out Your Spirit 47
	Spirit Blowing through Creation 191
	Wind upon the Water 200
	You Are the Voice 222
104:24	We Praise You 224
104:30	Send Us Your Spirit 189
104:33	A New Song 214
113:	Praise His Name 229
115:	Jesus, Heal Us 354
116:	Psalm 116 - Our Blessing Cup 48
116:12-13	Our Blessing Cup 347
116:12-18	The Name of God 342
116:15	The River Will Rise 322
117:	Confitemini Domino 237
	Laudate Dominum 216
	Psalm 117 - Holy Is God, Holy and Strong 49
	Sing of the Lord's Goodness 217
118:	Psalm 118 - Alleluia, Alleluia 51
	Psalm 118 - Let Us Rejoice 50
	Sing to the Mountains 234
118:1-4, 22-24	This Is the Day 226
118:24	Psallite Deo 177
118:26	Hosanna 165
119:	Jesus, Heal Us 354
121:	The Lord Is Near 259
	Psalm 121 - Our Help Comes from the Lord 52
122:	Psalm 122 - Let Us Go Rejoicing to the House of the Lord 53
123:	Hold Me in Life 241
124:	Our Help Is in the Name of the Lord 254
126:5	I Will Sing, I Will Sing 213
128:	Psalm 128 - Blest Are Those Who Love You 55
	Psalm 128 - O Blessed Are Those 54
	We Praise You 224
130:	Psalm 130 - With the Lord 57
	Psalm 130 - With the Lord There Is Mercy 56
130:3-4	Remember Your Love 158
130:6-7	My Soul in Stillness Waits 137
131:	My Soul Is Still 303
135:15-18	We Praise You 224
136:	Psalm 136 - Love Is Never Ending 58
136:7-9	We Praise You 224

Scripture Passages Related to Hymns/*continued*

138:	When from Our Exile 256
141:	Psalm 141 - Like Burning Incense 12
145:	Psalm 145 - I Will Praise Your Name 59
145:18	The Lord Is Near 259
145:18	The Lord Is Near 265
146:	Psalm 146 - Lord, Come and Save Us 60
146:2	A New Song 214
147:	Psalm 147 - Bless the Lord, My Soul 61
148:	In Praise of His Name 227
	Psalm 148 - Praise the Lord from the Heavens 62
150:	I Want to Praise Your Name 225
	Psalm 150 - Praise God in His Holy Dwelling 63
	Sing of the Lord's Goodness 217
ISAIAH	
6:3	Sing to the Mountains 234
6:8	Here I Am, Lord 291
9:1-2	City of God 294
9:1-5	Lord, Today 157
9:1-11	Arise, Shine! 155
11:1-5	Lord, Today 157
12:3	You Will Draw Water 266
32:16-17	Maranatha 141
35:1-4	Maranatha 141
40:11, 26-29, 31	We Will Rise Again 350
40:31	Our Help Is in the Name of the Lord 254
40:31-2	Though the Mountains May Fall 262
41:10	We Will Rise Again 350
43:2-3	Be Not Afraid 263
49:15	Return to Me 355
	Though the Mountains May Fall 262
53:1-5	Wherever You Go 174
54:6-10	Though the Mountains May Fall 262
55:1-2	All You Who Are Thirsty 204
	Come to the Water 202
55:10-11	Sow the Word 211
60:1-3	Arise, Shine! 155
61:1-2	He Has Anointed Me 292
67:7	Easter Alleluia 180
JEREMIAH	
8:22	Balm in Gilead 353
EZEKIEL	
11:19	Here I Am, Lord 291
34:10	Return to Me 355
36:26-28	Deep Within 159
37:23	I Will Be with You 188
47:1-12	O Healing River 242
DANIEL	
3:57-88	Nature's Praise 199
HOSEA	
6:1	Return to Me 355
14:2	Return to Me 355
	Deep Within 159
JOEL	
2:12	Return to Me 355
3:1	Song over the Waters 312
MICAH	
5:1	Lord, Today 157
6:8	We Are Called 301
MATTHEW	
2:	A Dulcimer Carol 150
	Brightest and Best 156
	Night of Silence 146
4:1-11	Now Let Us All with One Accord 162
	Tree of Life 163
5:3-12	Blest Are They 284
5:9	Jesus Still Lives 302
5:13-16	Bring Forth the Kingdom 280
5:13	Gather Us In 311
5:14-16	This Little Light of Mine 206
9:21-22	I Danced in the Morning 297

Scripture Passages Related to Hymns/*continued*

11:2-6 Hold Me in Life 241
11:28-30 Come to the Water 202
11:29-30 We Shall Rise Again 321
13:4-23 Bring Forth the Kingdom 280
13:4-30 Anthem 298
21:9 Hosanna 165
25:39-40 God of Day and God of Darkness 319
26:36-46 Stay Here and Keep Watch 166
Stay with Me 170
27:35 Were You There 171
27:50 Calvary 172
28:2 Were You There 171
28:5-6 Now the Green Blade Rises 175
Surrexit Christus 186
Surrexit Dominus Vere II 176
28:18 I Will Be with You 188

MARK

1:12-13 Now Let Us All with One Accord 162
1:14-20 Anthem 298
1:19-20 I Danced in the Morning 297
2:1-12 Now in This Banquet 336
4:3-6 Seed, Scattered and Sown 348
9:2-8 Tree of Life 163
11:9 Hosanna 165
14:32-42 Stay Here and Keep Watch 166
Stay with Me 170
15:25 Were You There 171
15:33 Were You There 171
15:39 Calvary 172
16:3 Were You There 171
16:5-6 Now the Green Blade Rises 175
Surrexit Christus 186
Surrexit Dominus Vere II 176
16:15 Song of the Risen One 181

LUKE

1:26-38 I Sing a Maid 327
1:46-55 All Who Claim the Faith of Jesus 326
Canticle of Mary - My Soul Gives Glory 14
1:67-79 Canticle of Zachary 316
Canticle of Zachary - Blessed Be the God of Israel 5
2: A Dulcimer Carol 150
Awake, Awake and Greet the New Morn 151
Carol at the Manger 152
Night of Silence 146
Once in Royal David's City 153
2:6-19 Song of the Stable 145
2:14 Gloria, Gloria 149
2:36-50 Maranatha 141
4:1-3 Now Let Us All with One Accord 162
4:18-19 He Has Anointed Me 292
6:20ff Be Not Afraid 263
6:21 The Day Is Near 136
9:25 The Love of the Lord 295
15:4-7 Return to Me 355
19:38 Hosanna 165
22:40-46 Stay Here and Keep Watch 166
Stay with Me 170
23:33 Were You There 171
23:42 Jesus, Remember Me 167
23:44 Were You There 171
23:47 Calvary 172
24:2 Were You There 171
24:5-6 Now the Green Blade Rises 175
Song of the Risen One 181
Surrexit Christus 186
Surrexit Dominus Vere II 176
24:13-15 In the Breaking of the Bread 340

JOHN

1:5 God Is Love 270
1:26 Song of God among Us 154
3:16 Love One Another 268
4:4-42 Tree of Life 163

Scripture Passages Related to Hymns/*continued*

4:14 The Water I Give 333
5:1-9 O Healing River 242
6: Behold the Lamb 344
Eat This Bread 341
I Am the Bread of Life 337
Look Beyond 343
6:68 Lord, to Whom Shall We Go 212
7:38 Peace Is Flowing Like a River 306
The River Will Rise 322
8:12 I Am the Light of the World 205
Light of Christ/Exsultet 178
9:1-41 Tree of Life 163
9:14-15 We Have Been Told 296
10:11 Easter Alleluia 180
10:17 Good Christians All 184
11:1-44 Tree of Life 163
11:25 I Am the Resurrection 179
12:12-13 Hosanna 165
12:23-25 Now the Green Blade Rises 175
12:24 Tree of Life 163
12:24-25 The Song of All Seed 289
13:1-17 Jesu, Jesu 168
No Greater Love 269
13:34-35 Good Friday Hymn 290
14:16 Spirit Friend 192
14:27 My Peace I Leave You 307
15:4 I Danced in the Morning 297
Now We Remain 299
15:4-5 We Have Been Told 296
15:5 Many Are the Light Beams 308
15:9, 13-14 No Greater Love 269
15:12-14 The Song of All Seed 289
19:18 Were You There 171
19:25 Calvary 172
20:1 Were You There 171
20:27-29 We Walk by Faith 252

ACTS
2:1-2 Song over the Waters 312
3:6 The Love of the Lord 295
4:12 Jesus the Lord 253

ROMANS
11:33-35 What Is Your Name 194
12:15 The Servant Song 285
13:14 Song to Jesus Christ 187

1 CORINTHIANS
2:9 We Live a Mystery 250
2:9-10 Eye Has Not Seen 275
6:11 Take Our Bread 243
10:16-17 One Bread, One Body 346
Seed, Scattered and Sown 348
10:17 Song of Gathering 309
11:23-26 Life-Giving Bread, Saving Cup 339
Now We Remain 299
Song of the Lord's Supper 161
11:26 Our Blessing Cup 347
12: Glorious in Majesty 287
Many Are the Light Beams 308
We Are Many Parts 310
12:4 One Bread, One Body 346
13: Not for Tongues 273

2 CORINTHIANS
4:11 Good Christians All 184
5:7 We Walk by Faith 252
5:17 Come Away to the Skies 185
Good Christians All 184

GALATIANS
3:28 One Bread, One Body 346
Song of Gathering 309
5:11 Christ Is Alive 183

EPHESIANS
4:24 Spirit of God within Me 190

Scripture Passages Related to Hymns/*continued*

5:8 I Want to Walk as a Child of the Light 208
Morning Hymn - God Is Alive 2
We Are Walking in the Light 207
You Are God's Work of Art 331
5:8-9 Jesus Still Lives 302
5:14 Awake, O Sleeper 330
Light of Christ/Exsultet 178

PHILIPPIANS
2:10-11 I Will Sing, I Will Sing 213
3:7-9 The Love of the Lord 295

COLOSSIANS
1:13 Spirit Friend 192
1:26-27 We Live a Mystery 250
2:13 Good Christians All 184

TITUS
3:5 Spirit of God within Me 190

HEBREWS
5:8 We Live a Mystery 250

1 PETER
1:3-5 Praise the Lord, My Soul 220
2:9 Light of Christ/Exsultet 178

2 PETER
1:19 People of the Night 140

1 JOHN
1:5 Evening Hymn - O Radiant Light 10
God Is Love 270
1:7 Morning Hymn - God Is Alive 2
4: God Is Love 270
Ubi Caritas 271
Where Charity and Love Prevail 267
4:7 Love One Another 268
Your Love, O God 352
4:12 Love One Another 268
5:13 Good Christians All 184
9:12,16 Easter Alleluia 180

REVELATION
5:12 Come Away to the Skies 185
18:23 Evening Hymn - O Radiant Light 10
19:7 Come Away to the Skies 185
21:4-5 Song of the Risen One 181
21:6 God of All Creation 196
21:22-24 I Want to Walk as a Child of the Light 208
21:23 Evening Hymn - O Radiant Light 10
22:5 Light of Christ/Exsultet 178
22:16 Come to Set Us Free 142
22:20 God of All People 143
Each Winter As the Year Grows Older 138

360 Liturgical Index

SEASONS AND FEASTS

ADVENT

244 Be Light for Our Eyes
5 Canticle of Zachary - Blessed Be the God of Israel
142 Come to Set Us Free
138 Each Winter As the Year Grows Older
143 God of All People
325 In the Lord, I Will Be Thankful
148 Let the Heavens Be Glad
324 Lord of Glory
141 Maranatha
137 My Soul in Stillness Waits
336 Now in This Banquet
140 People of the Night
210 Praise to You, O Christ, Our Savior
21 Psalm 25 - To You, O Lord
22 Psalm 25 - To You, O Lord
37 Psalm 80 - Lord, Make Us Turn to You
40 Psalm 85 - Lord, Let Us See Your Kindness
53 Psalm 122 - Let Us Go Rejoicing to the House of the Lord
60 Psalm 146 - Lord, Come and Save Us
356 Remember Your Mercy, Lord
230 Sing a New Song
218 Sing a New Song to the Lord
211 Sow the Word
136 The Day Is Near
139 Wait for the Lord
250 We Live a Mystery
350 We Will Rise Again
(also Topical Index: Second Coming, Messianic)

CHRISTMAS SEASON

150 A Dulcimer Carol
155 Arise, Shine!
151 Awake, Awake and Greet the New Morn
144 Born of Peace
156 Brightest and Best
152 Carol at the Manger
294 City of God
138 Each Winter As the Year Grows Older
149 Gloria, Gloria
148 Let the Heavens Be Glad
157 Lord, Today
146 Night of Silence
153 Once in Royal David's City
140 People of the Night
44 Psalm 98 - All the Ends of the Earth
147 Silent Night
154 Song of God among Us
145 Song of the Stable
(also Christmas Season)

MARY, MOTHER OF GOD

326 All Who Claim the Faith of Jesus
14 Canticle of Mary - My Soul Gives Glory
327 I Sing a Maid
141 Maranatha

EPIPHANY

155 Arise, Shine!
156 Brightest and Best
294 City of God
148 Let the Heavens Be Glad
157 Lord, Today
36 Psalm 72 - Lord, Every Nation on Earth Will Adore You
154 Song of God among Us
(also Christmas Season)

ASH WEDNESDAY

173 Ashes
30 Psalm 51 - Be Merciful, O Lord, for We Have Sinned
31 Psalm 51 - Create in Me

LENTEN SEASON

257 All That We Have
204 All You Who Are Thirsty
173 Ashes
202 Come to the Water
159 Deep Within
160 Eternal Lord of Love
258 From My Mother's Womb
272 Gift of Love
357 Healer of Our Every Ill
205 I Am the Light of the World
286 I Bind My Heart
334 I Have Loved You
208 I Want to Walk as a Child of the Light
203 I Will Lift Up My Eyes
239 Jesu Christe Miserere
354 Jesus, Heal Us
167 Jesus, Remember Me
253 Jesus the Lord
212 Lord, to Whom Shall We Go
255 My Refuge
269 No Greater Love
336 Now in This Banquet
162 Now Let Us All with One Accord
254 Our Help Is in the Name of the Lord
24 Psalm 30 - I Will Praise You, Lord
25 Psalm 33 - Let Your Mercy Be on Us
25 Psalm 33 - The Earth Is Full of the Goodness
30 Psalm 51 - Be Merciful, O Lord, for We Have Sinned
31 Psalm 51 - Create in Me
32 Psalm 62 - In God Alone
42 Psalm 91 - Be with Me
43 Psalm 95 - If Today You Hear His Voice
46 Psalm 103 - The Lord Is Kind and Merciful
57 Psalm 130 - With the Lord
56 Psalm 130 - With the Lord There Is Mercy
12 Psalm 141 - Like Burning Incense
60 Psalm 146 - Lord, Come and Save Us
61 Psalm 147 - Bless the Lord, My Soul
158 Remember Your Love
356 Remember Your Mercy, Lord

Liturgical Index/*continued*

283 Renew Your People
355 Return to Me
166 Stay Here and Keep Watch
170 Stay with Me
300 The Harvest of Justice
209 The Lord Is My Life
304 The Voice of God But Speaks of Peace
206 This Little Light of Mine
163 Tree of Life
301 We Are Called
207 We Are Walking in the Light
256 When from Our Exile
266 You Will Draw Water
(also Penance; Topical Index: Cross, Mercy, Repentance, Social Concern)

PASSION SUNDAY (PALM SUNDAY)
164 Adoramus Te Christe
165 Hosanna
167 Jesus, Remember Me
19 Psalm 22 - My God, My God, Why Have You Abandoned Me?
169 Ride On, Jesus, Ride
163 Tree of Life
(also Christ the King)

EASTER TRIDUUM

HOLY THURSDAY (EVENING MASS OF THE LORD'S SUPPER)
164 Adoramus Te Christe
168 Jesu, Jesu
269 No Greater Love
299 Now We Remain
48 Psalm 116 - Our Blessing Cup
348 Seed, Scattered and Sown
161 Song of the Lord's Supper
166 Stay Here and Keep Watch
170 Stay with Me
163 Tree of Life
271 Ubi Caritas
296 We Have Been Told
345 We Who Once Were Dead
267 Where Charity and Love Prevail
(also Good Friday, Eucharist)

GOOD FRIDAY
164 Adoramus Te Christe
172 Calvary
258 From My Mother's Womb
290 Good Friday Hymn
286 I Bind My Heart
167 Jesus, Remember Me
269 No Greater Love
19 Psalm 22 - My God, My God, Why Have You Abandoned Me?
166 Stay Here and Keep Watch
170 Stay with Me
163 Tree of Life
171 Were You There
174 Wherever You Go

EASTER VIGIL
204 All You Who Are Thirsty
180 Easter Alleluia
178 Light of Christ/Exsultet
175 Now the Green Blade Rises
58 Psalm 136 - Love Is Never Ending
181 Song of the Risen One
176 Surrexit Dominus Vere II
219 The Song of Moses
(also Easter Season)

EASTER SEASON
298 Anthem
332 Baptized in Water
337 I Am the Bread of Life
340 In the Breaking of the Bread
231 Lift Up Your Hearts
307 My Peace I Leave You
306 Peace Is Flowing Like a River
220 Praise the Lord, My Soul
305 Prayer for Peace
230 Sing a New Song
333 The Water I Give
296 We Have Been Told

ASCENSION
182 Hilariter
188 I Will Be with You
177 Psallite Deo
29 Psalm 47 - God Mounts His Throne
187 Song to Jesus Christ
(also Easter Season)

PENTECOST
332 Baptized in Water
292 He Has Anointed Me
357 Healer of Our Every Ill
308 Many Are the Light Beams
306 Peace Is Flowing Like a River
47 Psalm 104 - Lord, Send Out Your Spirit
189 Send Us Your Spirit
198 Sing Out, Earth and Skies
309 Song of Gathering
191 Spirit Blowing through Creation
192 Spirit Friend
190 Spirit of God within Me
193 Veni Sancte Spiritus
310 We Are Many Parts
200 Wind upon the Water
(also Confirmation)

SOLEMNITIES OF THE LORD

TRINITY SUNDAY
215 Alleluia, Sing!

Liturgical Index/*continued*

195 God Is One, Unique and Holy
194 What Is Your Name

BODY AND BLOOD OF CHRIST
299 Now We Remain
348 Seed, Scattered and Sown
161 Song of the Lord's Supper
(also Eucharist)

SACRED HEART
334 I Have Loved You
187 Song to Jesus Christ
296 We Have Been Told

CHRIST THE KING
332 Baptized in Water
287 Glorious in Majesty
184 Good Christians All
29 Psalm 47 - God Mounts His Throne
36 Psalm 72 - Lord, Every Nation on Earth Will Adore You
59 Psalm 145 - I Will Praise Your Name
169 Ride On, Jesus, Ride
230 Sing a New Song

TRIUMPH OF THE CROSS
164 Adoramus Te Christe
299 Now We Remain
(also Topical Index: Cross)

ALL SAINTS
284 Blest Are They
311 Gather Us In
297 I Danced in the Morning
299 Now We Remain
321 We Shall Rise Again

ALL SOULS
349 Song of Farewell

DEDICATION OF A CHURCH
311 Gather Us In
313 What Is This Place

BLESSED VIRGIN MARY
326 All Who Claim the Faith of Jesus
327 I Sing a Maid
141 Maranatha

RITES OF THE CHURCH

BAPTISM OF CHILDREN
332 Baptized in Water
196 God of All Creation
303 My Soul Is Still
20 Psalm 23 - Shepherd Me, O God
23 Psalm 27 - The Lord Is My Light
27 Psalm 34 - Taste and See
26 Psalm 34 - The Cry of the Poor
312 Song over the Waters
333 The Water I Give
329 Wonder of Wonders
331 You Are God's Work of Art

CHRISTIAN INITIATION OF ADULTS
204 All You Who Are Thirsty
298 Anthem
330 Awake, O Sleeper
332 Baptized in Water
280 Bring Forth the Kingdom
202 Come to the Water
180 Easter Alleluia
160 Eternal Lord of Love
311 Gather Us In
233 Glory and Praise to Our God
196 God of All Creation
297 I Danced in the Morning
334 I Have Loved You
208 I Want to Walk as a Child of the Light
231 Lift Up Your Hearts
2 Morning Hymn - God Is Alive
299 Now We Remain
242 O Healing River
306 Peace Is Flowing Like a River
220 Praise the Lord, My Soul
20 Psalm 23 - Shepherd Me, O God
23 Psalm 27 - The Lord Is My Light
27 Psalm 34 - Taste and See
26 Psalm 34 - The Cry of the Poor
28 Psalm 42 - Song of the Exile
31 Psalm 51 - Create in Me
3 Psalm 63 - In the Shadow of Your Wings
35 Psalm 66 - Let All the Earth
41 Psalm 89 - Forever I Will Sing the Goodness of the Lord
58 Psalm 136 - Love Is Never Ending
189 Send Us Your Spirit
198 Sing Out, Earth and Skies
309 Song of Gathering
312 Song over the Waters
187 Song to Jesus Christ
190 Spirit of God within Me
219 The Song of Moses
333 The Water I Give
193 Veni Sancte Spiritus
301 We Are Called
310 We Are Many Parts
207 We Are Walking in the Light
296 We Have Been Told
224 We Praise You
252 We Walk by Faith
200 Wind upon the Water
232 With Drums and Dancing
266 You Will Draw Water
277 You Will Show Me the Path of Life
(also Confirmation, Easter, Easter Vigil; Topical Index: Evangelization)

Liturgical Index/*continued*

CONFIRMATION

298 Anthem
332 Baptized in Water
263 Be Not Afraid
264 Blest Be the Lord
280 Bring Forth the Kingdom
292 He Has Anointed Me
297 I Danced in the Morning
208 I Want to Walk as a Child of the Light
223 Jubilate, Servite
261 On Eagle's Wings
47 Psalm 104 - Lord, Send Out Your Spirit
49 Psalm 117 - Holy Is God, Holy and Strong
59 Psalm 145 - I Will Praise Your Name
189 Send Us Your Spirit
198 Sing Out, Earth and Skies
247 Song of St. Patrick
191 Spirit Blowing through Creation
192 Spirit Friend
190 Spirit of God within Me
206 This Little Light of Mine
262 Though the Mountains May Fall
193 Veni Sancte Spiritus
301 We Are Called
207 We Are Walking in the Light
296 We Have Been Told
200 Wind upon the Water

(also Pentecost, Christian Initiation of Adults; Topical Index: Discipleship, Ministry, Mission)

EUCHARIST

214 A New Song
164 Adoramus Te Christe
204 All You Who Are Thirsty
298 Anthem
244 Be Light for Our Eyes
279 Because the Lord Is My Shepherd
344 Behold the Lamb
294 City of God
202 Come to the Water
237 Confitemini Domino
159 Deep Within
180 Easter Alleluia
341 Eat This Bread
311 Gather Us In
270 God Is Love
195 God Is One, Unique and Holy
290 Good Friday Hymn
291 Here I Am, Lord
165 Hosanna
337 I Am the Bread of Life
179 I Am the Resurrection
203 I Will Lift Up My Eyes
213 I Will Sing, I Will Sing
340 In the Breaking of the Bread
168 Jesu, Jesu
167 Jesus, Remember Me
335 Jesus, Wine of Peace
223 Jubilate, Servite
339 Life-Giving Bread, Saving Cup
343 Look Beyond
212 Lord, to Whom Shall We Go
268 Love One Another
308 Many Are the Light Beams
307 My Peace I Leave You
336 Now in This Banquet
299 Now We Remain
346 One Bread, One Body
347 Our Blessing Cup
229 Praise His Name
220 Praise the Lord, My Soul
305 Prayer for Peace
177 Psallite Deo
20 Psalm 23 - Shepherd Me, O God
27 Psalm 34 - Taste and See
28 Psalm 42 - Song of the Exile
3 Psalm 63 - In the Shadow of Your Wings
34 Psalm 63 - My Soul Is Thirsting for You, O Lord, My God
45 Psalm 100 - We Are His People
48 Psalm 116 - Our Blessing Cup
61 Psalm 147 - Bless the Lord, My Soul
158 Remember Your Love
348 Seed, Scattered and Sown
293 Send Me, Jesus (Thuma Mina)
218 Sing a New Song to the Lord
217 Sing of the Lord's Goodness
309 Song of Gathering
161 Song of the Lord's Supper
211 Sow the Word
166 Stay Here and Keep Watch
170 Stay with Me
186 Surrexit Christus
176 Surrexit Dominus Vere II
238 Table Prayer
243 Take Our Bread
338 Taste and See
300 The Harvest of Justice
209 The Lord Is My Life
274 The Lord Is My Shepherd
342 The Name of God
226 This Is the Day
271 Ubi Caritas
301 We Are Called
310 We Are Many Parts
207 We Are Walking in the Light
296 We Have Been Told
249 We Remember
252 We Walk by Faith
345 We Who Once Were Dead
313 What Is This Place
267 Where Charity and Love Prevail
248 Your Love Is Finer Than Life

(also Topical Index: Praise, Thanksgiving)

FUNERAL

353 Balm in Gilead
263 Be Not Afraid

Liturgical Index/*continued*

279 Because the Lord Is My Shepherd
344 Behold the Lamb
316 Canticle of Zachary
5 Canticle of Zachary - Blessed Be the God of Israel
251 Center of My Life
180 Easter Alleluia
341 Eat This Bread
10 Evening Hymn - O Radiant Light
275 Eye Has Not Seen
337 I Am the Bread of Life
179 I Am the Resurrection
208 I Want to Walk as a Child of the Light
188 I Will Be with You
335 Jesus, Wine of Peace
343 Look Beyond
235 May We Praise You
137 My Soul in Stillness Waits
303 My Soul Is Still
175 Now the Green Blade Rises
261 On Eagle's Wings
220 Praise the Lord, My Soul
20 Psalm 23 - Shepherd Me, O God
21 Psalm 25 - To You, O Lord
22 Psalm 25 - To You, O Lord
23 Psalm 27 - The Lord Is My Light
28 Psalm 42 - Song of the Exile
32 Psalm 62 - In God Alone
33 Psalm 63 - As Morning Breaks
3 Psalm 63 - In the Shadow of Your Wings
34 Psalm 63 - My Soul Is Thirsting for You, O Lord, My God
39 Psalm 84 - Happy Are They Who Dwell in Your House
38 Psalm 84 - How Lovely Is Your Dwelling Place
46 Psalm 103 - The Lord Is Kind and Merciful
48 Psalm 116 - Our Blessing Cup
53 Psalm 122 - Let Us Go Rejoicing to the House of the Lord
57 Psalm 130 - With the Lord
56 Psalm 130 - With the Lord There Is Mercy
62 Psalm 148 - Praise the Lord from the Heavens
276 Shelter Me, O God
230 Sing a New Song
349 Song of Farewell
338 Taste and See
209 The Lord Is My Life
274 The Lord Is My Shepherd
265 The Lord Is Near
342 The Name of God
322 The River Will Rise
296 We Have Been Told
250 We Live a Mystery
321 We Shall Rise Again
345 We Who Once Were Dead
350 We Will Rise Again
256 When from Our Exile
266 You Will Draw Water
248 Your Love Is Finer Than Life
(also Easter; Topical Index: Death, Eternal Life)

MARRIAGE

270 God Is Love
334 I Have Loved You
268 Love One Another
269 No Greater Love
273 Not for Tongues
27 Psalm 34 - Taste and See
26 Psalm 34 - The Cry of the Poor
46 Psalm 103 - The Lord Is Kind and Merciful
52 Psalm 121 - Our Help Comes from the Lord
53 Psalm 122 - Let Us Go Rejoicing to the House of the Lord
55 Psalm 128 - Blest Are Those Who Love You
54 Psalm 128 - O Blessed Are Those
59 Psalm 145 - I Will Praise Your Name
62 Psalm 148 - Praise the Lord from the Heavens
247 Song of St. Patrick
271 Ubi Caritas
207 We Are Walking in the Light
296 We Have Been Told
224 We Praise You
351 When Love Is Found
352 Your Love, O God
(also Topical Index: Love of God for Us, Love for Others, Praise, Thanksgiving, Vocation)

PASTORAL CARE OF THE SICK

257 All That We Have
151 Awake, Awake and Greet the New Morn
353 Balm in Gilead
263 Be Not Afraid
344 Behold the Lamb
246 Bless the Lord
14 Canticle of Mary - My Soul Gives Glory
251 Center of My Life
142 Come to Set Us Free
237 Confitemini Domino
138 Each Winter As the Year Grows Older
341 Eat This Bread
275 Eye Has Not Seen
258 From My Mother's Womb
357 Healer of Our Every Ill
334 I Have Loved You
208 I Want to Walk as a Child of the Light
188 I Will Be with You
340 In the Breaking of the Bread
354 Jesus, Heal Us
253 Jesus the Lord
335 Jesus, Wine of Peace
212 Lord, to Whom Shall We Go
141 Maranatha
255 My Refuge
137 My Soul in Stillness Waits
303 My Soul Is Still
175 Now the Green Blade Rises

Liturgical Index/*continued*

278 O Christe Domine Jesu
261 On Eagle's Wings
306 Peace Is Flowing Like a River
19 Psalm 22 - My God, My God, Why Have You Abandoned Me?
20 Psalm 23 - Shepherd Me, O God
21 Psalm 25 - To You, O Lord
22 Psalm 25 - To You, O Lord
23 Psalm 27 - The Lord Is My Light
24 Psalm 30 - I Will Praise You, Lord
25 Psalm 33 - Let Your Mercy Be on Us
25 Psalm 33 - The Earth Is Full of the Goodness
27 Psalm 34 - Taste and See
26 Psalm 34 - The Cry of the Poor
28 Psalm 42 - Song of the Exile
32 Psalm 62 - In God Alone
33 Psalm 63 - As Morning Breaks
34 Psalm 63 - My Soul Is Thirsting for You, O Lord, My God
35 Psalm 66 - Let All the Earth
39 Psalm 84 - Happy Are They Who Dwell in Your House
38 Psalm 84 - How Lovely Is Your Dwelling Place
42 Psalm 91 - Be with Me
46 Psalm 103 - The Lord Is Kind and Merciful
52 Psalm 121 - Our Help Comes from the Lord
60 Psalm 146 - Lord, Come and Save Us
61 Psalm 147 - Bless the Lord, My Soul
276 Shelter Me, O God
217 Sing of the Lord's Goodness
247 Song of St. Patrick
166 Stay Here and Keep Watch
170 Stay with Me
338 Taste and See
209 The Lord Is My Life
274 The Lord Is My Shepherd
259 The Lord Is Near
262 Though the Mountains May Fall
139 Wait for the Lord
250 We Live a Mystery
321 We Shall Rise Again
350 We Will Rise Again
256 When from Our Exile
174 Wherever You Go
248 Your Love Is Finer Than Life
(also Healing, Comfort)

PENANCE
214 A New Song
204 All You Who Are Thirsty
330 Awake, O Sleeper
353 Balm in Gilead
246 Bless the Lord
144 Born of Peace
172 Calvary
14 Canticle of Mary - My Soul Gives Glory
138 Each Winter As the Year Grows Older
233 Glory and Praise to Our God
357 Healer of Our Every Ill
205 I Am the Light of the World
334 I Have Loved You
213 I Will Sing, I Will Sing
239 Jesu Christe Miserere
354 Jesus, Heal Us
253 Jesus the Lord
231 Lift Up Your Hearts
307 My Peace I Leave You
137 My Soul in Stillness Waits
336 Now in This Banquet
162 Now Let Us All with One Accord
175 Now the Green Blade Rises
242 O Healing River
254 Our Help Is in the Name of the Lord
140 People of the Night
305 Prayer for Peace
19 Psalm 22 - My God, My God, Why Have You Abandoned Me?
21 Psalm 25 - To You, O Lord
22 Psalm 25 - To You, O Lord
24 Psalm 30 - I Will Praise You, Lord
25 Psalm 33 - Let Your Mercy Be on Us
25 Psalm 33 - The Earth Is Full of the Goodness
30 Psalm 51 - Be Merciful, O Lord, for We Have Sinned
31 Psalm 51 - Create in Me
42 Psalm 91 - Be with Me
43 Psalm 95 - If Today You Hear His Voice
46 Psalm 103 - The Lord Is Kind and Merciful
57 Psalm 130 - With the Lord
56 Psalm 130 - With the Lord There Is Mercy
12 Psalm 141 - Like Burning Incense
61 Psalm 147 - Bless the Lord, My Soul
158 Remember Your Love
356 Remember Your Mercy, Lord
283 Renew Your People
355 Return to Me
230 Sing a New Song
217 Sing of the Lord's Goodness
234 Sing to the Mountains
265 The Lord Is Near
304 The Voice of God But Speaks of Peace
262 Though the Mountains May Fall
174 Wherever You Go
232 With Drums and Dancing
222 You Are the Voice
(also Topical Index: Love of God for Us, Mercy, Praise, Repentance, Trust)

BENEDICTION *(see Eucharist, Body and Blood of Christ)*

SPRINKLING
242 O Healing River
312 Song over the Waters
333 The Water I Give

361 Topical Index

ALIENATION
152 Carol at the Manger
319 God of Day and God of Darkness

ANGELS
151 Awake, Awake and Greet the New Morn

ART
245 Come to Us, Creative Spirit

BLESSING
344 Behold the Lamb
246 Bless the Lord
236 Blessed Be God
5 Canticle of Zachary - Blessed Be the God of Israel
288 Come, My Children
227 In Praise of His Name
235 May We Praise You
346 One Bread, One Body
229 Praise His Name
46 Psalm 103 - The Lord Is Kind and Merciful
47 Psalm 104 - Lord, Send Out Your Spirit
55 Psalm 128 - Blest Are Those Who Love You
54 Psalm 128 - O Blessed Are Those
247 Song of St. Patrick
228 To God with Gladness Sing
163 Tree of Life
248 Your Love Is Finer Than Life

BROTHERHOOD AND SISTERHOOD
294 City of God
168 Jesu, Jesu
301 We Are Called
(also Discipleship, Ministry, Mission, Nation, Social Concern)

CALL TO WORSHIP *(see Gathering)*

CAPTIVITY
255 My Refuge
306 Peace Is Flowing Like a River

CELEBRATION
215 Alleluia, Sing!
182 Hilariter
249 We Remember
329 Wonder of Wonders

CHALLENGE OF THE GOSPEL
287 Glorious in Majesty
187 Song to Jesus Christ
163 Tree of Life

CHILDREN'S HYMNS/YOUTH *(i.e., particularly suitable for children and young people)*
214 A New Song
263 Be Not Afraid
287 Glorious in Majesty
233 Glory and Praise to Our God
208 I Want to Walk as a Child of the Light
261 On Eagle's Wings
229 Praise His Name
220 Praise the Lord, My Soul
293 Send Me, Jesus (Thuma Mina)
230 Sing a New Song
218 Sing a New Song to the Lord
234 Sing to the Mountains
192 Spirit Friend
243 Take Our Bread
206 This Little Light of Mine
226 This Is the Day
262 Though the Mountains May Fall
271 Ubi Caritas
267 Where Charity and Love Prevail
232 With Drums and Dancing
331 You Are God's Work of Art

CHRISTIAN LIFE
314 All People Here Who Remember
244 Be Light for Our Eyes
284 Blest Are They
280 Bring Forth the Kingdom
288 Come, My Children
202 Come to the Water
245 Come to Us, Creative Spirit
159 Deep Within
138 Each Winter As the Year Grows Older
311 Gather Us In
287 Glorious in Majesty
196 God of All Creation
292 He Has Anointed Me
205 I Am the Light of the World
286 I Bind My Heart
281 I Will Not Die
302 Jesus Still Lives
308 Many Are the Light Beams
2 Morning Hymn - God Is Alive
299 Now We Remain
283 Renew Your People
187 Song to Jesus Christ
211 Sow the Word
300 The Harvest of Justice
285 The Servant Song
289 The Song of All Seed
206 This Little Light of Mine
277 You Will Show Me the Path of Life

CHURCH
314 All People Here Who Remember
160 Eternal Lord of Love
311 Gather Us In
339 Life-Giving Bread, Saving Cup
282 Singing Songs of Expectation
249 We Remember
313 What Is This Place

CITY *(see Nation, Social Concern)*

Topical Index/*continued*

CITY OF GOD
280 Bring Forth the Kingdom
294 City of God
208 I Want to Walk as a Child of the Light
301 We Are Called
(also Eschatological, Eternal Life, Lamb)

COMFORT
151 Awake, Awake and Greet the New Morn
279 Because the Lord Is My Shepherd
344 Behold the Lamb
264 Blest Be the Lord
251 Center of My Life
138 Each Winter As the Year Grows Older
275 Eye Has Not Seen
258 From My Mother's Womb
292 He Has Anointed Me
208 I Want to Walk as a Child of the Light
188 I Will Be with You
203 I Will Lift Up My Eyes
137 My Soul in Stillness Waits
146 Night of Silence
278 O Christe Domine Jesu
261 On Eagle's Wings
153 Once in Royal David's City
347 Our Blessing Cup
254 Our Help Is in the Name of the Lord
20 Psalm 23 - Shepherd Me, O God
23 Psalm 27 - The Lord Is My Light
26 Psalm 34 - The Cry of the Poor
36 Psalm 72 - Lord, Every Nation on Earth Will Adore You
38 Psalm 84 - How Lovely Is Your Dwelling Place
42 Psalm 91 - Be with Me
56 Psalm 130 - With the Lord There Is Mercy
276 Shelter Me, O God
161 Song of the Lord's Supper
166 Stay Here and Keep Watch
170 Stay with Me
209 The Lord Is My Life
274 The Lord Is My Shepherd
259 The Lord Is Near
206 This Little Light of Mine
345 We Who Once Were Dead
350 We Will Rise Again
277 You Will Show Me the Path of Life
(also Providence, Trust)

COMMANDMENTS *(see Law)*

COMMISSIONING *(see Discipleship, Ministry, Mission; Liturgical Index: Confirmation)*

COMMITMENT
251 Center of My Life
245 Come to Us, Creative Spirit
291 Here I Am, Lord
286 I Bind My Heart
255 My Refuge
243 Take Our Bread
(also Discipleship, Mission)

COMMUNION *(see Liturgical Index: Eucharist)*

COMMUNION OF SAINTS
308 Many Are the Light Beams
(also Church; Liturgical Index: All Saints)

COMMUNITY
168 Jesu, Jesu
346 One Bread, One Body
(also Unity)

COMPASSION
152 Carol at the Manger
196 God of All Creation
357 Healer of Our Every Ill
162 Now Let Us All with One Accord
254 Our Help Is in the Name of the Lord
59 Psalm 145 - I Will Praise Your Name
191 Spirit Blowing through Creation
166 Stay Here and Keep Watch
170 Stay with Me
265 The Lord Is Near
171 Were You There
174 Wherever You Go

COMPLACENCY
136 The Day Is Near

CONFIDENCE *(see Trust)*

CONVERSION
298 Anthem
159 Deep Within
311 Gather Us In
297 I Danced in the Morning
299 Now We Remain
355 Return to Me
304 The Voice of God But Speaks of Peace
301 We Are Called
222 You Are the Voice

COUNTRY *(see Nation)*

COURAGE
257 All That We Have
298 Anthem
353 Balm in Gilead
263 Be Not Afraid
279 Because the Lord Is My Shepherd
264 Blest Be the Lord
142 Come to Set Us Free
275 Eye Has Not Seen
291 Here I Am, Lord
241 Hold Me in Life
307 My Peace I Leave You

Topical Index/*continued*

299 Now We Remain
278 O Christe Domine Jesu
261 On Eagle's Wings
19 Psalm 22 - My God, My God, Why Have You Abandoned Me?
276 Shelter Me, O God
282 Singing Songs of Expectation
161 Song of the Lord's Supper
192 Spirit Friend
166 Stay Here and Keep Watch
170 Stay with Me
136 The Day Is Near
274 The Lord Is My Shepherd
265 The Lord Is Near
206 This Little Light of Mine
163 Tree of Life
139 Wait for the Lord
301 We Are Called

COVENANT
204 All You Who Are Thirsty
332 Baptized in Water
14 Canticle of Mary - My Soul Gives Glory
316 Canticle of Zachary
5 Canticle of Zachary - Blessed Be the God of Israel
337 I Am the Bread of Life
334 I Have Loved You
340 In the Breaking of the Bread
335 Jesus, Wine of Peace
339 Life-Giving Bread, Saving Cup
343 Look Beyond
336 Now in This Banquet
162 Now Let Us All with One Accord
21 Psalm 25 - To You, O Lord
22 Psalm 25 - To You, O Lord
161 Song of the Lord's Supper
342 The Name of God
333 The Water I Give
224 We Praise You
321 We Shall Rise Again
345 We Who Once Were Dead
331 You Are God's Work of Art
(also Faithfulness of God, Love of God for Us, Evening)

CREATION
236 Blessed Be God
197 Canticle of the Sun
185 Come Away to the Skies
180 Easter Alleluia
233 Glory and Praise to Our God
196 God of All Creation
182 Hilariter
225 I Want to Praise Your Name
227 In Praise of His Name
318 Joyous Light of Heavenly Glory
317 Morning Has Broken
137 My Soul in Stillness Waits
199 Nature's Praise
47 Psalm 104 - Lord, Send Out Your Spirit
58 Psalm 136 - Love Is Never Ending
62 Psalm 148 - Praise the Lord from the Heavens
189 Send Us Your Spirit
198 Sing Out, Earth and Skies
234 Sing to the Mountains
191 Spirit Blowing through Creation
322 The River Will Rise
201 The Stars Declare His Glory
228 To God with Gladness Sing
224 We Praise You
350 We Will Rise Again
200 Wind upon the Water
329 Wonder of Wonders
222 You Are the Voice

CREATIVITY
245 Come to Us, Creative Spirit

CRISIS
258 From My Mother's Womb
28 Psalm 42 - Song of the Exile
(also Suffering; Liturgical Index: Pastoral Care of the Sick)

DANCE
196 God of All Creation
297 I Danced in the Morning
235 May We Praise You
255 My Refuge
21 Psalm 25 - To You, O Lord
22 Psalm 25 - To You, O Lord
35 Psalm 66 - Let All the Earth
356 Remember Your Mercy, Lord
230 Sing a New Song
217 Sing of the Lord's Goodness
190 Spirit of God within Me
232 With Drums and Dancing

DEATH
281 I Will Not Die
48 Psalm 116 - Our Blessing Cup
276 Shelter Me, O God
349 Song of Farewell
166 Stay Here and Keep Watch
170 Stay with Me
274 The Lord Is My Shepherd
321 We Shall Rise Again
(also Eternal Life; Liturgical Index: Easter, Funeral)

DEDICATION OF A CHURCH *(see Church; Liturgical Index: Dedication of a Church)*

DEPARTURE *(see Going Forth, Mission)*

DISCIPLESHIP
298 Anthem
244 Be Light for Our Eyes

Topical Index/*continued*

263 Be Not Afraid
279 Because the Lord Is My Shepherd
264 Blest Be the Lord
280 Bring Forth the Kingdom
202 Come to the Water
159 Deep Within
180 Easter Alleluia
290 Good Friday Hymn
292 He Has Anointed Me
291 Here I Am, Lord
241 Hold Me in Life
205 I Am the Light of the World
297 I Danced in the Morning
208 I Want to Walk as a Child of the Light
188 I Will Be with You
168 Jesu, Jesu
343 Look Beyond
2 Morning Hymn - God Is Alive
336 Now in This Banquet
299 Now We Remain
261 On Eagle's Wings
293 Send Me, Jesus (Thuma Mina)
276 Shelter Me, O God
161 Song of the Lord's Supper
181 Song of the Risen One
187 Song to Jesus Christ
192 Spirit Friend
295 The Love of the Lord
285 The Servant Song
289 The Song of All Seed
206 This Little Light of Mine
262 Though the Mountains May Fall
163 Tree of Life
310 We Are Many Parts
296 We Have Been Told
277 You Will Show Me the Path of Life
(also Commitment, Ministry, Mission, Social Concern)

ECOLOGY *(see Creation)*

ECUMENISM *(see Unity)*

ENCOURAGEMENT
298 Anthem
353 Balm in Gilead
279 Because the Lord Is My Shepherd
275 Eye Has Not Seen
241 Hold Me in Life
307 My Peace I Leave You
278 O Christe Domine Jesu
276 Shelter Me, O God
139 Wait for the Lord
301 We Are Called

ESCHATOLOGICAL *(see Second Coming)*

ETERNAL LIFE/HEAVEN
10 Evening Hymn - O Radiant Light
275 Eye Has Not Seen
323 Freedom Is Coming
337 I Am the Bread of Life
208 I Want to Walk as a Child of the Light
281 I Will Not Die
212 Lord, to Whom Shall We Go
235 May We Praise You
261 On Eagle's Wings
220 Praise the Lord, My Soul
20 Psalm 23 - Shepherd Me, O God
23 Psalm 27 - The Lord Is My Light
39 Psalm 84 - Happy Are They Who Dwell in Your House
38 Psalm 84 - How Lovely Is Your Dwelling Place
48 Psalm 116 - Our Blessing Cup
230 Sing a New Song
282 Singing Songs of Expectation
349 Song of Farewell
322 The River Will Rise
333 The Water I Give
250 We Live a Mystery
321 We Shall Rise Again
252 We Walk by Faith
248 Your Love Is Finer Than Life

EVANGELIZATION
204 All You Who Are Thirsty
298 Anthem
202 Come to the Water
159 Deep Within
311 Gather Us In
184 Good Christians All
205 I Am the Light of the World
297 I Danced in the Morning
188 I Will Be with You
213 I Will Sing, I Will Sing
141 Maranatha
137 My Soul in Stillness Waits
299 Now We Remain
140 People of the Night
309 Song of Gathering
187 Song to Jesus Christ
206 This Little Light of Mine
301 We Are Called
296 We Have Been Told

EVENING
314 All People Here Who Remember
173 Ashes
320 At Evening
332 Baptized in Water
244 Be Light for Our Eyes
14 Canticle of Mary - My Soul Gives Glory
183 Christ Is Alive
237 Confitemini Domino
160 Eternal Lord of Love
10 Evening Hymn - O Radiant Light
272 Gift of Love
287 Glorious in Majesty
195 God Is One, Unique and Holy

Topical Index/*continued*

319 God of Day and God of Darkness
184 Good Christians All
182 Hilariter
297 I Danced in the Morning
168 Jesu, Jesu
315 Jesus, Come to Us
318 Joyous Light of Heavenly Glory
231 Lift Up Your Hearts
178 Light of Christ/Exsultet
303 My Soul Is Still
175 Now the Green Blade Rises
299 Now We Remain
347 Our Blessing Cup
23 Psalm 27 - The Lord Is My Light
24 Psalm 30 - I Will Praise You, Lord
32 Psalm 62 - In God Alone
3 Psalm 63 - In the Shadow of Your Wings
36 Psalm 72 - Lord, Every Nation on Earth Will Adore You
52 Psalm 121 - Our Help Comes from the Lord
53 Psalm 122 - Let Us Go Rejoicing to the House of the Lord
58 Psalm 136 - Love Is Never Ending
12 Psalm 141 - Like Burning Incense
59 Psalm 145 - I Will Praise Your Name
282 Singing Songs of Expectation
349 Song of Farewell
161 Song of the Lord's Supper
181 Song of the Risen One
211 Sow the Word
295 The Love of the Lord
289 The Song of All Seed
163 Tree of Life
250 We Live a Mystery
345 We Who Once Were Dead
171 Were You There
313 What Is This Place
351 When Love Is Found
174 Wherever You Go
232 With Drums and Dancing
(also Light, Thanksgiving)

EXILE

152 Carol at the Manger
340 In the Breaking of the Bread
28 Psalm 42 - Song of the Exile
256 When from Our Exile
(also Pilgrimage)

FAITH

214 A New Song
314 All People Here Who Remember
298 Anthem
344 Behold the Lamb
284 Blest Are They
264 Blest Be the Lord
251 Center of My Life
142 Come to Set Us Free
237 Confitemini Domino
138 Each Winter As the Year Grows Older
275 Eye Has Not Seen
337 I Am the Bread of Life
179 I Am the Resurrection
334 I Have Loved You
315 Jesus, Come to Us
253 Jesus the Lord
223 Jubilate, Servite
343 Look Beyond
324 Lord of Glory
141 Maranatha
255 My Refuge
137 My Soul in Stillness Waits
342 The Name of God
261 On Eagle's Wings
140 People of the Night
220 Praise the Lord, My Soul
18 Psalm 19 - Lord, You Have the Words
19 Psalm 22 - My God, My God, Why Have You Abandoned Me?
20 Psalm 23 - Shepherd Me, O God
21 Psalm 25 - To You, O Lord
22 Psalm 25 - To You, O Lord
23 Psalm 27 - The Lord Is My Light
24 Psalm 30 - I Will Praise You, Lord
25 Psalm 33 - Let Your Mercy Be on Us
25 Psalm 33 - The Earth Is Full of the Goodness
27 Psalm 34 - Taste and See
26 Psalm 34 - The Cry of the Poor
28 Psalm 42 - Song of the Exile
29 Psalm 47 - God Mounts His Throne
30 Psalm 51 - Be Merciful, O Lord, for We Have Sinned
31 Psalm 51 - Create in Me
32 Psalm 62 - In God Alone
33 Psalm 63 - As Morning Breaks
34 Psalm 63 - My Soul Is Thirsting for You, O Lord, My God
35 Psalm 66 - Let All the Earth
36 Psalm 72 - Lord, Every Nation on Earth Will Adore You
37 Psalm 80 - Lord, Make Us Turn to You
39 Psalm 84 - Happy Are They Who Dwell in Your House
38 Psalm 84 - How Lovely Is Your Dwelling Place
41 Psalm 89 - Forever I Will Sing the Goodness of the Lord
42 Psalm 91 - Be with Me
43 Psalm 95 - If Today You Hear His Voice
44 Psalm 98 - All the Ends of the Earth
45 Psalm 100 - We Are His People
46 Psalm 103 - The Lord Is Kind and Merciful
47 Psalm 104 - Lord, Send Out Your Spirit
48 Psalm 116 - Our Blessing Cup
50 Psalm 118 - Let Us Rejoice
53 Psalm 122 - Let Us Go Rejoicing to the House of the Lord
55 Psalm 128 - Blest Are Those Who Love You
54 Psalm 128 - O Blessed Are Those
57 Psalm 130 - With the Lord

Topical Index/*continued*

56 Psalm 130 - With the Lord There Is Mercy
58 Psalm 136 - Love Is Never Ending
12 Psalm 141 - Like Burning Incense
59 Psalm 145 - I Will Praise Your Name
60 Psalm 146 - Lord, Come and Save Us
61 Psalm 147 - Bless the Lord, My Soul
356 Remember Your Mercy, Lord
355 Return to Me
276 Shelter Me, O God
218 Sing a New Song to the Lord
234 Sing to the Mountains
282 Singing Songs of Expectation
136 The Day Is Near
274 The Lord Is My Shepherd
259 The Lord Is Near
295 The Love of the Lord
219 The Song of Moses
333 The Water I Give
226 This Is the Day
163 Tree of Life
139 Wait for the Lord
250 We Live a Mystery
224 We Praise You
249 We Remember
252 We Walk by Faith
256 When from Our Exile
331 You Are God's Work of Art
222 You Are the Voice

FAITHFULNESS OF GOD
257 All That We Have
204 All You Who Are Thirsty
202 Come to the Water
233 Glory and Praise to Our God
334 I Have Loved You
315 Jesus, Come to Us
261 On Eagle's Wings
254 Our Help Is in the Name of the Lord
25 Psalm 33 - Let Your Mercy Be on Us
25 Psalm 33 - The Earth Is Full of the Goodness
41 Psalm 89 - Forever I Will Sing the Goodness of the Lord
45 Psalm 100 - We Are His People
49 Psalm 117 - Holy Is God, Holy and Strong
59 Psalm 145 - I Will Praise Your Name
158 Remember Your Love
217 Sing of the Lord's Goodness
262 Though the Mountains May Fall
277 You Will Show Me the Path of Life
(also Love of God for Us, Mercy, Providence)

FAMILY LIFE
225 I Want to Praise Your Name
53 Psalm 122 - Let Us Go Rejoicing to the House of the Lord
55 Psalm 128 - Blest Are Those Who Love You
54 Psalm 128 - O Blessed Are Those

FASTING
160 Eternal Lord of Love
162 Now Let Us All with One Accord

FEAR
257 All That We Have
151 Awake, Awake and Greet the New Morn
263 Be Not Afraid
152 Carol at the Manger
288 Come, My Children
325 In the Lord, I Will Be Thankful
354 Jesus, Heal Us
302 Jesus Still Lives
255 My Refuge
299 Now We Remain
261 On Eagle's Wings
23 Psalm 27 - The Lord Is My Light
158 Remember Your Love
136 The Day Is Near
265 The Lord Is Near
163 Tree of Life

FOOD
302 Jesus Still Lives
309 Song of Gathering

FORGIVENESS *(see Love of God for Us, Mercy, Reconciliation; Liturgical Index: Penance)*

FREEDOM
257 All That We Have
5 Canticle of Zachary - Blessed Be the God of Israel
142 Come to Set Us Free
323 Freedom Is Coming
213 I Will Sing, I Will Sing
141 Maranatha
255 My Refuge
242 O Healing River
306 Peace Is Flowing Like a River
220 Praise the Lord, My Soul
210 Praise to You, O Christ, Our Savior
58 Psalm 136 - Love Is Never Ending
192 Spirit Friend
301 We Are Called
(also Liberation)

FRIENDSHIP
320 At Evening
353 Balm in Gilead
195 God Is One, Unique and Holy
269 No Greater Love
192 Spirit Friend
296 We Have Been Told

GATHERING
314 All People Here Who Remember
215 Alleluia, Sing!
298 Anthem
155 Arise, Shine!

Topical Index/*continued*

173 Ashes
185 Come Away to the Skies
245 Come to Us, Creative Spirit
311 Gather Us In
287 Glorious in Majesty
213 I Will Sing, I Will Sing
227 In Praise of His Name
315 Jesus, Come to Us
223 Jubilate, Servite
231 Lift Up Your Hearts
324 Lord of Glory
137 My Soul in Stillness Waits
175 Now the Green Blade Rises
220 Praise the Lord, My Soul
210 Praise to You, O Christ, Our Savior
43 Psalm 95 - If Today You Hear His Voice
45 Psalm 100 - We Are His People
53 Psalm 122 - Let Us Go Rejoicing to the House of the Lord
230 Sing a New Song
218 Sing a New Song to the Lord
217 Sing of the Lord's Goodness
234 Sing to the Mountains
309 Song of Gathering
312 Song over the Waters
226 This Is the Day
228 To God with Gladness Sing
313 What Is This Place
232 With Drums and Dancing
222 You Are the Voice

GIVING
173 Ashes
332 Baptized in Water
344 Behold the Lamb
185 Come Away to the Skies
237 Confitemini Domino
325 In the Lord, I Will Be Thankful
339 Life-Giving Bread, Saving Cup
231 Lift Up Your Hearts
347 Our Blessing Cup
24 Psalm 30 - I Will Praise You, Lord
3 Psalm 63 - In the Shadow of Your Wings
45 Psalm 100 - We Are His People
46 Psalm 103 - The Lord Is Kind and Merciful
48 Psalm 116 - Our Blessing Cup
51 Psalm 118 - Alleluia, Alleluia
50 Psalm 118 - Let Us Rejoice
58 Psalm 136 - Love Is Never Ending
59 Psalm 145 - I Will Praise Your Name
283 Renew Your People
234 Sing to the Mountains
238 Table Prayer
300 The Harvest of Justice
342 The Name of God
228 To God with Gladness Sing
224 We Praise You

GOING FORTH
214 A New Song
263 Be Not Afraid
264 Blest Be the Lord
294 City of God
287 Glorious in Majesty
291 Here I Am, Lord
182 Hilariter
337 I Am the Bread of Life
297 I Danced in the Morning
227 In Praise of His Name
340 In the Breaking of the Bread
223 Jubilate, Servite
261 On Eagle's Wings
220 Praise the Lord, My Soul
52 Psalm 121 - Our Help Comes from the Lord
293 Send Me, Jesus (Thuma Mina)
230 Sing a New Song
218 Sing a New Song to the Lord
217 Sing of the Lord's Goodness
234 Sing to the Mountains
192 Spirit Friend
206 This Little Light of Mine
262 Though the Mountains May Fall
232 With Drums and Dancing

GOSPEL *(see Word of God)*

GRACE *(see Love of God for Us, Providence)*

GRATITUDE *(see Thanksgiving)*

GRIEVING
138 Each Winter As the Year Grows Older
175 Now the Green Blade Rises

GROWTH
173 Ashes
211 Sow the Word

GUIDANCE
196 God of All Creation
235 May We Praise You
255 My Refuge
21 Psalm 25 - To You, O Lord
22 Psalm 25 - To You, O Lord
36 Psalm 72 - Lord, Every Nation on Earth Will Adore You
356 Remember Your Mercy, Lord
190 Spirit of God within Me

HARVEST
300 The Harvest of Justice
(also Thanksgiving)

HEALING
353 Balm in Gilead
244 Be Light for Our Eyes
357 Healer of Our Every Ill
354 Jesus, Heal Us
335 Jesus, Wine of Peace

Topical Index/*continued*

242 O Healing River
306 Peace Is Flowing Like a River
20 Psalm 23 - Shepherd Me, O God
60 Psalm 146 - Lord, Come and Save Us
61 Psalm 147 - Bless the Lord, My Soul
355 Return to Me
191 Spirit Blowing through Creation
166 Stay Here and Keep Watch
170 Stay with Me
249 We Remember
174 Wherever You Go
(also Liturgical Index: Pastoral Care of the Sick)

HEAVEN *(see Eternal Life)*

HOLINESS
319 God of Day and God of Darkness
18 Psalm 19 - Lord, You Have the Words
49 Psalm 117 - Holy Is God, Holy and Strong
267 Where Charity and Love Prevail
(also Christian Life, Love for Others, Love of God for Us, Social Concern)

HOLY SPIRIT *(see Liturgical Index: Pentecost, Confirmation)*

HOMECOMING
152 Carol at the Manger
281 I Will Not Die
304 The Voice of God Speaks But of Peace
224 We Praise You
256 When from Our Exile
(also Exile)

HOMELAND
280 Bring Forth the Kingdom

HOMELESS
196 God of All Creation
136 The Day Is Near

HOPE *(see Trust)*

HORROR OF WAR
138 Each Winter As the Year Grows Older
302 Jesus Still Lives
136 The Day Is Near

HUMILITY
14 Canticle of Mary - My Soul Gives Glory
303 My Soul Is Still
301 We Are Called

HUNGER
204 All You Who Are Thirsty
298 Anthem
344 Behold the Lamb
341 Eat This Bread
337 I Am the Bread of Life
302 Jesus Still Lives
336 Now in This Banquet
300 The Harvest of Justice
248 Your Love Is Finer Than Life

IMMORTALITY *(see Death, Eternal Life)*

INCARNATION
155 Arise, Shine!
144 Born of Peace
156 Brightest and Best
152 Carol at the Manger
183 Christ Is Alive
272 Gift of Love
157 Lord, Today
210 Praise to You, O Christ, Our Savior
154 Song of God among Us
145 Song of the Stable
211 Sow the Word
267 Where Charity and Love Prevail
(also Liturgical Index: Christmas Season)

INSTITUTION OF MINISTRIES *(see Discipleship, Ministry, Mission)*

INTERFAITH
214 A New Song
264 Blest Be the Lord
251 Center of My Life
142 Come to Set Us Free
334 I Have Loved You
223 Jubilate, Servite
324 Lord of Glory
141 Maranatha
255 My Refuge
137 My Soul in Stillness Waits
261 On Eagle's Wings
18 Psalm 19 - Lord, You Have the Words
19 Psalm 22 - My God, My God, Why Have You Abandoned Me?
20 Psalm 23 - Shepherd Me, O God
21 Psalm 25 - To You, O Lord
22 Psalm 25 - To You, O Lord
23 Psalm 27 - The Lord Is My Light
24 Psalm 30 - I Will Praise You, Lord
25 Psalm 33 - Let Your Mercy Be on Us
25 Psalm 33 - The Earth Is Full of the Goodness
27 Psalm 34 - Taste and See
26 Psalm 34 - The Cry of the Poor
28 Psalm 42 - Song of the Exile
29 Psalm 47 - God Mounts His Throne
30 Psalm 51 - Be Merciful, O Lord, for We Have Sinned
31 Psalm 51 - Create in Me
32 Psalm 62 - In God Alone
33 Psalm 63 - As Morning Breaks
34 Psalm 63 - My Soul Is Thirsting for You, O Lord, My God
35 Psalm 66 - Let All the Earth

Topical Index/*continued*

36 Psalm 72 - Lord, Every Nation on Earth Will Adore You
37 Psalm 80 - Lord, Make Us Turn to You
39 Psalm 84 - Happy Are They Who Dwell in Your House
38 Psalm 84 - How Lovely Is Your Dwelling Place
41 Psalm 89 - Forever I Will Sing the Goodness of the Lord
42 Psalm 91 - Be with Me
43 Psalm 95 - If Today You Hear His Voice
44 Psalm 98 - All the Ends of the Earth
45 Psalm 100 - We Are His People
46 Psalm 103 - The Lord Is Kind and Merciful
47 Psalm 104 - Lord, Send Out Your Spirit
48 Psalm 116 - Our Blessing Cup
50 Psalm 118 - Let Us Rejoice
53 Psalm 122 - Let Us Go Rejoicing to the House of the Lord
55 Psalm 128 - Blest Are Those Who Love You
54 Psalm 128 - O Blessed Are Those
57 Psalm 130 - With the Lord
56 Psalm 130 - With the Lord There Is Mercy
58 Psalm 136 - Love Is Never Ending
12 Psalm 141 - Like Burning Incense
59 Psalm 145 - I Will Praise Your Name
60 Psalm 146 - Lord, Come and Save Us
61 Psalm 147 - Bless the Lord, My Soul
356 Remember Your Mercy, Lord
355 Return to Me
276 Shelter Me, O God
218 Sing a New Song to the Lord
234 Sing to the Mountains
274 The Lord Is My Shepherd
259 The Lord Is Near
342 The Name of God
219 The Song of Moses
226 This Is the Day
139 Wait for the Lord
224 We Praise You
222 You Are the Voice

JESUS CHRIST
164 Adoramus Te Christe
314 All People Here Who Remember
257 All That We Have
298 Anthem
320 At Evening
353 Balm in Gilead
332 Baptized in Water
244 Be Light for Our Eyes
183 Christ Is Alive
138 Each Winter As the Year Grows Older
180 Easter Alleluia
323 Freedom Is Coming
272 Gift of Love
287 Glorious in Majesty
270 God Is Love
179 I Am the Resurrection
286 I Bind My Heart
297 I Danced in the Morning
208 I Want to Walk as a Child of the Light
340 In the Breaking of the Bread
239 Jesu Christe Miserere
168 Jesu, Jesu
315 Jesus, Come to Us
354 Jesus, Heal Us
167 Jesus, Remember Me
302 Jesus Still Lives
253 Jesus the Lord
178 Light of Christ/Exsultet
212 Lord, to Whom Shall We Go
308 Many Are the Light Beams
175 Now the Green Blade Rises
299 Now We Remain
306 Peace Is Flowing Like a River
140 People of the Night
210 Praise to You, O Christ, Our Savior
305 Prayer for Peace
169 Ride On, Jesus, Ride
293 Send Me, Jesus (Thuma Mina)
189 Send Us Your Spirit
247 Song of St. Patrick
161 Song of the Lord's Supper
181 Song of the Risen One
187 Song to Jesus Christ
176 Surrexit Dominus Vere II
300 The Harvest of Justice
295 The Love of the Lord
163 Tree of Life
296 We Have Been Told
250 We Live a Mystery
249 We Remember
252 We Walk by Faith
345 We Who Once Were Dead
174 Wherever You Go

JOURNEY
280 Bring Forth the Kingdom
259 The Lord Is Near
285 The Servant Song
(also Pilgrimage)

JOY
215 Alleluia, Sing!
155 Arise, Shine!
151 Awake, Awake and Greet the New Morn
284 Blest Are They
14 Canticle of Mary - My Soul Gives Glory
197 Canticle of the Sun
185 Come Away to the Skies
180 Easter Alleluia
184 Good Christians All
292 He Has Anointed Me
357 Healer of Our Every Ill
182 Hilariter
213 I Will Sing, I Will Sing
325 In the Lord, I Will Be Thankful
231 Lift Up Your Hearts
2 Morning Hymn - God Is Alive

Topical Index/*continued*

255 My Refuge
140 People of the Night
177 Psallite Deo
29 Psalm 47 - God Mounts His Throne
3 Psalm 63 - In the Shadow of Your Wings
35 Psalm 66 - Let All the Earth
50 Psalm 118 - Let Us Rejoice
53 Psalm 122 - Let Us Go Rejoicing to the House of the Lord
234 Sing to the Mountains
154 Song of God among Us
181 Song of the Risen One
186 Surrexit Christus
176 Surrexit Dominus Vere II
304 The Voice of God But Speaks of Peace
277 You Will Show Me the Path of Life

JUDGMENT
138 Each Winter As the Year Grows Older
218 Sing a New Song to the Lord
(also Second Coming; Liturgical Index: Christ the King)

JUSTICE
298 Anthem
244 Be Light for Our Eyes
280 Bring Forth the Kingdom
183 Christ Is Alive
138 Each Winter As the Year Grows Older
319 God of Day and God of Darkness
260 How Can I Keep from Singing?
203 I Will Lift Up My Eyes
281 I Will Not Die
253 Jesus the Lord
318 Joyous Light of Heavenly Glory
141 Maranatha
336 Now in This Banquet
242 O Healing River
36 Psalm 72 - Lord, Every Nation on Earth Will Adore You
40 Psalm 85 - Lord, Let Us See Your Kindness
283 Renew Your People
169 Ride On, Jesus, Ride
198 Sing Out, Earth and Skies
154 Song of God among Us
312 Song over the Waters
136 The Day Is Near
300 The Harvest of Justice
304 The Voice of God But Speaks of Peace
301 We Are Called
313 What Is This Place
194 What Is Your Name
200 Wind upon the Water
(also Peace, Social Concern)

KINGDOM *(see Reign of God)*

LABOR
202 Come to the Water
340 In the Breaking of the Bread

LAMB
344 Behold the Lamb
185 Come Away to the Skies
208 I Want to Walk as a Child of the Light
(also Second Coming, Eternal Life)

LAW
204 All You Who Are Thirsty
159 Deep Within
18 Psalm 19 - Lord, You Have the Words
201 The Stars Declare His Glory

LIBERATION
14 Canticle of Mary - My Soul Gives Glory
316 Canticle of Zachary
5 Canticle of Zachary - Blessed Be the God of Israel
294 City of God
288 Come, My Children
323 Freedom Is Coming
290 Good Friday Hymn
213 I Will Sing, I Will Sing
302 Jesus Still Lives
318 Joyous Light of Heavenly Glory
242 O Healing River
254 Our Help Is in the Name of the Lord
306 Peace Is Flowing Like a River
60 Psalm 146 - Lord, Come and Save Us
338 Taste and See
342 The Name of God
(also Freedom)

LIBERTY *(see Freedom)*

LIFE
314 All People Here Who Remember
244 Be Light for Our Eyes
284 Blest Are They
280 Bring Forth the Kingdom
197 Canticle of the Sun
183 Christ Is Alive
288 Come, My Children
142 Come to Set Us Free
202 Come to the Water
245 Come to Us, Creative Spirit
159 Deep Within
138 Each Winter As the Year Grows Older
10 Evening Hymn - O Radiant Light
275 Eye Has Not Seen
323 Freedom Is Coming
311 Gather Us In
272 Gift of Love
287 Glorious in Majesty
196 God of All Creation
184 Good Christians All
292 He Has Anointed Me
182 Hilariter
337 I Am the Bread of Life
205 I Am the Light of the World
179 I Am the Resurrection

Topical Index/*continued*

286 I Bind My Heart
225 I Want to Praise Your Name
208 I Want to Walk as a Child of the Light
281 I Will Not Die
302 Jesus Still Lives
335 Jesus, Wine of Peace
339 Life-Giving Bread, Saving Cup
212 Lord, to Whom Shall We Go
308 Many Are the Light Beams
235 May We Praise You
2 Morning Hymn - God Is Alive
199 Nature's Praise
175 Now the Green Blade Rises
299 Now We Remain
261 On Eagle's Wings
140 People of the Night
220 Praise the Lord, My Soul
210 Praise to You, O Christ, Our Savior
18 Psalm 19 - Lord, You Have the Words
20 Psalm 23 - Shepherd Me, O God
23 Psalm 27 - The Lord Is My Light
39 Psalm 84 - Happy Are They Who Dwell in Your House
38 Psalm 84 - How Lovely Is Your Dwelling Place
48 Psalm 116 - Our Blessing Cup
53 Psalm 122 - Let Us Go Rejoicing to the House of the Lord
55 Psalm 128 - Blest Are Those Who Love You
54 Psalm 128 - O Blessed Are Those
283 Renew Your People
348 Seed, Scattered and Sown
230 Sing a New Song
198 Sing Out, Earth and Skies
282 Singing Songs of Expectation
349 Song of Farewell
181 Song of the Risen One
187 Song to Jesus Christ
211 Sow the Word
190 Spirit of God within Me
243 Take Our Bread
300 The Harvest of Justice
209 The Lord Is My Life
295 The Love of the Lord
322 The River Will Rise
285 The Servant Song
289 The Song of All Seed
304 The Voice of God But Speaks of Peace
333 The Water I Give
206 This Little Light of Mine
250 We Live a Mystery
321 We Shall Rise Again
252 We Walk by Faith
345 We Who Once Were Dead
200 Wind upon the Water
222 You Are the Voice
277 You Will Show Me the Path of Life
248 Your Love Is Finer Than Life

LIGHT

298 Anthem
155 Arise, Shine!
320 At Evening
330 Awake, O Sleeper
244 Be Light for Our Eyes
236 Blessed Be God
156 Brightest and Best
280 Bring Forth the Kingdom
294 City of God
142 Come to Set Us Free
202 Come to the Water
10 Evening Hymn - O Radiant Light
311 Gather Us In
233 Glory and Praise to Our God
270 God Is Love
195 God Is One, Unique and Holy
319 God of Day and God of Darkness
205 I Am the Light of the World
208 I Want to Walk as a Child of the Light
315 Jesus, Come to Us
302 Jesus Still Lives
178 Light of Christ/Exsultet
157 Lord, Today
137 My Soul in Stillness Waits
336 Now in This Banquet
140 People of the Night
220 Praise the Lord, My Soul
210 Praise to You, O Christ, Our Savior
305 Prayer for Peace
158 Remember Your Love
154 Song of God among Us
312 Song over the Waters
209 The Lord Is My Life
265 The Lord Is Near
206 This Little Light of Mine
163 Tree of Life
301 We Are Called
207 We Are Walking in the Light
200 Wind upon the Water
331 You Are God's Work of Art
222 You Are the Voice

LONELINESS

258 From My Mother's Womb
335 Jesus, Wine of Peace

LOVE OF GOD FOR US

257 All That We Have
204 All You Who Are Thirsty
155 Arise, Shine!
344 Behold the Lamb
246 Bless the Lord
280 Bring Forth the Kingdom
316 Canticle of Zachary
185 Come Away to the Skies
202 Come to the Water
272 Gift of Love
270 God Is Love
195 God Is One, Unique and Holy

Topical Index/*continued*

196 God of All Creation
184 Good Christians All
290 Good Friday Hymn
291 Here I Am, Lord
260 How Can I Keep from Singing?
334 I Have Loved You
188 I Will Be with You
239 Jesu Christe Miserere
168 Jesu, Jesu
231 Lift Up Your Hearts
178 Light of Christ/Exsultet
268 Love One Another
235 May We Praise You
269 No Greater Love
336 Now in This Banquet
162 Now Let Us All with One Accord
175 Now the Green Blade Rises
347 Our Blessing Cup
306 Peace Is Flowing Like a River
229 Praise His Name
220 Praise the Lord, My Soul
305 Prayer for Peace
27 Psalm 34 - Taste and See
46 Psalm 103 - The Lord Is Kind and Merciful
58 Psalm 136 - Love Is Never Ending
59 Psalm 145 - I Will Praise Your Name
60 Psalm 146 - Lord, Come and Save Us
283 Renew Your People
355 Return to Me
169 Ride On, Jesus, Ride
189 Send Us Your Spirit
230 Sing a New Song
161 Song of the Lord's Supper
191 Spirit Blowing through Creation
238 Table Prayer
338 Taste and See
265 The Lord Is Near
295 The Love of the Lord
262 Though the Mountains May Fall
163 Tree of Life
271 Ubi Caritas
296 We Have Been Told
250 We Live a Mystery
249 We Remember
351 When Love Is Found
267 Where Charity and Love Prevail
174 Wherever You Go
232 With Drums and Dancing
222 You Are the Voice
277 You Will Show Me the Path of Life
248 Your Love Is Finer Than Life

LOVE FOR GOD

172 Calvary
180 Easter Alleluia
54 Psalm 128 - O Blessed Are Those
296 We Have Been Told
267 Where Charity and Love Prevail

LOVE FOR OTHERS

280 Bring Forth the Kingdom
290 Good Friday Hymn
357 Healer of Our Every Ill
291 Here I Am, Lord
286 I Bind My Heart
168 Jesu, Jesu
302 Jesus Still Lives
339 Life-Giving Bread, Saving Cup
268 Love One Another
2 Morning Hymn - God Is Alive
269 No Greater Love
273 Not for Tongues
336 Now in This Banquet
346 One Bread, One Body
305 Prayer for Peace
283 Renew Your People
189 Send Us Your Spirit
198 Sing Out, Earth and Skies
190 Spirit of God within Me
300 The Harvest of Justice
271 Ubi Caritas
301 We Are Called
310 We Are Many Parts
296 We Have Been Told
351 When Love Is Found
267 Where Charity and Love Prevail
(also Brotherhood and Sisterhood)

MAJESTY AND POWER

288 Come, My Children
29 Psalm 47 - God Mounts His Throne
51 Psalm 118 - Alleluia, Alleluia
50 Psalm 118 - Let Us Rejoice
218 Sing a New Song to the Lord
219 The Song of Moses
201 The Stars Declare His Glory
228 To God with Gladness Sing

MARY *(see Liturgical Index)*

MERCY

246 Bless the Lord
264 Blest Be the Lord
280 Bring Forth the Kingdom
172 Calvary
14 Canticle of Mary - My Soul Gives Glory
241 Hold Me in Life
239 Jesu Christe Miserere
354 Jesus, Heal Us
253 Jesus the Lord
231 Lift Up Your Hearts
141 Maranatha
254 Our Help Is in the Name of the Lord
21 Psalm 25 - To You, O Lord
22 Psalm 25 - To You, O Lord
24 Psalm 30 - I Will Praise You, Lord
25 Psalm 33 - Let Your Mercy Be on Us
30 Psalm 51 - Be Merciful, O Lord, for We Have Sinned

Topical Index/*continued*

31 Psalm 51 - Create in Me
46 Psalm 103 - The Lord Is Kind and Merciful
57 Psalm 130 - With the Lord
56 Psalm 130 - With the Lord There Is Mercy
158 Remember Your Love
356 Remember Your Mercy, Lord
169 Ride On, Jesus, Ride
218 Sing a New Song to the Lord
217 Sing of the Lord's Goodness
265 The Lord Is Near
304 The Voice of God But Speaks of Peace
262 Though the Mountains May Fall
321 We Shall Rise Again

MESSIANIC
142 Come to Set Us Free
281 I Will Not Die
148 Let the Heavens Be Glad
157 Lord, Today
141 Maranatha
137 My Soul in Stillness Waits
210 Praise to You, O Christ, Our Savior
19 Psalm 22 - My God, My God, Why Have You Abandoned Me?
36 Psalm 72 - Lord, Every Nation on Earth Will Adore You
37 Psalm 80 - Lord, Make Us Turn to You
40 Psalm 85 - Lord, Let Us See Your Kindness
41 Psalm 89 - Forever I Will Sing the Goodness of the Lord
136 The Day Is Near
139 Wait for the Lord
(also Second Coming)

MINISTRY
294 City of God
245 Come to Us, Creative Spirit
311 Gather Us In
290 Good Friday Hymn
292 He Has Anointed Me
291 Here I Am, Lord
297 I Danced in the Morning
188 I Will Be with You
168 Jesu, Jesu
336 Now in This Banquet
293 Send Me, Jesus (Thuma Mina)
189 Send Us Your Spirit
230 Sing a New Song
217 Sing of the Lord's Goodness
161 Song of the Lord's Supper
312 Song over the Waters
211 Sow the Word
191 Spirit Blowing through Creation
192 Spirit Friend
289 The Song of All Seed
163 Tree of Life
271 Ubi Caritas
193 Veni Sancte Spiritus
267 Where Charity and Love Prevail
232 With Drums and Dancing
(also Commitment, Discipleship, Mission, Service)

MISSION
214 A New Song
244 Be Light for Our Eyes
263 Be Not Afraid
279 Because the Lord Is My Shepherd
264 Blest Be the Lord
280 Bring Forth the Kingdom
294 City of God
184 Good Christians All
290 Good Friday Hymn
292 He Has Anointed Me
291 Here I Am, Lord
297 I Danced in the Morning
188 I Will Be with You
340 In the Breaking of the Bread
343 Look Beyond
261 On Eagle's Wings
293 Send Me, Jesus (Thuma Mina)
181 Song of the Risen One
312 Song over the Waters
211 Sow the Word
289 The Song of All Seed
206 This Little Light of Mine
262 Though the Mountains May Fall
310 We Are Many Parts

MORNING
214 A New Song
221 Adoramus Te Domine II - Gloria
151 Awake, Awake and Greet the New Morn
236 Blessed Be God
316 Canticle of Zachary
5 Canticle of Zachary - Blessed Be the God of Israel
237 Confitemini Domino
213 I Will Sing, I Will Sing
227 In Praise of His Name
223 Jubilate, Servite
231 Lift Up Your Hearts
235 May We Praise You
317 Morning Has Broken
2 Morning Hymn - God Is Alive
229 Praise His Name
220 Praise the Lord, My Soul
18 Psalm 19 - Lord, You Have the Words
25 Psalm 33 - Let Your Mercy Be on Us
25 Psalm 33 - The Earth Is Full of the Goodness
28 Psalm 42 - Song of the Exile
29 Psalm 47 - God Mounts His Throne
30 Psalm 51 - Be Merciful, O Lord, for We Have Sinned
31 Psalm 51 - Create in Me
33 Psalm 63 - As Morning Breaks
3 Psalm 63 - In the Shadow of Your Wings
34 Psalm 63 - My Soul Is Thirsting for You, O Lord, My God

Topical Index/*continued*

35 Psalm 66 - Let All the Earth
37 Psalm 80 - Lord, Make Us Turn to You
39 Psalm 84 - Happy Are They Who Dwell in Your House
38 Psalm 84 - How Lovely Is Your Dwelling Place
40 Psalm 85 - Lord, Let Us See Your Kindness
43 Psalm 95 - If Today You Hear His Voice
44 Psalm 98 - All the Ends of the Earth
45 Psalm 100 - We Are His People
49 Psalm 117 - Holy Is God, Holy and Strong
51 Psalm 118 - Alleluia, Alleluia
50 Psalm 118 - Let Us Rejoice
60 Psalm 146 - Lord, Come and Save Us
61 Psalm 147 - Bless the Lord, My Soul
62 Psalm 148 - Praise the Lord from the Heavens
63 Psalm 150 - Praise God in His Holy Dwelling
230 Sing a New Song
218 Sing a New Song to the Lord
217 Sing of the Lord's Goodness
234 Sing to the Mountains
304 The Voice of God But Speaks of Peace
228 To God with Gladness Sing
232 With Drums and Dancing
222 You Are the Voice

MUSIC MINISTRY
245 Come to Us, Creative Spirit
230 Sing a New Song
217 Sing of the Lord's Goodness
232 With Drums and Dancing

MYSTERY OF GOD
161 Song of the Lord's Supper
187 Song to Jesus Christ
163 Tree of Life
250 We Live a Mystery
194 What Is Your Name

NATION
155 Arise, Shine!
144 Born of Peace
156 Brightest and Best
152 Carol at the Manger
183 Christ Is Alive
272 Gift of Love
319 God of Day and God of Darkness
157 Lord, Today
210 Praise to You, O Christ, Our Savior
217 Sing of the Lord's Goodness
154 Song of God among Us
145 Song of the Stable
211 Sow the Word
267 Where Charity and Love Prevail

NATURE *(see Life)*

NEW CREATION
214 A New Song
173 Ashes
332 Baptized in Water
244 Be Light for Our Eyes
183 Christ Is Alive
185 Come Away to the Skies
159 Deep Within
138 Each Winter As the Year Grows Older
160 Eternal Lord of Love
184 Good Christians All
260 How Can I Keep from Singing?
281 I Will Not Die
175 Now the Green Blade Rises
220 Praise the Lord, My Soul
189 Send Us Your Spirit
217 Sing of the Lord's Goodness
198 Sing Out, Earth and Skies
181 Song of the Risen One
187 Song to Jesus Christ
190 Spirit of God within Me
243 Take Our Bread
163 Tree of Life
224 We Praise You
200 Wind upon the Water
232 With Drums and Dancing
222 You Are the Voice

OBEDIENCE
250 We Live a Mystery

OFFERING
257 All That We Have
173 Ashes
245 Come to Us, Creative Spirit
12 Psalm 141 - Like Burning Incense
161 Song of the Lord's Supper
243 Take Our Bread
226 This Is the Day
249 We Remember

PASCHAL MYSTERY
138 Each Winter As the Year Grows Older
160 Eternal Lord of Love
137 My Soul in Stillness Waits
140 People of the Night
217 Sing of the Lord's Goodness
187 Song to Jesus Christ

PASTORAL CARE
289 The Song of All Seed
271 Ubi Caritas
267 Where Charity and Love Prevail
(also Discipleship, Ministry)

PATIENCE
241 Hold Me in Life
250 We Live a Mystery

PATRIOTIC *(see Nation)*

Topical Index/*continued*

PEACE
298 Anthem
320 At Evening
151 Awake, Awake and Greet the New Morn
284 Blest Are They
280 Bring Forth the Kingdom
138 Each Winter As the Year Grows Older
196 God of All Creation
319 God of Day and God of Darkness
290 Good Friday Hymn
357 Healer of Our Every Ill
260 How Can I Keep from Singing?
302 Jesus Still Lives
141 Maranatha
307 My Peace I Leave You
137 My Soul in Stillness Waits
303 My Soul Is Still
306 Peace Is Flowing Like a River
305 Prayer for Peace
40 Psalm 85 - Lord, Let Us See Your Kindness
53 Psalm 122 - Let Us Go Rejoicing to the House of the Lord
283 Renew Your People
198 Sing Out, Earth and Skies
312 Song over the Waters
304 The Voice of God But Speaks of Peace
228 To God with Gladness Sing
313 What Is This Place
266 You Will Draw Water

PERSEVERANCE
241 Hold Me in Life

PETITION/PRAYER
257 All That We Have
244 Be Light for Our Eyes
344 Behold the Lamb
246 Bless the Lord
152 Carol at the Manger
142 Come to Set Us Free
245 Come to Us, Creative Spirit
138 Each Winter As the Year Grows Older
311 Gather Us In
196 God of All Creation
143 God of All People
319 God of Day and God of Darkness
290 Good Friday Hymn
357 Healer of Our Every Ill
241 Hold Me in Life
208 I Want to Walk as a Child of the Light
239 Jesu Christe Miserere
315 Jesus, Come to Us
354 Jesus, Heal Us
167 Jesus, Remember Me
318 Joyous Light of Heavenly Glory
324 Lord of Glory
141 Maranatha
255 My Refuge
137 My Soul in Stillness Waits
273 Not for Tongues
336 Now in This Banquet
162 Now Let Us All with One Accord
242 O Healing River
240 O Lord, Hear My Prayer
140 People of the Night
305 Prayer for Peace
19 Psalm 22 - My God, My God, Why Have You Abandoned Me?
20 Psalm 23 - Shepherd Me, O God
30 Psalm 51 - Be Merciful, O Lord, for We Have Sinned
31 Psalm 51 - Create in Me
37 Psalm 80 - Lord, Make Us Turn to You
38 Psalm 84 - How Lovely Is Your Dwelling Place
47 Psalm 104 - Lord, Send Out Your Spirit
57 Psalm 130 - With the Lord
56 Psalm 130 - With the Lord There Is Mercy
12 Psalm 141 - Like Burning Incense
60 Psalm 146 - Lord, Come and Save Us
356 Remember Your Mercy, Lord
283 Renew Your People
293 Send Me, Jesus (Thuma Mina)
189 Send Us Your Spirit
276 Shelter Me, O God
198 Sing Out, Earth and Skies
247 Song of St. Patrick
191 Spirit Blowing through Creation
190 Spirit of God within Me
166 Stay Here and Keep Watch
170 Stay with Me
243 Take Our Bread
201 The Stars Declare His Glory
304 The Voice of God But Speaks of Peace
193 Veni Sancte Spiritus
252 We Walk by Faith
345 We Who Once Were Dead
194 What Is Your Name
200 Wind upon the Water
248 Your Love Is Finer Than Life

PILGRIMAGE
280 Bring Forth the Kingdom
340 In the Breaking of the Bread
137 My Soul in Stillness Waits
336 Now in This Banquet
282 Singing Songs of Expectation
300 The Harvest of Justice
259 The Lord Is Near
285 The Servant Song
224 We Praise You

POVERTY
204 All You Who Are Thirsty
298 Anthem
155 Arise, Shine!
288 Come, My Children
202 Come to the Water
275 Eye Has Not Seen
319 God of Day and God of Darkness

Topical Index/*continued*

286 I Bind My Heart
253 Jesus the Lord
26 Psalm 34 - The Cry of the Poor
300 The Harvest of Justice

POVERTY OF SPIRIT
284 Blest Are They

PRAISE
214 A New Song
164 Adoramus Te Christe
221 Adoramus Te Domine II - Gloria
215 Alleluia, Sing!
332 Baptized in Water
236 Blessed Be God
264 Blest Be the Lord
14 Canticle of Mary - My Soul Gives Glory
197 Canticle of the Sun
316 Canticle of Zachary
5 Canticle of Zachary - Blessed Be the God of Israel
251 Center of My Life
183 Christ Is Alive
185 Come Away to the Skies
288 Come, My Children
245 Come to Us, Creative Spirit
237 Confitemini Domino
180 Easter Alleluia
10 Evening Hymn - O Radiant Light
149 Gloria, Gloria
287 Glorious in Majesty
233 Glory and Praise to Our God
184 Good Christians All
182 Hilariter
165 Hosanna
225 I Want to Praise Your Name
213 I Will Sing, I Will Sing
227 In Praise of His Name
223 Jubilate, Servite
216 Laudate Dominum
339 Life-Giving Bread, Saving Cup
231 Lift Up Your Hearts
178 Light of Christ/Exsultet
235 May We Praise You
317 Morning Has Broken
2 Morning Hymn - God Is Alive
199 Nature's Praise
229 Praise His Name
220 Praise the Lord, My Soul
210 Praise to You, O Christ, Our Savior
177 Psallite Deo
24 Psalm 30 - I Will Praise You, Lord
25 Psalm 33 - Let Your Mercy Be on Us
25 Psalm 33 - The Earth Is Full of the Goodness
27 Psalm 34 - Taste and See
26 Psalm 34 - The Cry of the Poor
29 Psalm 47 - God Mounts His Throne
33 Psalm 63 - As Morning Breaks
3 Psalm 63 - In the Shadow of Your Wings
35 Psalm 66 - Let All the Earth
36 Psalm 72 - Lord, Every Nation on Earth Will Adore You
37 Psalm 80 - Lord, Make Us Turn to You
41 Psalm 89 - Forever I Will Sing the Goodness of the Lord
43 Psalm 95 - If Today You Hear His Voice
44 Psalm 98 - All the Ends of the Earth
45 Psalm 100 - We Are His People
47 Psalm 104 - Lord, Send Out Your Spirit
49 Psalm 117 - Holy Is God, Holy and Strong
51 Psalm 118 - Alleluia, Alleluia
53 Psalm 122 - Let Us Go Rejoicing to the House of the Lord
59 Psalm 145 - I Will Praise Your Name
60 Psalm 146 - Lord, Come and Save Us
61 Psalm 147 - Bless the Lord, My Soul
62 Psalm 148 - Praise the Lord from the Heavens
63 Psalm 150 - Praise God in His Holy Dwelling
283 Renew Your People
169 Ride On, Jesus, Ride
230 Sing a New Song
218 Sing a New Song to the Lord
217 Sing of the Lord's Goodness
198 Sing Out, Earth and Skies
234 Sing to the Mountains
186 Surrexit Christus
176 Surrexit Dominus Vere II
238 Table Prayer
338 Taste and See
300 The Harvest of Justice
219 The Song of Moses
201 The Stars Declare His Glory
226 This Is the Day
262 Though the Mountains May Fall
228 To God with Gladness Sing
224 We Praise You
256 When from Our Exile
232 With Drums and Dancing
222 You Are the Voice

PRESENCE OF GOD
143 God of All People
208 I Want to Walk as a Child of the Light
188 I Will Be with You
335 Jesus, Wine of Peace
178 Light of Christ/Exsultet
137 My Soul in Stillness Waits
282 Singing Songs of Expectation
192 Spirit Friend
256 When from Our Exile

PRIESTHOOD *(see Discipleship, Mission)*

PROMISE
5 Canticle of Zachary - Blessed Be the God of Israel
340 In the Breaking of the Bread
335 Jesus, Wine of Peace
342 The Name of God

Topical Index/*continued*

PROPHECY *(see Word of God)*

PROVIDENCE
204 All You Who Are Thirsty
144 Born of Peace
5 Canticle of Zachary - Blessed Be the God of Israel
202 Come to the Water
180 Easter Alleluia
334 I Have Loved You
203 I Will Lift Up My Eyes
335 Jesus, Wine of Peace
146 Night of Silence
25 Psalm 33 - Let Your Mercy Be on Us
25 Psalm 33 - The Earth Is Full of the Goodness
26 Psalm 34 - The Cry of the Poor
34 Psalm 63 - My Soul Is Thirsting for You, O Lord, My God
35 Psalm 66 - Let All the Earth
42 Psalm 91 - Be with Me
47 Psalm 104 - Lord, Send Out Your Spirit
50 Psalm 118 - Let Us Rejoice
52 Psalm 121 - Our Help Comes from the Lord
58 Psalm 136 - Love Is Never Ending
60 Psalm 146 - Lord, Come and Save Us
61 Psalm 147 - Bless the Lord, My Soul
338 Taste and See
228 To God with Gladness Sing
350 We Will Rise Again
232 With Drums and Dancing

RECONCILIATION
246 Bless the Lord
210 Praise to You, O Christ, Our Savior
262 Though the Mountains May Fall
267 Where Charity and Love Prevail

REDEMPTION *(see Salvation)*

REFUGE
258 From My Mother's Womb
260 How Can I Keep from Singing?
340 In the Breaking of the Bread
255 My Refuge
261 On Eagle's Wings
12 Psalm 141 - Like Burning Incense
276 Shelter Me, O God
259 The Lord Is Near
265 The Lord Is Near

REIGN OF GOD
314 All People Here Who Remember
204 All You Who Are Thirsty
284 Blest Are They
280 Bring Forth the Kingdom
183 Christ Is Alive
202 Come to the Water
311 Gather Us In
196 God of All Creation
165 Hosanna
281 I Will Not Die
167 Jesus, Remember Me
335 Jesus, Wine of Peace
339 Life-Giving Bread, Saving Cup
2 Morning Hymn - God Is Alive
161 Song of the Lord's Supper
301 We Are Called
329 Wonder of Wonders
266 You Will Draw Water

REMEMBRANCE
314 All People Here Who Remember
356 Remember Your Mercy, Lord
218 Sing a New Song to the Lord
249 We Remember

RENEWAL
214 A New Song
246 Bless the Lord
138 Each Winter As the Year Grows Older
283 Renew Your People
230 Sing a New Song
218 Sing a New Song to the Lord
191 Spirit Blowing through Creation
192 Spirit Friend
200 Wind upon the Water

REPENTANCE
172 Calvary
162 Now Let Us All with One Accord
30 Psalm 51 - Be Merciful, O Lord, for We Have Sinned
31 Psalm 51 - Create in Me
355 Return to Me

REST
263 Be Not Afraid
279 Because the Lord Is My Shepherd
251 Center of My Life
202 Come to the Water
260 How Can I Keep from Singing?
259 The Lord Is Near
266 You Will Draw Water

RESURRECTION *(see Liturgical Index: Easter)*

SACRAMENT
343 Look Beyond
345 We Who Once Were Dead

SACRIFICE
160 Eternal Lord of Love
190 Spirit of God within Me

SAINTS *(see Liturgical Index: All Saints, Apostles, Martyrs)*

SALVATION
14 Canticle of Mary - My Soul Gives Glory

Topical Index/*continued*

316 Canticle of Zachary
5 Canticle of Zachary - Blessed Be the God of Israel
142 Come to Set Us Free
180 Easter Alleluia
272 Gift of Love
208 I Want to Walk as a Child of the Light
255 My Refuge
299 Now We Remain
254 Our Help Is in the Name of the Lord
44 Psalm 98 - All the Ends of the Earth
218 Sing a New Song to the Lord
234 Sing to the Mountains
191 Spirit Blowing through Creation
209 The Lord Is My Life
219 The Song of Moses
345 We Who Once Were Dead

SEASONS
236 Blessed Be God
138 Each Winter As the Year Grows Older
182 Hilariter
146 Night of Silence
175 Now the Green Blade Rises

SECOND COMING
142 Come to Set Us Free
323 Freedom Is Coming
287 Glorious in Majesty
325 In the Lord, I Will Be Thankful
148 Let the Heavens Be Glad
324 Lord of Glory
141 Maranatha
137 My Soul in Stillness Waits
140 People of the Night
220 Praise the Lord, My Soul
28 Psalm 42 - Song of the Exile
53 Psalm 122 - Let Us Go Rejoicing to the House of the Lord
230 Sing a New Song
218 Sing a New Song to the Lord
136 The Day Is Near
322 The River Will Rise
139 Wait for the Lord
250 We Live a Mystery
249 We Remember
321 We Shall Rise Again
350 We Will Rise Again

SECURITY
241 Hold Me in Life
334 I Have Loved You
335 Jesus, Wine of Peace
303 My Soul Is Still
247 Song of St. Patrick
266 You Will Draw Water

SEEKING
334 I Have Loved You
240 O Lord, Hear My Prayer
310 We Are Many Parts

SENDING FORTH *(see Going Forth, Missions)*

SERVICE
251 Center of My Life
287 Glorious in Majesty
168 Jesu, Jesu
308 Many Are the Light Beams
342 The Name of God
285 The Servant Song
301 We Are Called
310 We Are Many Parts
296 We Have Been Told
(also Ministry)

SHARING
320 At Evening
168 Jesu, Jesu
161 Song of the Lord's Supper
300 The Harvest of Justice
310 We Are Many Parts

SHEPHERD
246 Bless the Lord
180 Easter Alleluia
335 Jesus, Wine of Peace
20 Psalm 23 - Shepherd Me, O God
274 The Lord Is My Shepherd
228 To God with Gladness Sing
350 We Will Rise Again

SICKNESS *(see Comfort, Healing, Suffering; Liturgical Index: Pastoral Care of the Sick)*

SIN
344 Behold the Lamb
246 Bless the Lord
236 Blessed Be God
5 Canticle of Zachary - Blessed Be the God of Israel
288 Come, My Children
227 In Praise of His Name
235 May We Praise You
346 One Bread, One Body
229 Praise His Name
30 Psalm 51 - Be Merciful, O Lord, for We Have Sinned
31 Psalm 51 - Create in Me
46 Psalm 103 - The Lord Is Kind and Merciful
47 Psalm 104 - Lord, Send Out Your Spirit
55 Psalm 128 - Blest Are Those Who Love You
54 Psalm 128 - O Blessed Are Those
247 Song of St. Patrick
228 To God with Gladness Sing
163 Tree of Life
248 Your Love Is Finer Than Life
(also Repentance; Liturgical Index: Penance)

Topical Index/*continued*

SOCIAL CONCERN
204 All You Who Are Thirsty
298 Anthem
320 At Evening
144 Born of Peace
152 Carol at the Manger
183 Christ Is Alive
294 City of God
202 Come to the Water
138 Each Winter As the Year Grows Older
323 Freedom Is Coming
319 God of Day and God of Darkness
291 Here I Am, Lord
260 How Can I Keep from Singing?
286 I Bind My Heart
203 I Will Lift Up My Eyes
281 I Will Not Die
168 Jesu, Jesu
302 Jesus Still Lives
318 Joyous Light of Heavenly Glory
242 O Healing River
153 Once in Royal David's City
283 Renew Your People
198 Sing Out, Earth and Skies
312 Song over the Waters
136 The Day Is Near
300 The Harvest of Justice
289 The Song of All Seed
304 The Voice of God But Speaks of Peace
301 We Are Called
267 Where Charity and Love Prevail
266 You Will Draw Water

SOLIDARITY
298 Anthem
294 City of God
275 Eye Has Not Seen
287 Glorious in Majesty
167 Jesus, Remember Me
302 Jesus Still Lives
308 Many Are the Light Beams
346 One Bread, One Body
53 Psalm 122 - Let Us Go Rejoicing to the House of the Lord
192 Spirit Friend
166 Stay Here and Keep Watch
170 Stay with Me
300 The Harvest of Justice
285 The Servant Song
289 The Song of All Seed
345 We Who Once Were Dead
194 What Is Your Name
174 Wherever You Go

SONG
197 Canticle of the Sun
183 Christ Is Alive
185 Come Away to the Skies
260 How Can I Keep from Singing?
225 I Want to Praise Your Name
208 I Want to Walk as a Child of the Light
213 I Will Sing, I Will Sing
2 Morning Hymn - God Is Alive
44 Psalm 98 - All the Ends of the Earth
63 Psalm 150 - Praise God in His Holy Dwelling
230 Sing a New Song
218 Sing a New Song to the Lord
217 Sing of the Lord's Goodness
198 Sing Out, Earth and Skies
234 Sing to the Mountains
186 Surrexit Christus
209 The Lord Is My Life
219 The Song of Moses
226 This Is the Day
301 We Are Called
232 With Drums and Dancing

SORROW *(see Comfort, Mercy, Repentance, Sin, Trust, Providence; Liturgical Index: Penance)*

STEWARDSHIP *(see Sharing, Service, Ministry)*

STRANGER
320 At Evening
152 Carol at the Manger
300 The Harvest of Justice

STRENGTH
155 Arise, Shine!
142 Come to Set Us Free
159 Deep Within
260 How Can I Keep from Singing?
208 I Want to Walk as a Child of the Light
203 I Will Lift Up My Eyes
339 Life-Giving Bread, Saving Cup
255 My Refuge
19 Psalm 22 - My God, My God, Why Have You Abandoned Me?
32 Psalm 62 - In God Alone
39 Psalm 84 - Happy Are They Who Dwell in Your House
234 Sing to the Mountains
309 Song of Gathering
181 Song of the Risen One
166 Stay Here and Keep Watch
170 Stay with Me
136 The Day Is Near
209 The Lord Is My Life
259 The Lord Is Near
219 The Song of Moses
206 This Little Light of Mine
163 Tree of Life
139 Wait for the Lord
350 We Will Rise Again
266 You Will Draw Water

STRUGGLE
258 From My Mother's Womb
340 In the Breaking of the Bread

Topical Index/*continued*

SUFFERING
173 Ashes
284 Blest Are They
258 From My Mother's Womb
233 Glory and Praise to Our God
28 Psalm 42 - Song of the Exile
181 Song of the Risen One
166 Stay Here and Keep Watch
170 Stay with Me
295 The Love of the Lord
174 Wherever You Go

TEMPTATION
162 Now Let Us All with One Accord
163 Tree of Life

TESTIMONY/WITNESS *(see Christian Life, Ministry, Mission, Solidarity)*

THANKSGIVING
173 Ashes
332 Baptized in Water
344 Behold the Lamb
185 Come Away to the Skies
237 Confitemini Domino
325 In the Lord, I Will Be Thankful
339 Life-Giving Bread, Saving Cup
231 Lift Up Your Hearts
347 Our Blessing Cup
24 Psalm 30 - I Will Praise You, Lord
3 Psalm 63 - In the Shadow of Your Wings
45 Psalm 100 - We Are His People
46 Psalm 103 - The Lord Is Kind and Merciful
48 Psalm 116 - Our Blessing Cup
51 Psalm 118 - Alleluia, Alleluia
50 Psalm 118 - Let Us Rejoice
58 Psalm 136 - Love Is Never Ending
59 Psalm 145 - I Will Praise Your Name
283 Renew Your People
234 Sing to the Mountains
238 Table Prayer
342 The Name of God
228 To God with Gladness Sing
224 We Praise You

THIRST
204 All You Who Are Thirsty
202 Come to the Water
341 Eat This Bread
337 I Am the Bread of Life
203 I Will Lift Up My Eyes
137 My Soul in Stillness Waits
242 O Healing River
28 Psalm 42 - Song of the Exile
33 Psalm 63 - As Morning Breaks
3 Psalm 63 - In the Shadow of Your Wings
34 Psalm 63 - My Soul Is Thirsting for You, O Lord, My God
333 The Water I Give
248 Your Love Is Finer Than Life

TRUST
257 All That We Have
298 Anthem
155 Arise, Shine!
151 Awake, Awake and Greet the New Morn
353 Balm in Gilead
263 Be Not Afraid
279 Because the Lord Is My Shepherd
344 Behold the Lamb
236 Blessed Be God
264 Blest Be the Lord
144 Born of Peace
316 Canticle of Zachary
152 Carol at the Manger
251 Center of My Life
138 Each Winter As the Year Grows Older
341 Eat This Bread
275 Eye Has Not Seen
258 From My Mother's Womb
311 Gather Us In
233 Glory and Praise to Our God
196 God of All Creation
357 Healer of Our Every Ill
241 Hold Me in Life
260 How Can I Keep from Singing?
179 I Am the Resurrection
334 I Have Loved You
188 I Will Be with You
340 In the Breaking of the Bread
325 In the Lord, I Will Be Thankful
315 Jesus, Come to Us
354 Jesus, Heal Us
302 Jesus Still Lives
335 Jesus, Wine of Peace
324 Lord of Glory
212 Lord, to Whom Shall We Go
307 My Peace I Leave You
255 My Refuge
137 My Soul in Stillness Waits
303 My Soul Is Still
146 Night of Silence
336 Now in This Banquet
278 O Christe Domine Jesu
240 O Lord, Hear My Prayer
261 On Eagle's Wings
254 Our Help Is in the Name of the Lord
140 People of the Night
220 Praise the Lord, My Soul
19 Psalm 22 - My God, My God, Why Have You Abandoned Me?
20 Psalm 23 - Shepherd Me, O God
21 Psalm 25 - To You, O Lord
23 Psalm 27 - The Lord Is My Light
24 Psalm 30 - I Will Praise You, Lord
25 Psalm 33 - Let Your Mercy Be on Us
25 Psalm 33 - The Earth Is Full of the Goodness
27 Psalm 34 - Taste and See
28 Psalm 42 - Song of the Exile
32 Psalm 62 - In God Alone
33 Psalm 63 - As Morning Breaks

Topical Index/*continued*

3 Psalm 63 - In the Shadow of Your Wings
34 Psalm 63 - My Soul Is Thirsting for You, O Lord, My God
42 Psalm 91 - Be with Me
52 Psalm 121 - Our Help Comes from the Lord
57 Psalm 130 - With the Lord
56 Psalm 130 - With the Lord There Is Mercy
12 Psalm 141 - Like Burning Incense
158 Remember Your Love
276 Shelter Me, O God
282 Singing Songs of Expectation
247 Song of St. Patrick
338 Taste and See
136 The Day Is Near
274 The Lord Is My Shepherd
259 The Lord Is Near
265 The Lord Is Near
304 The Voice of God But Speaks of Peace
262 Though the Mountains May Fall
139 Wait for the Lord
321 We Shall Rise Again
252 We Walk by Faith
350 We Will Rise Again
256 When from Our Exile
351 When Love Is Found
232 With Drums and Dancing
266 You Will Draw Water
277 You Will Show Me the Path of Life

TRUTH
138 Each Winter As the Year Grows Older
21 Psalm 25 - To You, O Lord
40 Psalm 85 - Lord, Let Us See Your Kindness
348 Seed, Scattered and Sown
190 Spirit of God within Me
304 The Voice of God But Speaks of Peace

UNITY
214 A New Song
344 Behold the Lamb
311 Gather Us In
287 Glorious in Majesty
270 God Is Love
213 I Will Sing, I Will Sing
168 Jesu, Jesu
339 Life-Giving Bread, Saving Cup
308 Many Are the Light Beams
346 One Bread, One Body
210 Praise to You, O Christ, Our Savior
49 Psalm 117 - Holy Is God, Holy and Strong
189 Send Us Your Spirit
282 Singing Songs of Expectation
309 Song of Gathering
238 Table Prayer
310 We Are Many Parts
267 Where Charity and Love Prevail
(also Love for Others, Peace, Solidarity)

VICTORY OVER SIN AND DEATH
183 Christ Is Alive
184 Good Christians All
213 I Will Sing, I Will Sing

VISION
138 Each Winter As the Year Grows Older
357 Healer of Our Every Ill
281 I Will Not Die

VOCATION
270 God Is Love
290 Good Friday Hymn
291 Here I Am, Lord
343 Look Beyond
2 Morning Hymn - God Is Alive
210 Praise to You, O Christ, Our Savior
224 We Praise You
(also Discipleship, Mission)

WATER
204 All You Who Are Thirsty
✓202 Come to the Water
233 Glory and Praise to Our God
196 God of All Creation
203 I Will Lift Up My Eyes
242 O Healing River
312 Song over the Waters
333 The Water I Give
163 Tree of Life
266 You Will Draw Water

WAY, TRUTH AND LIFE *(see Truth)*

WELCOME *(see Gathering)*

WISDOM
275 Eye Has Not Seen
233 Glory and Praise to Our God
18 Psalm 19 - Lord, You Have the Words
259 The Lord Is Near
224 We Praise You
277 You Will Show Me the Path of Life

WITNESS/TESTIMONY *(see Christian Life, Ministry, Mission, Solidarity)*

WORD OF GOD
142 Come to Set Us Free
245 Come to Us, Creative Spirit
212 Lord, to Whom Shall We Go
140 People of the Night
210 Praise to You, O Christ, Our Savior
18 Psalm 19 - Lord, You Have the Words
154 Song of God among Us
211 Sow the Word
136 The Day Is Near

WORK *(see Labor)*

WORLD *(see Nation)*

WORSHIP *(see Praise)*

Index of Composers, Authors and Sources 362

Afro-American Spiritual 169 171 172 206 353
Alexander, Cecil Francis 153
Alford, Henry 252
Alington, Cyril A. 184
Ault, Gary 257
Balhoff, Mike 157 158 224 238 259 292
Baring-Gould, Sabin 282
Barr, Tony 136 154
Barrickman, David 309
Batastini, Robert 153 171 184 208 243 260 313 341 353
Beeck, Franz Jozef van 194
Benoit, Paul 267
Berthier, Jacques 118 125 139 149 166 167 170 176 177 186 193 216 221 223 237 239 240 271 278 307 325 341
Braud, Dominic 199
Burnham, Jack W. 185
Cain, Thomas H. 160
Carter, Sydney 297
Celtic 117 327
Chepponis, James J. 268 328 339
Children's Bells, The 317
Coles, V.S.S. 326
Colgan, Rev. Tobias, OSB 174
Colvin, Tom 168 192
Connolly, Michael 204 236 250
Conry, Tom 136 144 154 173 194 203 266 281 298 314 322
Cothran, Jeff 287
Cotter, Jeanne 86 114 181 189 196 212 222 329
Crum, John M.C. 175
Currie, Randolph N. 283
Cyprian of Carthage 308
Daigle, Gary 157 158 224 238 257 259 292
Dearmer, Percy 182
Didache 339 346 348
Ducote, Darryl 157 158 224 238 259 292 343
Dudley-Smith, Timothy 145 190 201 218 273 328
Dufford, Bob, SJ 234 263
Dutch Traditional 289
Dyer, Max 213
English 316 351
Farjeon, Eleanor 317
Farrell, Bernadette 142 210
Feitan, Dan 348
Foley, John, SJ 26 202 235 346
Ford, Paul 272
Freeman, James Dillet 178
French Carol 175
Frostenson, Anders 308
Gaelic 317 332
Gauntlett, Henry J. 153
Gay, Annabeth 138
Gay, William 138
Ghana Folk Song 168
Gillard, Richard 285
Gonja Folk Song 192
Good Friday Liturgy 164
Grail, The 12 24 33 43 49 52 54 62 251 356
Green, Fred Pratt 320
Gregory the Great 162
Gruber, Franz X. 147
Gunnison, Eric 348
Haas, David 1 2 3 5 6 7 8 18 23 31 32 43 44 45 51 59 85 86 87 88 89 90 91 92 93 94 95 114 134 140 143 145 159 165 179 181 189 196 201 212 215 222 244 270 284 288 296 299 300 301 303 305 315 320 329 331 333 335 342 345 350 354
Harvey, T.C. 266
Haugen, Marty 19 20 21 25 27 28 29 30 35 37 40 41 42 44 46 48 50 55 56 58 60 61 65 67 68 71 74 76 77 78 79 80 82 96 97 98 99 100 101 102 103 104 105 106 107 121 137 138 151 152 154 155 156 163 164 175 178 180 183 191 192 197 198 200 226 244 247 248 249 252 274 275 277 280 282 290 296 308 310 311 312 317 318 319 326 330 332 336 357
Hayakawa, Greg 205
Hays, Henry Bryan, OSB 304
Heber, Reginald 156
Hooker, John Leon 162
Hughes, Howard, SM 62
Huijbers, Bernard 136 187 194 241 254 256 314
Hurd, Bob 123 225 258 272 276 340 355
Hytrek, Sr. Theophane, OSF 227 233 234 264 324
Ingeman, Bernard Severin 282
Ingram, Rev. F. 289 345
International Commission on English in the Liturgy 18 19 21 22 25 27 30 33 40 41 43 46 47 49 50 53 54 56 349
Inwood, Paul 24 54 133 217 251 356
Jacobse, Muus 345
Janco, Steven R. 211
Jerusalem Bible 174
Jewish Melody 287
Joncas, Michael 9 10 11 12 14 15 16 17 22 33 34 36 38 49 52 53 57 108 109 110 111 112 113 160 161 209 228 229 242 261 265 269 273 284 295 298 316 327 334 347 349
Jordan, J. Tash 1
Kantor, Daniel 146
Kelly, Rev. Columba, OSB 174
Keyes, Jeffrey 253
Kingsbury, Craig S. 205 225 272 276 344 355
Kirchengesang 182
Landry, Carey 306
LeBlanc, Robert 199
Lewis, Freeman 162
Lisicky, Paul 47
Loomis, Patrick 144 195 246 322
MacAller, Dominic 258 340
Manion, Tim 324
Maraire, Abraham 115
Marchal, Michael 349
Marshall, Jane 168
Martin, Barbara Jackson 169
Mawbray, David 245
McGoldrick, Redmond 187 254 256 289
Mealy, Norman 184
Means, Alexander 290

Index of Composers, Authors and Sources/*continued*

Miller, R.J. 348
Mohr, Joseph 147
Moore, James E. 124 188 206 207 214 338
Moore, William 282
Mueller, J.T. 14
Neder-landtsche gedenck-klanck 313
New American Bible 34
O'Carroll, Fintan 117
O'Connor, Roc, SJ 227 231
Oomen, A. 289
Oosterhuis, Huub 136 154 187 194 241 254 256 289 313
Oxford Book of Carols 175 182
Parker, Tom 220
Piae Cantiones 272
Pizzutti, Margaret 306
Pope, Michael, SJ 262 291
Porter, Thomas J. 39
Proulx, Richard 129 130 131
Pruner, Marcia 129
Pulkingham, Betty Carr 219 285
Quaker 260
Quinn, James, SJ 5 162 228 316
Ridge, M.D. 119 126 127 128 195 327
Sacred Harp, The 319
Sands, Ernest 217
Savoy, Thomas F. 245
Saward, Michael 332
Schoenbachler, Tim 141
Schulz-Widmar, Russell 352
Schutte, Dan 230 232 233 262 264 291 294
Senchur, Becket 135
Shaker 120 297
Shaw, Martin 182
Sionstoner 326
Smith, David 241 313 345
Soderberg, Sheryl 255
South African 168 293 323
Southern Harmony 119 156 185 290
Spee, Friedrich von 182
Stirks, Saul 148
Storey, William G. 10
Tabourot, J. 187
Taizé Community 118 125 139 149 166 167 170 176 177 186 193 216 221 223 237 239 240 271 278 307 325 341
Tallis, Thomas 352
Thomerson, Kathleen 208
Toolan, Suzanne, SM 286 302 337
Traditional 207 242 306
Trupia, Robert C. 272
Tucker, F. Bland 326
Vermulst, Jan M. 63
Vessels, Dennis 255
Vulpius, Melchior 184
Walker, Christopher 117 217 279
Walker, Edward 246
Watt, Lauchlan McLean 286
Weissrock, John 231 291 294
Welch, Lucia 283
West, Martin 351
Westendorf, Omer 63 267
Widestrand, Olle 308
Willett, Martin 150 190 344
Wilson, David G. 218
Wise, Joe 116 122 132 148 243 274 309
Wren, Brian 183 195 329 351
Young, Jeremy 321
Young, John F. 147
Zavelli, Keith 211

Metrical Index of Tunes 363

Included here are those hymns written in more or less standard meters. Hymns with irregular and peculiar meters have been omitted.

CM (COMMON METER - 8 6 8 6)
252 SHANTI
267 CHRISTIAN LOVE

CMD (COMMON METER DOUBLE)
5 HURON
316 FOREST GREEN

LM (LONG METER - 88 88)
10 O RADIANT LIGHT
162 BOURBON
182 HILARITER
183 AGINCOURT
351 O WALY WALY
352 TALLIS' CANON

LMD (LONG METER DOUBLE)
14 MAGNIFICAT

5 5 5 4 D
145 PRIOR LAKE
317 332 BUNESSAN
320 EVENING HYMN
329 VIKTORIA

6 6 6 6 4 44 4
228 CYMBALA

66 86 66
328 BALDWIN

7 6 8 6 8 6
201 DEERFIELD

7 6 8 6 8 6 8 6
190 SCHOLA

7 7 7 7 WITH REFRAIN
198 SING OUT

8 5 8 5 84 3
245 CREATOR SPIRITUS

8 7 8 7
163 THOMAS
285 THE SERVANT SONG

8 7 8 7 WITH REFRAIN
260 HOW CAN I KEEP FROM SINGING
273 COMFORT

8 7 8 7 8 7
195 GHENT
326 TILLFLYKT

8 7 8 7 D
152 318 JOYOUS LIGHT
282 HOLY MANNA
319 BEACH SPRING

888 WITH ALLELUIAS
184 GELOBT SEI GOTT

11 10 11 10
175 NOËL NOUVELET

364 Index of Tunes

AGINCOURT 183
BALDWIN 328
BALM IN GILEAD 353
BEACH SPRING 319
BOURBON 162
BREAD OF LIFE 337
BUNESSAN 317, 332
CANTATE DOMINO 218
CAROL OF HOPE 138
CHEREPONI 168
CHRISTIAN LOVE 267
COMFORT 273
CREATION 196
CREATOR SPIRITUS 245
CYMBALA 228
DEERFIELD 201
EVENING HYMN 320
FENN HOUSE 160
FOREST GREEN 316
GELOBT SEI GOTT 184
GHENT 195
HILARITER 182
HOLY MANNA 282
HOUSTON 208
HURON 5
IRBY 153
JOYOUS LIGHT 152, 318
KINGDOM 143
KOMT NU MET ZANG 313
MAGNIFICAT 14
MIDDLEBURY 185
NATOMAH 192
NATURE'S PRAISE 199
NOËL NOUVELET 175
O FILLII ET FILIAE 180
O WALY WALY 351
OAK POINT 345
PERSONET HODIE 272
PRIOR LAKE 145
PULKINGHAM 213
REJOICE, REJOICE 151
RESURRECTION 321
SCHOLA 190
SHAKER SONG 297
SHALOM 304
SHANTI 252
SHEPHERD'S SONG 140
SHIBBOLET BASADEH 287
SING OUT 198
STAR IN THE EAST 156
STILLE NACHT 147
SUMMIT HILL 2
TALLIS' CANON 352
THE FLIGHT OF THE EARLS 327
THOMAS 163
THUMA MINA 293
TILLFLYKT 326
VIKTORA 329
WERE YOU THERE 171
WONDROUS LOVE 290

Index of First Lines and Common Titles 365

150 A Dulcimer Carol
214 A New Song
164 Adoramus Te Christe
221 Adoramus Te Domine II - Gloria
314 All People Here Who Remember
295 All That I Counted as Gain
257 All That We Have
44 All the Ends of the Earth
326 All Who Claim the Faith of Jesus
333 All Who Drink the Water
204 All You Who Are Thirsty
51 Alleluia, Alleluia
215 Alleluia, Sing!
337 And I Will Raise You Up
298 Anthem
155 Arise, Shine!
28 As a Deer Longs
33 As Morning Breaks
211 As the Rain
173 Ashes
320 At Evening
151 Awake, Awake and Greet the New Morn
294 Awake from Your Slumber
330 Awake, O Sleeper

353 Balm in Gilead
332 Baptized in Water
244 Be Light for Our Eyes
30 Be Merciful, O Lord
263 Be Not Afraid
42 Be with Me
279 Because the Lord Is My Shepherd
344 Behold the Lamb
227 Bless the Lord
246 Bless the Lord
61 Bless the Lord, My Soul
236 Blessed Be God
215 Blessed Be Our God
316 Blessed Be the God
5 Blessed Be the God of Israel
284 Blest Are They
55 Blest Are Those
264 Blest Be the Lord
144 Born of Peace
156 Brightest and Best
280 Bring Forth the Kingdom

172 Calvary
14 Canticle of Mary
197 Canticle of the Sun
5 Canticle of Zachary
316 Canticle of Zachary
152 Carol at the Manger
251 Center of My Life
145 Chill of the Night Fall
183 Christ Is Alive
294 City of God
146 Cold Are the People
244 Come and Be Light for Our Eyes
185 Come Away to the Skies
301 Come! Live in the Light
189 Come, Lord Jesus
288 Come, My Children
198 Come, O God of All the Earth
141 Come, O Lord
217 Come Then, All You Nations
321 Come to Me, All You Weary
142 Come to Set Us Free
202 Come to the Water
245 Come to Us, Creative Spirit
237 Confitemini Domino
31 Create in Me

159 Deep Within

138 Each Winter As the Year Grows Older
261 Eagle's Wings
180 Easter Alleluia
341 Eat This Bread
160 Eternal Lord of Love
10 Evening Hymn - O Radiant Light
36 Every Nation on Earth
275 Eye Has Not Seen

136 For Words and Deeds
137 For You, O Lord
41 Forever I Will Sing
323 Freedom Is Coming
258 From My Mother's Womb

311 Gather Us In
272 Gift of Love
328 Give Thanks to God on High
149 Gloria, Gloria
287 Glorious in Majesty
233 Glory and Praise to Our God
180 Glory to God Who Does Wondrous Things
2 God Is Alive
270 God Is Love
195 God Is One, Unique and Holy
196 God of All Creation
322 God of All Living
143 God of All People
143 God of All Places
319 God of Day and God of Darkness
196 God of the Ocean and Sea
29 God Mounts His Throne
192 God Sends Us His Spirit
312 God, You Have Moved
184 Good Christians All
290 Good Friday Hymn

39 Happy Are They
300 Harvest of Justice
292 He Has Anointed Me
357 Healer of Our Every Ill
291 Here I Am, Lord
311 Here in This Place
182 Hilariter

Index of First Lines and Common Titles/*continued*

241 Hold Me in Life
152 Holy Child within the Manger
49 Holy Is God
165 Hosanna
260 How Can I Keep from Singing?
38 How Lovely Is Your Dwelling

337 I Am the Bread of Life
205 I Am the Light of the World
179 I Am the Resurrection
286 I Bind My Heart
297 I Danced in the Morning
334 I Have Loved You
327 I Sing a Maid
291 I, the Lord of Sea and Sky
225 I Want to Praise Your Name
208 I Want to Walk as a Child of the Light
188 I Will Be with You
203 I Will Lift Up My Eyes
281 I Will Not Die
24 I Will Praise You, Lord
213 I Will Sing, I Will Sing
214 I Will Sing the Lord
342 I Will Take the Cup of Life
43 If Today You Hear His Voice
32 In God Alone
227 In Praise of His Name
340 In the Breaking of the Bread
325 In the Lord, I Will Be Thankful
3 In the Shadow of Your Wings
255 In You, O God
303 In You, O Lord

239 Jesu Christe Miserere
168 Jesu, Jesu
315 Jesus, Come to Us
354 Jesus, Heal Us
167 Jesus, Remember Me
302 Jesus Still Lives
253 Jesus the Lord
335 Jesus, Wine of Peace
318 Joyous Light of Heavenly Glory
223 Jubilate Deo
223 Jubilate, Servite

216 Laudate Dominum
324 Leaping the Mountains
154 Lest the Word
35 Let All the Earth
148 Let the Heavens Be Glad
53 Let Us Go Rejoicing
50 Let Us Rejoice
25 Let Your Mercy Be on Us
339 Life-Giving Bread, Saving Cup
231 Lift Up Your Hearts
178 Light of Christ/Exsultet
350 Like a Shepherd
12 Like Burning Incense
343 Look Beyond
60 Lord, Come and Save Us
277 Lord, Come Show Us the Path of Life
40 Lord, Let Us See Your Kindness
37 Lord, Make Us Turn to You
297 Lord of the Dance
47 Lord, Send Out Your Spirit
324 Lord of Glory
212 Lord, to Whom Shall We Go
157 Lord, Today
18 Lord, You Have the Words
58 Love Is Never Ending
268 Love One Another
283 Loving Father, Gracious God

308 Many Are the Light Beams
141 Maranatha
273 May Love Be Ours
247 May the Spirit of Christ
300 May We Find Riches
235 May We Praise You
317 Morning Has Broken
2 Morning Hymn - God Is Alive
19 My God, My God
260 My Life Flows On
307 My Peace I Leave You
255 My Refuge
14 My Soul Gives Glory
137 My Soul in Stillness Waits
303 My Soul Is Still
34 My Soul Is Thirsting

199 Nature's Praise
309 Neither Greek, nor Jew
146 Night of Silence
269 No Greater Love
273 Not for Tongues
336 Now in This Banquet
320 Now It Is Evening
162 Now Let Us All with One Accord
175 Now the Green Blade Rises
299 Now We Remain

54 O Blessed Are Those
278 O Christe Domine Jesu
323 O Freedom
248 O God, I Seek You
242 O Healing River
202 O Let All Who Thirst
240 O Lord, Hear My Prayer
251 O Lord, You Are the Center
10 O Radiant Light
265 O the Lord Is Near
261 On Eagle's Wings
150 On This Blessed Morn
153 Once in Royal David's City
346 One Bread, One Body
48 Our Blessing Cup
347 Our Blessing Cup
52 Our Help Comes from the Lord
254 Our Help Is in the Name of the Lord

Index of First Lines and Common Titles/*continued*

305 Peace before Us
306 Peace Is Flowing Like a River
140 People of the Night
63 Praise God in His Holy Dwelling
232 Praise God with Drums and Dancing
229 Praise His Name
62 Praise the Lord from the Heavens
220 Praise the Lord, My Soul
199 Praise the Lord, Oceans and Rivers
210 Praise to You, O Christ, Our Savior
225 Praise with the Trumpet
305 Prayer for Peace
177 Psallite Deo
18 Psalm 19 - Lord, You Have the Words
19 Psalm 22 - My God, My God, Why Have You Abandoned Me?
20 Psalm 23 - Shepherd Me, O God
21 Psalm 25 - To You, O Lord
22 Psalm 25 - To You, O Lord
23 Psalm 27 - The Lord Is My Light
24 Psalm 30 - I Will Praise You, Lord
25 Psalm 33 - Let Your Mercy Be on Us
25 Psalm 33 - The Earth Is Full of the Goodness
27 Psalm 34 - Taste and See
26 Psalm 34 - The Cry of the Poor
28 Psalm 42 - Song of the Exile
29 Psalm 47 - God Mounts His Throne
30 Psalm 51 - Be Merciful, O Lord, for We Have Sinned
31 Psalm 51 - Create in Me
32 Psalm 62 - In God Alone
33 Psalm 63 - As Morning Breaks
3 Psalm 63 - In the Shadow of Your Wings
34 Psalm 63 - My Soul Is Thirsting for You, O Lord, My God
35 Psalm 66 - Let All the Earth
36 Psalm 72 - Lord, Every Nation on Earth Will Adore You
37 Psalm 80 - Lord, Make Us Turn to You
39 Psalm 84 - Happy Are They Who Dwell in Your House
38 Psalm 84 - How Lovely Is Your Dwelling Place
40 Psalm 85 - Lord, Let Us See Your Kindness
41 Psalm 89 - Forever I Will Sing the Goodness of the Lord
42 Psalm 91 - Be with Me
43 Psalm 95 - If Today You Hear His Voice
44 Psalm 98 - All the Ends of the Earth
45 Psalm 100 - We Are His People
46 Psalm 103 - The Lord Is Kind and Merciful
47 Psalm 104 - Lord, Send Out Your Spirit
48 Psalm 116 - Our Blessing Cup
49 Psalm 117 - Holy Is God, Holy and Strong
51 Psalm 118 - Alleluia, Alleluia
50 Psalm 118 - Let Us Rejoice
52 Psalm 121 - Our Help Comes from the Lord
53 Psalm 122 - Let Us Go Rejoicing to the House of the Lord
55 Psalm 128 - Blest Are Those Who Love You
54 Psalm 128 - O Blessed Are Those
57 Psalm 130 - With the Lord
56 Psalm 130 - With the Lord There Is Mercy
58 Psalm 136 - Love Is Never Ending
12 Psalm 141 - Like Burning Incense
59 Psalm 145 - I Will Praise Your Name
60 Psalm 146 - Lord, Come and Save Us
61 Psalm 147 - Bless the Lord, My Soul
62 Psalm 148 - Praise the Lord from the Heavens
63 Psalm 150 - Praise God in His Holy Dwelling

151 Rejoice, Rejoice
158 Remember Your Love
356 Remember Your Mercy, Lord
283 Renew Your People
355 Return to Me
169 Ride On, Jesus, Ride

348 Seed, Scattered and Sown
293 Send Me, Jesus (Thuma Mina)
189 Send Us Your Spirit
276 Shelter Me, O God
20 Shepherd Me, O God
147 Silent Night
230 Sing a New Song
218 Sing a New Song to the Lord
217 Sing of the Lord's Goodness
198 Sing Out, Earth and Skies
234 Sing to the Mountains
2 Sing Your Joy
282 Singing Songs of Expectation
349 Song of Farewell
309 Song of Gathering
154 Song of God among Us
247 Song of St. Patrick
28 Song of the Exile
161 Song of the Lord's Supper
181 Song of the Risen One
145 Song of the Stable
312 Song over the Waters
187 Song to Jesus Christ
211 Sow the Word
191 Spirit Blowing through Creation
192 Spirit Friend
190 Spirit of God within Me
166 Stay Here and Keep Watch
170 Stay with Me
186 Surrexit Christus
176 Surrexit Dominus Vere II

238 Table Prayer

Index of First Lines and Common Titles/*continued*

243 Take Our Bread
27 Taste and See
338 Taste and See
26 The Cry of the Poor
136 The Day Is Near
25 The Earth Is Full
300 The Harvest of Justice
197 The Heavens Are Telling
26 The Lord Hears
46 The Lord Is Kind and Merciful
209 The Lord Is My Life
23 The Lord Is My Light
274 The Lord Is My Shepherd
219 The Lord Is My Strength
259 The Lord Is Near
265 The Lord Is Near
295 The Love of the Lord
342 The Name of God
322 The River Will Rise
285 The Servant Song
289 The Song of All Seed
219 The Song of Moses
201 The Stars Declare His Glory
237 The Table Which You Set
304 The Voice of God But Speaks of Peace
333 The Water I Give
182 The Whole Bright World
353 There Is a Balm
269 There Is No Greater Love
206 This Little Light of Mine
50 This Is the Day
226 This Is the Day
178 This Is the Light of Christ
344 Those Who Were in the Dark
262 Though the Mountains May Fall
293 Thuma Mina
292 To Bring Glad Tidings
228 To God with Gladness Sing
289 To Live on Earth
21, 22 To You, O Lord
163 Tree of Life

271 Ubi Caritas

193 Veni Sancte Spiritus

139 Wait for the Lord
301 We Are Called
298 We Are Called, We Are Chosen
45 We Are His People
310 We Are Many Parts
207 We Are Walking in the Light
140 We Are Your People of the Night
58 We Give Thanks unto You
296 We Have Been Told
253 We Have No Name
299 We Hold the Death of the Lord
250 We Live a Mystery
224 We Praise You
249 We Remember
161 We Remember One Who Loved Us Well
173 We Rise Again from Ashes
321 We Shall Rise Again
252 We Walk by Faith
345 We Who Once Were Dead
350 We Will Rise Again
171 Were You There
313 What Is This Place
194 What Is Your Name
290 What Wondrous Love
144 When All the Earth
256 When from Our Exile
351 When Love Is Found
267 Where Charity and Love Prevail
174 Wherever You Go
174 Who Could Believe
181 Why Do You Look for the Living
285 Will You Let Me Be Your Servant
200 Wind upon the Water
232 With Drums and Dancing
56, 57 With the Lord There Is Mercy
329 Wonder of Wonders

331 You Are God's Work of Art
222 You Are the Voice
280 You Are Salt
229 You Servants of the Lord
263 You Shall Cross the Barren Desert
261 You Who Dwell
187 You Who Have Passed By
266 You Will Draw Water
277 You Will Show Me the Path of Life
248 Your Love Is Finer Than Life
352 Your Love, O God